Robert Lebling has lived and worked as a journalist in Egypt, Lebanon, Saudi Arabia, the United Kingdom and the United States. He is author, with Donna Pepperdine, of *Natural Remedies of Arabia*. Married with two daughters, he is currently a writer and communications specialist based in Dhahran, Saudi Arabia.

'Robert Lebling's exhaustive and very readable account of jinn lore and legends traces the fascinating history of these strange beings ... mortals interested in knowing more about these magical creatures must content themselves with Lebling's absorbing study.'

Gary Lachman, *Times Literary Supplement*

'The boundaries of Lebling's work surpassed my wildest dreams. Lebling has left no stone unturned in his enquiry, roaming through traditional Eastern literature as well as the modern media. The result is a truly extraordinary masterwork, a treasury within itself that can be consulted at random, dipped into as a bedside book, or read from cover to cover in a fabulous feast for the imagination and the enquiring mind.'

Tahir Shah

'A comprehensive reference ... easily the most authoritative and accessible recent work on the topic... . The book may strike a note with a younger audience fascinated by the occult, but many students of the Middle East, Islam and ancient history should find it a valuable addition to their libraries as well.'

Stephen L. Brundage, Saudi Aramco World

'A long overdue compendium of the knowledge and history of the jinn ... a lifelong reference to the mysteries of the Middle East and their influence on both Western and Eastern cultures.'

Arabnews.com

'A superb study... . A glorious feast of anthropological forteana... . Even those familiar with Islamic literature will delight in Lebling's pursuit of the "sons of smokeless fire."'

Fortean Times

Legends of the Fire Spirits

Jinn and Genies from Arabia to Zanzibar

Robert Lebling

Foreword by Tahir Shah

New paperback edition published in 2014 by I.B.Tauris & Co Ltd
6 Salem Road, London W2 4BU
175 Fifth Avenue, New York NY 10010
www.ibtauris.com

First published in hardback in 2010 by I.B.Tauris & Co Ltd

Jacket photograph: The Hand of Fatima, shown painted on a house wall in Algeria, is a powerful charm and sacred symbol used in Arab and Muslim lands to protect the innocent from evil jinn or demons and from the effects of the 'evil eye'. It symbolises generosity, hospitality, power and divine providence. As a whole, the hand represents the Muslim Holy Family: the thumb stands for the Prophet Muhammad, the index finger his daughter Fatima, the second finger her husband Ali, and the third and fourth fingers their sons Hassan and Hussein respectively.

ISBN: 978 1 78076 904 2
eISBN: 978 0 85773 063 3

A full CIP record for this book is available from the British Library

Printed and bound in Great Britain by Page Bros, Norwich

It is itself the morning; its clear radiance dispels
The night when it shoots out sparks like rubies
As the patrolling angels do, when, at night, they stone
With the stars the rebellious demon Afrits.

– Abu Nuwas, poet

The Prophet said, 'There are three types of jinn: one type which flies in the air all the time, another type which exists as snakes and dogs, and an earthbound type which resides in one place and wanders about.'

– Al-Tabarani, hadith scholar

The microscope shows you the creatures on the leaf; no mechanical tube is yet invented to discover the nobler and more gifted things that hover in the illimitable air. Yet between these last and man is a mysterious and terrible affinity. ... Now, in space there are millions of beings, not literally spiritual, for they have all, like the animalculæ unseen by the naked eye, certain forms of matter, though matter so delicate, air-drawn, and subtile, that it is, as it were, but a film, a gossamer, that clothes the spirit. ... Yet, in truth, these races differ most widely ... some of surpassing wisdom, some of horrible malignity; some hostile as fiends to men, others gentle as messengers between earth and heaven.

– Sir Edward Bulwer-Litton, novelist

The very fact that our vision of the world can be falsified as a result of further movement, observation, probing, etc., implies that there is more in the world than what we have perceived and known.

– David Bohm, physicist

Contents

Foreword

Five years ago I moved from a cramped London flat into a sprawling Moroccan mansion set squarely in the middle of a Casablanca shantytown. Looking back, it was a relocation touched by lunacy, but it was all the more unwise because the house was said to be infested with Jinn.

The Occidental world has never found it easy to grasp the strange netherworld of spirits that followers of Islam universally believe exist in a realm overlaid by our own. Although descended from an Oriental family with its roots in the mountain fortress of Afghanistan's Hindu Kush, I was born and brought up in the West. I thought I knew the East. I was well accustomed from childhood to understand the finer points of Arab etiquette, and I had been taught its tales, gleaned from *Alf layla wa layla* (*The Thousand and One Nights*). That fabulous treasury of stories had introduced me early on to the extraordinary possibilities of a world peopled by invisible legions of Jinn. So when we came to live here at Dar Khalifa, the Caliph's House, I felt as if nothing could surprise me.

How wrong I was.

From the first moment that we crossed the threshold, I realised that I was way out of my depth. The house had been empty for almost a decade. Whereas in the West an empty home might appeal to squatters, in the East there is a danger of quite a different kind. The unlawful occupants of our new home were not human, but superhuman.

The guardians, who came with the house as if through some mediaeval right sale, warned us from the outset that there was extreme danger all around. When I declared that we would be moving into the house right away to supervise the renovations, they laughed nervously – that is, until they realised I was serious. Terrified, contorted expressions then swept across their faces, and they begged us to leave. The Jinn would not take kindly to intruders, they told me. For in the years that the house had been empty, it had become *their* home. Dare to trespass and they might kill us, the leader of the guardians declared. Irritated, yet willing to go along for the sake of respecting local sensitivities, I asked what to do. The chief guardian, whose name was Osman, swept his out arms wide and yelled: 'You must hold an exorcism!'

Back in London I would have had no idea where to find an exorcist, let alone a troop of them. But Morocco is very different. It may be perched in Africa's north-west corner, just eight miles from the gates of Europe, but in many ways it is the deepest, darkest Orient. And that is what is so appealing about it.

I asked around and, very soon, found myself in the old imperial city of Mèknes. According to all my informants it was the centre of exorcists. And they were right. A few minutes after my arrival I was offered dozens of exorcists from the Aissawa brotherhood. I negotiated a price for twenty, and the exorcist dealer threw in a further four of them for free. The only catch was that I obliged to pay in advance.

A day or so later I arrived home and was greeted by the guardians' long looks. The Jinn were already exacting their revenge, they told me. A dead cat had been found in the garden with its head cut off. A tree had fallen in the wind and broken a window. And the maid, hired to look after our little baby, had run off screaming for no reason at all. I held out a hand at arms length and whispered confidently, 'The exorcists are coming.'

The guardians perked up.

They asked when exactly the visitors would arrive.

I shrugged.

'They'll come when they are ready,' I said.

My wife said that I was mad to have handed over wads of money to exorcists I didn't know. She said she could hear them all the way in Mèknes, howling with laughter.

A day passed, then another.

I kicked myself for having been so ingenuous as to pay in advance. But then at that moment I heard the wild, whooping sound of men in high spirits, against a backdrop of grinding noise. A huge cement truck inched its way down our lane. On the back were riding the exorcists, as if on some infernal chariot. I pointed at them and grinned, and the guardians grinned too.

Through days and nights the exorcists wreaked their terrible work. They slaughtered and skinned a goat at what they said was the heart of the house. As the person obliged to purchase the animal, I found myself naturally interested in how its execution would feature in the cleansing of my home of supernatural elements. When stripped of its skin, the carcass was beheaded, and its gallbladder swallowed by one of the exorcists. The others slit open its belly and rifled through the organs, which gleamed like jewels in the candlelight.

One of the group poured milk in all corners of the house, and another did the same with blood. Drums beat, and high-pitched homemade oboes wailed. The drumming became faster and faster as the night wore on. And as it did so, the exorcists stepped into another plane, a kind of twilight zone of their own imagination.

They cut their wrists with knives and drank their own blood and then collapsed on the ground in trance. Yet more exorcists massed in a dark damp room at the far end of the house. They barricaded themselves inside, killed chickens and drank more blood.

And all the while the drums beat and the oboes shrieked out. I wondered whether the walls would tumble down as they had done in Jericho.

I whispered sternly to the leader of the exorcists that they could leave. He laughed a wild hearty laugh, and I swear his eyes flashed red with fire. He would quit our home, he said, only when the jinn had been sucked out of the walls and swallowed. I explained that my wife was growing impatient and that she was uncomfortable at having the walls and floor strewn with freshly purged blood. The leader of the exorcists caught my glance in his. Widening his eyes in the most terrifying manner, he told me that he had never been in a house so consumed with evil spirits.

Then he asked for more money, and for another goat.

The next day, after brokering a deal which involved a handful of crisp hundred-dirham notes, the exorcists clambered aboard the cement truck. They rolled back down the lane and through the shantytown to the open road. My wife gave me one of those looks that instilled pure fear. I bragged out loud that the house was now squeaky clean, that the last thing we ever needed to worry about again was the prospect of being tormented by Jinn.

That was all six years ago. In the weeks and months since, I have found myself living in a country where the belief in these normally invisible spirits is complete and unshakable. Jinn are described in the Qur'an and are a part of life for all God-fearing Muslims in Morocco and across the Islamic world.

The Qur'an tells us that when God created Man from clay, he created a second race of beings – Jinn – from 'smokeless fire'. Jinn are not ghosts, that is, they are not spirits of the dead. Far from it. They are living entities just like us. They are born, get married and die like humans. Some are good and others bad, some ugly, while others are radiantly beautiful. Indeed, there are many tales of mortal men being wooed by the charms of voluptuous women, only to realise later that they are not human, but Jinn. The difference between us and them is that they have magical powers and can decide whether to be visible or not. They can fly through the air, change their form and are capable of magical feats.

The nineteenth century's fascination with *The Arabian Nights* saw the deeds and misdeeds of Jinn enter Victorian drawing-rooms. The creatures slipped into Western communal folklore through the tales of Aladdin, Sindbad and others, mixed in with epic quests, treasure, flying carpets and enchanted lands. And through the endless adaptations for children and all the Hollywood renditions, Jinn became known to us all.

But gone was the Oriental imagery – the sly, ferocious race that lives among us – replaced by a comic jumble of towering yet quite loveable creatures, who go by the name of 'genies'.

Anyone who has spent any time in the Arab world knows the difference between Hollywood's depiction and that which is found embedded deep in local culture. Living in a country like Morocco, where belief in Jinn is all-pervasive, involves experiencing situations such as the ones we faced at the Caliph's House. It brings an extraordinary level of cultural possibility that simply doesn't exist in the Occidental world. Imagine that all around me there may be invisible spirits, sitting, standing, laughing, chatting, cackling, or crouching on the floor. Some of them are minute, while others tower hundreds of feet into the air. The more you think about it and live with it, the more appealing the idea of Jinn becomes. And the longer you live in a place where everyone believes, the more you find yourself believing, too.

Long before I moved to Morocco, I had searched for a readable book about Jinn and their world. But there wasn't one. When I asked friends who were scholars in Islamic culture and tradition, they recommended barely readable texts written by academics for academics. Years passed. Then, through a kind of magic that was from the realm of Jinn themselves, Robert Lebling contacted me out of the blue. He spoke of a work, a great labour of love, which would reveal to the West all it needed to know about Jinn.

My prayers had been answered.

The boundaries of Lebling's *Legends of the Fire Spirits* surpassed my wildest dreams. The book's scope exceeds simply listing stories of Jinn taken from Islamic texts and Arab folklore.

Lebling has left no stone unturned in his enquiry, roaming through traditional Eastern literature as well as the modern media, in search of anything which gives us a better understanding of Jinn and their world. The result is a truly extraordinary masterwork, a treasury within itself that can be consulted at random, dipped into as a bedside book, or read from cover to cover in a fabulous feast for the imagination and the enquiring mind.

Through *Legends of the Fire Spirits* we learn that the belief in Jinn is certainly Pre-Islamic, and that there are various distinct forms of these creatures. The Qur'an devotes an entire Surah to them, a form of life that is inextricably linked to the cultural and religious tapestry of Arab and Islamic lands.

Lebling details clearly how followers of Islam perceive the realm of Jinn, what the Prophet Muhammed said about them, and how regional and geographic divide has shaped them within local culture. An entire section is devoted to the study and appreciation of jinn by geographic location – through Morocco, Tunisia and Egypt, to Arabia and Palestine, Turkey, Iraq and Iran, as well as through Nigeria, Malaysia, Zanzibar and beyond.

We learn that the Arabic word for 'crazy' – *Majnun* – comes from the same root as the word 'Jinn', suggesting that a deranged person is possessed in some way. We also learn that Jinn are believed to lurk in wells and lavatories, in addition to their haunting empty buildings, such as our home. Space is given to King Solomon, the one human who could control Jinn through the magical ring he wore. And Lebling describes the extraordinary encounters between those of us created from clay and the others who were shaped from smokeless fire. These include examples of humans who unwittingly married Jinn, and others such as the fourteenth-century Moroccan magician Muhammad ibn al-Hajj al-Tilimsani, whose work *Suns of Lights and Treasures of Secrets* provides a spell for anyone wishing to seduce the daughter of the White King of the Jinn.

Legends of the Fire Spirits provides a window into Arab and Islamic society that is usually clouded over, opaque to all except Arabists and scholars of Islam. The subject is one known to Muslims embracing belief that stands at the heart of the Islamic faith but one that until now has been largely misrepresented and misunderstood in the West.

As someone who lives with the daily possibility of Jinn spotting, I would urge everyone wishing a deeper understanding of Arab society and culture to make careful use of *Legends of the Fire Spirits*. To anyone considering the purchase of a haunted home in Morocco or elsewhere in the region, this book will become an indispensible handbook in the months and years to come.

As for life at the Caliph's House, all is not well. One of the guardians recently almost severed his hand while sharpening an axe in the garden. Then, last week, the maid tripped and cut her foot badly, and on the same day the swimming pool turned an eerie shade of yellow. The guardians have been imploring me to hold another exorcism. The very thought of it fills me with worry. Most of all, I don't know how on earth I'll break it to my wife. But, as all my friends assure me, everyone knows that even the best exorcism has to be renewed once in a while.

Tahir Shah
Dar Khalifa, Casablanca
2010

Acknowledgements

This book is a result of a personal quest for understanding a compelling and enduring phenomenon in the Middle East. It is not a work of scholars, for I am not one; it is an adventure in discovery for general readers, particularly the curious and the open-minded. Notes and references are included to serve as guideposts for further exploration. Not every jinn tradition or country could be covered here, but it is hoped that the coverage provided in this book is broad enough and deep enough to be satisfying. The jinn lore and legends assembled and discussed here were tracked down and sometimes translated by the author. Some of the discussions originated in the author's Jinn Group, an online community created in 1999 and now hosted by Yahoo!® (http://groups.yahoo.com/group/jinn). I would like to thank the members of that group for their enlightening and ever-fascinating contributions. My thanks go to Saudi Aramco and its library system, particularly the Technical Information Center in Dhahran, for providing me access to a wealth of hard-to-find books, papers and monographs. My appreciation also goes to the many friends and colleagues in Saudi Arabia and other countries who have kept me up-to-date on ancient and current jinn lore. Among these individuals, special thanks go to Guriyan M. Al-Hajri of Ain Dar, for teaching me about the desert and its ways. I am deeply grateful to Tahir Shah and Tatiana Wilde for their constant encouragement in this prolonged undertaking. Finally and foremost, my deepest thanks go to Linda, Sara and Brittany, who have constantly encouraged my writing and shown amazing patience in the process.

Notes on Transliteration

Transliterating Arabic is a daunting task. There is no standard English spelling for Arabic words. The word 'jinn' – from which we get 'genie' – is rendered in many ways: jinn, jenn, djinn, djin, jin, ginn, ğinn, among others. Sometimes 'jinn' is singular, referring to one creature; sometimes (more correctly, according to the Arabic) it is plural. There is a grammatically correct masculine singular form ('jinni' or 'jinnee' and its variants) and a feminine equivalent ('jinniya' and its variants). In addition to 'jinn' itself, there are a number of other plural forms, such as 'jnun', 'jnoun', 'djnun' or 'djnoun' (favoured in Arab North Africa), 'jann' or 'jan' (a general or collective term used often to refer to ordinary jinn or all jinn), the Anglicised form 'jinns', and more.

This work cites many authors over many years, and each of them has his or her own way of rendering Arabic words. When directly quoting these writers, I have left their spellings unchanged. Consider it the charm of the East.

Introduction

The Nature of Jinn

The swarm of jinn is passing,
And it whirls, hissing.
Old conifers, stirred by their flight,
Crackle like burning pine.
Their herd, heavy and swift,
Flying in the vacant space,
Seems a livid cloud
With lightning flashing at its edge.

–Victor Hugo, 'Les Djinns'

The drama and power of the fire spirits we call genies or jinn, as presented in the literatures of the world, are enough to take our breath away. These beings are mysterious, they are frightening, they cause humankind endless grief. And yet there is a spark of goodness among them as well, and they can help as well as hinder. Readers in the West shake their heads in amazement as they read the tales, and some wonder, 'Could such creatures actually exist?'

Imagine a species of intelligent beings that live secretly among us. Imagine that they often appear humanoid or even human but possess amazing powers that we lack. They can change their shapes, can fly through the air and can even render themselves invisible. They watch us, study us and react to us. Occasionally they abduct humans and even mate with them, producing hybrid offspring. In today's North America or Europe, such creatures are discussed in all seriousness by many – they are called 'aliens' or 'Greys'. In the Middle East, Africa and Asia, beings that fit this description are called 'jinn'.

Many in the West are unwilling to concede the existence of jinn (which is their Arabic name).[1] This reluctance is grounded partly in a rationalist tradition, which rejects the existence of most things that cannot be seen or experienced otherwise (though science does admit the existence of the infrared and ultraviolet light spectra, despite the fact that these things cannot be detected by the human eye). Additionally, in our culture's collective experience, the anecdotal evidence for this phenomenon is quite sparse: very few of us have ever claimed to have seen a jinn.

Many in Western cultures refuse to admit that jinn exist because they are viewed as an element of fantasy literature, an imaginative *Arabian Nights* creation that has entertained children for generations but has no basis in fact. Aladdin's magic lamp is a storyteller's figment, not a part of our concrete world. When Westerners conjure up a mental picture of a genie, the first image to come to mind may be Barbara Eden in harem pants, from the old TV series *I Dream of Jeannie*, or the huge blue buffoon with Robin Williams' voice from Disney's animated film *Aladdin*.

It may come as a surprise to many in the West to learn that jinn are taken seriously and regarded as real, tangible beings by a large segment of the world's population. Millions of people in North Africa, the Middle East and other Islamic regions have been brought up to consider jinn as a normal, natural part of the world around them. Admittedly this belief has eroded somewhat, as educated elites in Muslim countries, influenced by Western thought, have come to view the jinn as essentially a spiritual or even metaphorical concept.

But Muslims committed to the literal truth of the Qur'an – as the word of Allah[2] conveyed to the Prophet Muhammad by the angel Gabriel – dare not reject the notion of jinn entirely.[3] The Qur'an describes jinn as actual, intelligent life forms – beings that, though different from humans, share some attributes with them.[4] Jinn populate the world with offspring. They too are male and female and raise families. They possess free will and make choices in life. They accept or reject God. Some become renegades and are classified as demons or ghouls. Others practise established religions and live what humans would consider conventional, 'normal' lives among their own kind. Jinn generally keep to their own communities. But they also, on occasion, interact with humans, sometimes emotionally or sexually, and in positive or negative ways. These interactions can occur haphazardly or unavoidably, when the worlds of jinn and humans touch or intersect. They can also happen when jinn make a conscious decision to seek out, contact or confront human beings.

In the Arab and Islamic worlds, jinn haunt abandoned houses and crumbling ruins, inhabit caves and sewers and sink-holes, wander through deserts, guard hidden or buried treasures, take the form of snakes and other beasts, possess humans, and perform wonders at the bidding of magicians. But what may seem to be jinn activity is not always so. Even those who believe firmly in jinn concede that swindlers, grifters and scammers often use this belief to manipulate the guileless and defraud the innocent.

According to Islamic tradition, God created angels from light, humans from clay and jinn from smokeless fire. Jinn – a word derived from an Arabic root meaning to 'conceal' or 'cover with darkness' – are said to have the ability to hide themselves from humans, often by disguising themselves as animals such as snakes, dogs and cats. Many jinn listened to the teachings of the Prophet, found them persuasive and became Muslims. Various local traditions, including those in Palestine and Arabia, also recognise the existence of Christian and Jewish jinn. In some countries, such as the Maldives and Indonesia, jinn are said to adopt sometimes other faiths, such as Buddhism and Hinduism.

Scholars in Muslim countries – theologians, philosophers and even scientists – have wrestled with the nature of jinn ever since the foundation of Islam in the seventh century. In the thirteenth century, the celebrated Persian physician, astronomer and geographer Zakariya al-Qazwini wrote a work in Arabic about the universe that defined jinn as follows: 'It is held that the Jinn are aerial animals, with transparent bodies, which can assume various forms.'[5] He noted that opinions differed on what jinn really are: 'Some consider the Jinn ... as unruly men; but these persons are of the Moatezileh [a sect of Muslim free-thinkers]: and some hold, that God ... created the Angels of the light of fire, and the Jinn of its flame ... and that [all] these kinds of beings are [usually] invisible to men, but that they assume what forms they please, and when their form becomes condensed they are visible.'

In fourteenth-century Mamluk Egypt, a scholar named Muhammad al-Damiri made another effort to explain these remarkable creatures in a zoological – some say 'para-zoological' – opus called *Hayat al-Hayawan* (The Life of Animals). The *Hayat* is an ambitious book that describes 731 different animal species – with numerous digressions into theological opinion, folklore and the traditions of the Prophet – and draws on 585 other prose works and 222 poetic sources. Al-Damiri fits jinn comfortably into the world of animals. He describes them as 'ethereal bodies capable of forming themselves into different shapes. They have reason, understanding and capability for hard work. They are different from humans ... . It is said they are called jinn because they are wary and not seen.' He cites a tradition of Abu al-Darada', a companion of the Prophet: 'God created three types of jinn: a type which are snakes, scorpions and vermin of the earth; a type like the breeze in the air; and a type like humans who are subject to judgement and punishment.'

Muhammad Asad (1900–1992) – a highly regarded, European Muslim thinker and author who converted from Judaism[6] (his birth name was Leopold Weiss) – described jinn as 'certain sentient organisms of so fine a nature and of a physiological composition so different from our own that they are not normally accessible to our sense-perception ... . [I]f we assume, as we must, that there are living organisms whose biological premises are entirely different from our own, it is only logical to assume that our physical senses can establish contact with them only under very exceptional circumstances; hence the description of them as "invisible beings".'

Asad felt that the 'occasional, very rare crossing of paths between their life-mode and ours may well give rise to strange – because unexplainable – manifestations, which man's primitive fantasy has subsequently interpreted as ghosts, demons and other such "supernatural" apparitions'. His explanation suggests that jinn inhabit another dimension and that they occasionally enter ours and interact with us. Such concepts traditionally belong in the realms of science fiction – but should they? Recent work by physicists from many countries on the cutting edge of quantum and superstring theory supports the notion that our universe possesses many more dimensions than the four we are accustomed to – length, width, height and time. It may be, then, that much more exists than we can ordinarily perceive, and that the idea of jinn is not so fanciful after all.

To understand why Arabs and Muslims take the concept and nature of jinn so seriously, we need to journey there and experience the phenomenon close-up and if possible first-hand. The exploration of jinn lore and legend in this book begins in the ancient Arab East, where the jinn phenomenon was first reported. We will look at how the jinn became part of Islam, the revealed religion that laid claim to the mantle of successor of the Judaeo-Christian tradition, and investigate a wide variety of jinn legends, beginning in Arabia. Spiralling outward from the Arabian heartlands we will look at how others in the Islamic world view jinn – from Iraq to Palestine and Syria, to Egypt, Arab North Africa and Spain, Turkey, Iran, the Indian Ocean and its Asian and African shores. Finally we will explore the impact of jinn lore on the literatures and cultures of the world.

The phenomenon of jinn is one thing, the interpretation of jinn quite another. While the phenomenon, the experience, of jinn interests us greatly, the only way humans can share an experience is by explaining it, interpreting it. By sampling and analysing a wealth of interpretations of the jinn phenomenon, we aspire to approach the truth.

My hope is that this journey will tell the story of these remarkable beings in sufficient detail and with enough flavour to satisfy the curious, entertain the imaginative and lay down a useful path for further research and inquiry.

Chapter One

Origins

It is related in histories, that a race of Jinn, in ancient times, before the creation of Adam, inhabited the earth, and covered it, the land and the sea, and the plains and the mountains; and the favours of God were multiplied upon them, and they had government, and prophecy, and religion, and law; but they transgressed and offended, and opposed their prophets, and made wickedness to abound in the earth; whereupon God, whose name be exalted, sent against them an army of Angels, who took possession of the earth, and drove away the Jinn to the regions of the islands, and made many of them prisoners ...

– Zakariya al-Qazwini, cosmographer

Jinn are best known as an Arab and/or Islamic phenomenon. In Arab tradition, the jinn is a spirit creature, often linked to nature, with the ability to manifest itself physically. The jinn have great powers, sometimes miraculous abilities, which humans normally lack.

Jinn are usually divided into five major 'categories': jann, jinn, shaitan, ifrit and marid. These terms sometimes overlap and are often not as precise as one would like. Jann is a collective term referring to the masses of jinn of all types; the term is sometimes interchangeable with jinn. 'Jinn' is used more often to refer to specific individuals or families or tribes of fire spirits. Jinn can be good or evil, but shaitans ('satans' or devils) are the children and servants of the chief devil, Iblis (the equivalent of the West's Satan), and are always evil. Ifrits are more powerful than shaitans and are most often evil.[1] Marids are evil as well and most powerful of all. All of the above categories have the ability to shapeshift or shield themselves with invisibility, so their appearance varies depending on circumstances.

The various categories of jinn were created separately, according to a creation myth reported by the Arab historian Abu al-Hasan Ali al-Mas'udi (896–956), called by some 'the Herodotus of the Arabs'. In his celebrated *Meadows of Gold*, al-Mas'udi explains the sequence of this creation:

> It is said that God created the demons from the *semoum* (burning wind); that from the demon he created his woman, as he created Eve from Ádam; that the demon having had relations with his woman, she became pregnant from him and laid thirty eggs. One of these eggs cracked open, giving birth to the *qotrobaht*, which was, so to speak, the mother of all the *qotrobs*, demons that have the form of a cat. From another egg emerged the *iblises*, in whose number must be counted El Harith Abou Murrah and which make their home within walls. From another egg were hatched the *maradahs*, which inhabit islands. Another produced the *ghouls*, which chose for their refuge ruins and deserts; another, the *si'lahs*, which hide in the mountains; the others, the *ouahaouis*, which inhabit the air in the form of winged serpents, and fly from place to place. From another egg emerged the *daouasiks*; from yet another the *hamasiks*; from still another the *hamamis*, and so forth.[2]

Most of these types of jinn will be encountered and explained later in this book. The egg motif appears in the earliest creation myths of many peoples, including the Greeks, Egyptians, Hindus and Chinese, suggesting a pre-Islamic origin for al-Mas'udi's account. But its exact source is unknown.

The Arabs' belief in jinn long predates Islam and played a role of considerable importance in the seventh-century environment in which the Islamic faith was born. According to this ancient belief, spirits were believed to haunt dark and desolate locales in the desert, and people needed to protect themselves from these beings. 'It is often assumed that belief in the jinn who were thought to dwell in the desert originated with the Bedouin and was passed from them to the settled tribes,' notes German scholar Joseph Henninger.[3] He says: 'This assumption does not seem to me to be well founded.'

Bedouin tribesmen who are at home in the desert experience much less fear in those regions than do villagers or townspeople who are often terrified by the desert and are convinced that all sorts of demons and monsters live there. Among the Arabs today, Henninger asserts, 'belief in spirits is much more intense among the [settled] agricultural population than among the Bedouin'. This is not to say, however, that the Bedouins of the Arabian Peninsula disbelieve in the jinn. This belief is very much a part of their everyday lives. But nomadic Arabs are generally less frightened by the jinn than are their settled counterparts.

Another scholar, American archaeologist William F. Albright, believed that the word *jinn* is not originally Arabic but is derived from Aramaic. Aramaic-speaking Christians used the term to designate pagan gods reduced to the status of demons. Albright concluded from this that the jinn themselves were introduced into Arabic folklore only late in the pre-Islamic period. Not all scholars agree on this point. Some maintain that the Arabic word *jinn* is older, and that the Palmyran (ancient Syrian) word *jny'* or *gny'*, which we shall encounter later, derives from the earlier Arabic form.

Henninger did a study of local Arabian pre-Islamic divinities – called 'idols' (*asnam*) or 'companions' (*shuraka'*) by Hisham ibn al-Kalbi (d.821) and other early Muslim authors. Cults worshipping these divinities were limited to specific areas or tribes. The Hudhayl tribe, for example, worshipped a god called Suwa' in a village near Yanbu' on the Red Sea coast, according to Ibn al-Kalbi. The Tayyi tribe had an idol called al-Fals, a red rock shaped like a man atop a black mountain, which was worshipped up until the birth of Islam and was destroyed by the Prophet's son-in-law 'Ali. Such pre-Islamic deities are often called companions because they were sometimes – mistakenly, from the Muslim viewpoint – associated with Allah. Apart from Ibn al-Kalbi's slender volume from the eighth century, *The Book of Idols*,[4] very few specifics have survived about the hundreds of early Arabian deities. In some cases we don't even know their real names or where they were worshipped. Sometimes they are referred to only by a title, for instance, as 'lord of such and such a place'. The myths which might have told us more about these divinities and their character are almost entirely lost, eclipsed and in some cases suppressed by Islam and its proselytisation. So it is often problematic deciding whether a specific deity originated with the nomadic Bedouins of the deserts or with the settled peoples of the Middle East. At various times before Islam, Bedouin tribes often adopted divinities from settled communities so as to facilitate rudimentary trade and social interaction with these areas. But the nomadic people of the Syrian and Arabian deserts may also have had their own gods; Henninger cites the example of a god named after a mountain – Dushara or Dusares[5] – who was almost certainly of Bedouin origin.

Henninger describes pre-Islamic deity worship as a 'chaotic picture' and is reluctant to characterise the large array of gods as a 'pantheon'. 'Among these gods there may be some that were originally jinn, mythical ancestors or legendary heroes, elevated little by little to the rank of god,' he says. 'On the other hand, some of the gods developed directly from the personification of natural forces (in [the pre-Islamic deity] Quzah, for example, one may still discern the features of a storm god). It should not be thought, however, that these gods must first have passed through a spirit or demon stage, and that celestial beings are posterior to earth spirits.'

Some Western scholars of the Middle East believe that the earliest jinn were conceptualised as malicious demons living in deserted or contaminated places and often taking the form of animals. Other Middle East scholars say the jinn originated as early deities of such peoples as the Sumerians and Akkadians, often nature gods and goddesses, who were later dethroned and displaced by more sophisticated beliefs but not totally discarded or forgotten.

Although the specific origins of jinn belief are in dispute and shrouded in confusion and mystery, it is known that the earliest jinn were believed to come from the desert. But belief in these creatures crystallised not in the deserts of the Middle East themselves, but in settled and sown areas, where agriculture had taken root and cities – civilisations – were being built, particularly in Mesopotamia, the 'land between the rivers', home of the Sumerians, Babylonians and Assyrians and now the land we called Iraq. The Bedouins who roamed the trackless deserts of greater Arabia with their flocks of sheep, goats and camels feared the spirit creatures of these regions much less than did the city and village folk, who dreaded the remote sand wastes because they were thought to harbour the unknown and the mysterious.

Pazuzu, the ancient Mesopotamian wind demon, is an example of a desert spirit, a primordial jinn, who struck terror in the hearts of city dwellers of Eridu, Ur, Nippur, Uruk, Akkad and other Sumerian cities some 4,000–6,000 years ago. Jinn are often associated with the wind and are said to travel by it. Pazuzu, a demon brought into Western consciousness by the novel and film *The Exorcist*, is an early form of nature spirit, probably a fallen deity of antiquity relegated to the world of the jinn. Pazuzu is first mentioned by the Sumerians and is later identified in Assyrian and Babylonian mythology as the son of Hanpa (or Hanbi), who is lord of all demons and sometimes identified with Satan himself. Novelist William Burroughs, in his *Cities of the Red Night*, called Pazuzu 'Lord of Fevers and Plagues, Dark Angel of the Four Winds with rotting genitals from which he howls through sharpened teeth over stricken cities'. This seems to refer to the common depiction of Pazuzu with an erect penis ending in a serpent's head. In general, the demon is portrayed as a human-animal hybrid, with a canine or leonine head, animal horns, a human beard, two pairs of bird wings on his back and a scorpion's tail.[6] The animal parts associated with his image are by and large those of beasts of the desert wastelands.

Pazuzu is often associated with a southwest wind, but recent research suggests that this may be an error and should be a cold, northeast wind.[7] Some scholars consider this wind demon to be one of the most malevolent elemental forces in world mythology. He was certainly a scavenger of desert wastelands, carrying loathsome disease, desolation and starvation. Significantly, William Woods states in his *History of the Devil*, 'In Mesopotamia the horned demon, Pazuzu, rode on the wind and carried malaria ... ', thus affirming the demon's destructive role as 'lord of fevers and plagues'.[8] Although he is certainly evil, Pazuzu curiously sometimes appears on ancient amulets as a defence against other demons. In the brutal eras of antiquity, occasionally appeasement was the smartest survival tactic.

Portraying a wind demon such as Pazuzu as a creature of the desert may derive from the Egyptian concept of Set, the destroyer, most ancient of the gods, who was represented as a strange, dog-like animal, not unlike that scavenging denizen of the desert, the jackal.

We need to keep in mind that Pazuzu, despite his perceived desert origins, frightened settled populations, not Bedouins.

The ancient Babylonians, who succeeded the Sumerians in Mesopotamia, were a Semitic people believed to have originated in Arabia. They were great practitioners of magic, and their lore was replete with grotesque and frightening demons that could be summoned by sorcery or driven off by talismans. Many of these demons were primordial jinn.

Scottish folklorist Lewis Spence says, 'Babylonian demons were legion and most of them exceedingly malevolent.'[9] A good example was the *utukku*, an evil spirit that normally lurked in the desert, where it lay in wait for unsuspecting travellers. But this particular demon did not limit itself to remote wastelands. It haunted graveyards, a common abode for jinn, and sometimes made its home in the mountains and even in the sea. Any man who spied an utukku was certain to face a grim fate.

The Babylonians feared another lurking demon called the *rabisu*, which hid in unfrequented spots and leapt out upon passers-by (the modus operandi, as we shall see later, of a fairly specialised jinn called the *ghul*). Yet another early jinn was the *labartu*, a Lilith-like figure, said to be the daughter of the ancient sky deity Anu. She was believed to live in craggy mountains or in dismal swamps and was particularly addicted to destroying children. Babylonian mothers would shield their children from the horrors of this demon by placing protective talismans on cords or chains around their youngsters' necks.

Another Babylonian demon called the *sedu* was possibly a guardian spirit, like the *qarin/qarinah* which we shall visit later. But it was also seen as having evil propensities. The sedu and a similar demon called the *lamassu* were often appealed to at the end of written invocations that have survived to this day on clay tablets. 'These malign influences were probably the prototypes of the Arabian jinn, to whom they have many points of resemblance,' Spence observes.

In northern Mesopotamia, the Assyrians feared a variety of spirits that were described as half-human and half-supernatural. Some of these demons engaged in sexual relations with humans – another jinn characteristic. The offspring of these demon-human unions was said to be a spirit creature called the *alu*, sometimes identified as a wind demon (like Pazuzu) which haunted desolate ruins and abandoned buildings and would enter houses like a ghost and steal people's sleep.

Primordial jinn were sometimes portrayed in reliefs and sculptures by Babylonian and other artists of Mesopotamia. A few representations of the utukku have survived the ravages of time. They show a creature with a powerful human body, large wings, and a beast's head – a cross between a bird of prey and a lizard.

Other unique representations of the jinn in the Arab East have been found in the oasis-city of Palmyra in what is now Syria. Palmyra, also called Tadmor or Tudmur, was a trade emporium and a crossroads of peoples and cultures in ancient times, first settled by the Amorites and Aramaeans, then conquered by the Romans in the first century. Taken by the Arabs in the seventh century, it endured until the sixteenth. Because of its location on the principal east-west caravan route, Palmyra's culture and society were influenced by Phoenicians, Hebrews, Babylonians, Persians and Greeks. Its cultural tapestry was rich and diverse. When the Romans seized the city, Palmyra's main temple, said to have been built by King Solomon of the Israelites, had already stood for two thousand years. Impressive ruins, including temples to Semitic deities such as Ba'al of the Canaanites, Nabu of Babylon and the goddess Allat of Arabia, survive to this day. Ancient jinn reigned in Palmyra as tutelary or guardian deities.

Palmyra is perhaps most famous for Zenobia, the beautiful and brilliant third-century Syrian queen who led a revolt against Rome and created a breakaway Palmyrene Empire in Egypt and the Levant. She ruled this short-lived realm for about five years, until she was defeated and taken to Rome in golden chains by the soldier-emperor Aurelian in 274. Zenobia's claim of descent from Dido of Carthage and the Greek queen Cleopatra VII of Egypt demonstrates the cultural and social complexity of Palmyra and its people.

Palmyra's Arabian jinn-gods are often called *gny'* (*jny'*) or *ginnaya* (plur. *ginnayê*), an Aramaic term that some Western scholars have tried to link with the Roman-origin *genii* (singular *genius*), tutelary or household deities.[10] The ginnayê of Palmyra are indeed similar in function to the Latin genii, and the resemblance was probably encouraged during the period of Roman occupation. Roman genii protected individuals, families and places. Even as late as the European Renaissance, the

Latin term 'genius' had not taken on its modern meaning of a person endowed with great intellect and creativity. In Leonardo da Vinci's time, extraordinary accomplishments of artists or scientists were attributed to their genius, or attendant spirit.[11] The Palmyrene jinn were protective and supportive as well, but they were indigenous and ancient, dating back millennia.

Like the jinn of today's Bedouins, Palmyra's ginnayê were said to resemble human beings in appearance and behaviour. The artists of Palmyra portrayed them in the specific roles that the deities played in Palmyrene society. For example, a surviving stele shows images in relief of Ashar and Saad, two well-known Palmyrene ginnayê, dressed in Roman-style togas; Ashar is shown mounted on horseback, with a quiver of arrows attached to his saddle, and Saad is standing beside the horse, holding a round shield. These ginnayê were tasked with taking care of or protecting human lives and enterprises – hence the weapons – and thus the people of Palmyra gave them the appellation *šbb'*, or 'close', revealing their position as guardians to their human charges.

Ginnayê were regarded as protectors of caravans, cattle and desert villages, and shrines were built in their honour. The ruins of these sanctuaries remain today as isolated reminders of Palmyra's golden era. The Arabs of Palmyra and the surrounding area were mostly Bedouin in origin and many combined two ways of life, shepherding and farming, much as the Bani Tamim of Saudi Arabia's Jabal Shammar region did until the nineteenth century. As tribesmen passed from a nomadic lifestyle to a sedentary one, the tutelary jinn-gods were always present, offering security in times of change. Ginnayê protected the Bedouins in their wanderings as they drove camels, sheep and goats from one pasture to another, and they also gave comfort to those raising crops and facing the hazards of drought, storms and pestilence.

The ginnayê of ancient Palmyra also protected the trading caravans. Camels loaded with all kinds of trade goods could fall victim to bandits and other renegades. The caravans were furnished with escorts through the desert and this human protection was supplemented by the supernatural presence of ginnayê.

During the Roman occupation of Palmyra, from the first to fourth centuries, the hamlets around the city were not only centres of settled life but also relay and staging points for the merchant caravans. In this bustling setting the cult of tutelary ginnayê proliferated.

Palmyra scholar Javier Teixidor asserts that ginnayê were frequently invoked in pairs by citizens who sought their protection, and that reliefs found in the ruins of the ancient city usually portray each one in a characteristic guise. Why they were often venerated in pairs remains a mystery. But the personalities of these spirit beings were rather clearly delineated. For example, one of the prominent jinn deities of Palmyra is Abgal, often portrayed as a youth with long hair and moustache, wearing local dress and grasping a lance. Abgal sometimes stands alone, but he is often shown with other gods whose cults flourished in the desert among Arab nomads, including Azizos, Maan, Ashar and Shalman – gods of the plains like himself.

A well-known pairing is Maan and Saad. In an altar inscription at Ras esh-Shaar, Syria, dating to August 194 AD, Maan is described as a 'good and bountiful god'. He carries a lance and rides a horse. Saad, his associate deity, rides a camel. Maan's feast day was celebrated in Palmyra every August 16. Beef dishes were prepared for the occasion.

Ashar, whom we have seen earlier in the company of Saad, is also sometimes teamed with Abgal. In such cases, Ashar appears as a horseman in Arab dress, hefting a lance and shield. Ashar and Saad are portrayed at Dura-Europos with identical Parthian hairstyles (huge puffs of curls on each side of the face), bushy moustaches and identical local garments.

Shlmn and Shlmt are male and female respectively. Some scholars maintain they are siblings and identify them with the Assyrian deities Shulman and Shulmanitu. Shlmn, called 'good and bountiful' like Maan, is invoked along with Abgal on an altar at Ras esh-Shaar.

The jinn god Shai' al-Qaum is a protector of caravans. His Arabic name means 'protector of the people', or 'the one who accompanies the people', suggesting that his cult was particularly favoured by nomadic tribes. There are parallels between this god and the angel of Yahweh in Exodus 23:20: 'Look, I am sending an angel to precede you, to guard you as you go and bring you to the place that I have prepared.'[12]

The Hebrews of antiquity – from the kingdoms of David, Solomon and their successors in Palestine to the Babylonian captivity to the

Roman conquest in 70 AD – were for long familiar with jinn and the lore associated with them.

According to Talmudic tradition, after Adam and Eve were driven from the Garden of Eden, Adam was separated from Eve for 130 years. During this time female spirits had intercourse with Adam, and male spirits with Eve, and from these unions the *mazikeen*[13] were born. Some Talmudic scholars have called them ghouls and demons. Others have characterised them as 'fairies', somewhat reminiscent of the European Celtic variety: winged creatures that could fly and practise magic. Victorian explorer-translator Sir Richard F. Burton believed the mazikeen were equivalent to jinn.[14] They were able to foretell the future and could shapeshift. Like humans, they enjoyed feasting and drinking, and they married and had children.

Belief in jinn continued unabated in the Arab East through Roman and Byzantine times to the coming of Islam in the seventh century, when these spirit beings were integrated into the new faith through Qur'anic revelation and the personal experiences of the Prophet. Two streams of knowledge were at work here: One was the folk interpretation of jinn, which, as we have seen, is largely Mesopotamian in origin, developed in cities, towns and villages with an eye towards the desert, and incorporating age-old regional beliefs about nature spirits, demons and divinities. The other stream was channelled by Greek and Roman philosophers and proto-scientists, and focused on the role of 'demons' (in Greek, *daimones*) as intermediaries between men and gods. Belief in demons was widespread in the Graeco-Roman world; it may have originated in Mesopotamia as well but underwent considerable evolution and refinement at the hands of such thinkers as Socrates, Plato, Aristotle, Plutarch, Porphyry and Augustine.

The demons of the pre-Christian era were natural spirits, inhabiting high places and the upper air, neither good nor evil in their essence, but often protective and inspirational, and conveyors of knowledge and talent. Socrates believed that the inspiration for his philosophical abilities came from a personal demon. Diotima of Mantinea, a female philosopher and tutor of Socrates, says in Plato's *Symposium*: 'Everything demonic is intermediate between God and mortal. God has no contact with man; only through the demonic is there intercourse and conversation between man and gods, whether in the waking state or during sleep.' Aristotle thought demons were responsible for human dreams. Plutarch and Porphyry speculated that since demons inhabited the upper air, they may have come from the Moon.[15]

The Platonist and Neo-Platonist philosophers, who powerfully influenced early Christian theology, maintained that some demons were good and some were evil. This distinction eventually found its way into Islamic thinking. The Christian theologians, however, moved towards the belief that all demons were evil. Tertullian, a second-century Christian theologian of Berber descent,[16] said demons prey on 'the captive and outwitted minds of men'. He declared: 'They have their abode in the air, the stars are their neighbours, their commerce is with the clouds.' St. Augustine, another North African convert from paganism, reported that pagans of his day believed that 'gods occupy the loftiest regions, men the lowest, the demons the middle region ... They have immortality of the body, but passions of the mind in common with men.' But in his *City of God*, written in the fifth century, Augustine, reflecting the growing Christian sentiment of his day, says demons have no redeeming value and are totally evil. He calls them 'aerial animals ... most eager to inflict harm, utterly alien from righteousness, swollen with pride, pale with envy, subtle in deceit'.

Graeco-Roman concepts of demons were quite familiar to the people of the Middle East and the Arabian Peninsula, through conquest, colonisation and peaceful interaction (including the spread of religion by travelling merchants). These concepts did not supplant local beliefs but may have influenced or supplemented them. Greek and Roman notions of demons certainly had an impact on Islamic philosophers, theologians and other scholars of the Umayyad and Abbasid eras, since these thinkers actively built on the knowledge of their Graeco-Roman predecessors.

Islam

In Western Arabia, where Islam was born, one of the many roles of jinn was to inspire poets and soothsayers. Poetry was a particularly popular oral art among the people of Arabia. The ability to recite beautiful poetry or foretell the future was thought to be a sign of being possessed by jinn. Even madmen were afforded special protected status by the Arabian tribes, because they were thought to be *majnun*, or 'jinn-possessed'. As the historian al-Tabari relates, the Prophet himself originally feared that his revelations might not be divine, but rather the work of jinn.[17] Despite his initial doubts, the Prophet was persuaded by his wife Khadija and her cousin Waraqa, among others, that his revelations were divinely inspired.

Throughout his life, the Prophet remained suspicious of poets, who exercised great influence among the tribes. One poet, however, Hassan ibn Thabit (d.665), won Muhammad's favour by using his poetic skills in competition against the bards of other tribes and on behalf of the Prophet's mission and became known as the 'Poet of the Prophet'. Hassan claimed he first acquired his poetic talent in his home city of Yathrib (later called Medina), when a female jinn accosted him in the streets, knocked him down and pressed upon his chest, forcing him to recite three verses of poetry. Throughout his life, Hassan maintained that his poetry was jinn-inspired. The Prophet disagreed, asserting that Hassan derived his inspiration from Allah.[18]

The earliest Muslim interpretations of jinn regard them as having free will, like humans, able to choose between good and evil. The Qur'an itself has a chapter devoted to these spirit beings: Sura 72, Al-Jinn. This sura begins by mentioning a group of jinn who listened to the recitation of the Qur'an and decided to accept Islam: 'They said, "We have really heard a wonderful Recital! It gives guidance to the Right, and we have believed therein: We shall not join (in worship) any (gods) with our Lord."'

An ancient mosque in Mecca is dedicated to the jinn who accepted the Prophet's message. Masjid al-Jinn (Mosque of the Jinn) is either the locale where the jinn actually listened to the Prophet recite the Qur'an, or the place where he received the revelation of the sura called Al-Jinn. Sir Richard F.Burton visited the mosque during his pilgrimage to Mecca in 1853:

> Descending a flight of steps, – for this Mosque, like all ancient localities at Meccah, is as much below as above ground, – we entered a small apartment containing water-pots for drinking and all the appurtenances of ablution. In it is shown the Mauza al-Khatt (place

> of the writing), where Mohammed wrote a letter to Abu Mas'ud after the homage of the Jinnis. A second and interior flight of stone steps led to another diminutive oratory, where the Prophet used to pray and receive the archangel Gabriel.[19]

These jinn made a commitment to monotheism, the core of Islam. Other Qur'anic passages indicate that jinn had heard of earlier revelations, such as that of Moses and the Trinitarian doctrine of Christianity.

For Muslims, the beings we call jinn – however they may be conceptualised – are an integral and ever-present part of the language and theology of their faith. The existence of these creatures is assumed and reiterated in numerous places in the Qur'an. The book, at its very outset, calls Allah *rabb al-'alamin*, 'lord of the worlds', understood from the earliest days of Islam to mean all possible worlds that could exist, including the worlds of humans, of jinn and of heaven. The Qur'an often mentions mankind and jinn together as the two types of creatures capable of receiving – and accepting or rejecting – the divine message. Muhammad, as founder of the faith, regarded the reality of jinn – as did his compatriots – as commonplace and indisputable. The *hadiths*, or recorded sayings and traditions of the Prophet and his circle, mention jinn and their activities on numerous occasions, as routinely as they mention the existence and deeds of humans.

Muhammad ibn Isma'il al-Bukhari, who lived from 810 to 870 AD, was one of the greatest and most reliable compilers of hadiths. His multi-volume collection of carefully culled and attested accounts dating from the time of the Prophet (some two centuries earlier) is called *Al-Sahih* (*The Complete*). Al-Bukhari's hadiths involving jinn are generally regarded as the most authoritative accounts on the subject.

Some of the most popular hadiths are those of the Prophet's companion Abu Hurayrah, who narrated more than 5,300 incidents from Muhammad's life. In one of these, the Prophet is quoted as saying that a 'big ifrit' or jinn demon came to him one night and tried to interrupt his prayers, but Muhammad overpowered him. Muhammad said, 'I wanted to fasten him to one of the pillars of the mosque so that all of you could see him in the morning'; the Prophet, however, relented and sent the defeated ifrit away 'humiliated'.[20]

In another hadith, Muhammad's cousin Ibn Abbas relates an occasion when the Prophet was preaching and a barrier was suddenly and mysteriously created between the 'devils' and the 'news from heaven'. Previously, jinn had been able to eavesdrop on happenings in heaven and thereby acquire news of the future, which they could impart to soothsayers and other magicians. Without warning, this divine 'back channel' was cut off, and the jinn lost one of their powers. At the same time, fire was thrown down upon the jinn – perhaps a shower of meteorites. They soon discovered that the new barrier in heaven against their eavesdropping was the result of Muhammad's recitation of the Qur'an to his followers. These jinn then went to their fellows and told them about the 'wonderful Recital'. As we have seen earlier, these jinn embraced Islam and thus were no longer called devils. This conversation among the jinn was subsequently revealed by God to Muhammad.[21]

Abdur Rahman ibn Awf, one of the earliest converts to Islam, related a tradition passed on by the reliable jurist and hadith transmitter Masruq ibn al-Ajda', that on the night the jinn heard Muhammad reciting the Qur'an, 'a tree informed the Prophet about them'.[22] What kind of tree it was and how the information was conveyed remain a mystery. But we do know that the Prophet was something of an environmentalist in his day; he had a fondness for trees and encouraged their planting, saying those who grew them would be rewarded in heaven.

The association of jinn with magic and fortunetelling, an ancient linkage that predates Islam by millennia, survived the coming of the Prophet and, in fact, thrived for many centuries after the establishment of the faith. Even the most illustrious of the early Muslims did not find such a relationship surprising. For example, 'Abdullah ibn 'Umar (caliph's son, companion of the Prophet and renowned jurist) said that his father, Caliph 'Umar, once met a man who had been a foreteller – a soothsayer or a predictor of the future – before the coming of Islam. Such foretellers, as we have seen, often claimed to rely on the jinn for their predictions. 'Umar said to the man, 'Tell me the most astonishing thing your female Jinn has told you of.' The man replied, 'One-day while I was in the market, she came to me scared and said, "Haven't you seen the Jinns and their despair and they were overthrown after their defeat [and prevented from listening to the news of the heaven] so that they [stopped going to the sky and] kept following camel-riders [i.e. 'Arabs']?"' 'Umar said, 'He is right,' and added, 'One day while I was near their idols, there came a man with a calf and slaughtered it as a sacrifice [for the idols]. An [unseen] creature shouted at him, and I have never heard harsher than his voice. He was crying, "O you bold evil-doer! A matter of success! An eloquent man is saying: None has the right to be worshipped except you [O Allah]." On that the people fled, but I said, "I shall not go away till I know what is behind this." Then the cry came again: "O you bold evil-doer! A matter of success! An eloquent man is saying: None has the right to be worshipped except Allah." I then went away and a few days later it was said, "A prophet has appeared."'[23]

One of Muhammad's companions particularly revered by today's Shi'ites, Jabir ibn Abdullah, recounts in a hadith how the Prophet counselled people on ways of dealing with mischievous jinn. 'Cover your utensils and tie your water skins, and close your doors and keep your children close to you at night, as the Jinns spread out at such time and snatch things away,' Muhammad said. Another account says that in this instance the Prophet used the word 'devils' instead of 'Jinns'.[24]

According to Muhammad's third wife, 'Aisha bint Abu Bakr, who was the source of many hadiths about her husband, some people asked the Prophet about soothsayers. He said, 'They are nothing.' They persisted, saying, 'O Allah's Apostle! Some of their talks come true.' Muhammad then replied, 'That word which happens to be true is what a Jinn snatches away by stealth [from Heaven] and pours it in the ears of his friend [the foreteller] with a sound like the cackling of a hen. The soothsayers then mix with that word one hundred lies.'[25]

To believers, jinn are just another type of creature created by Allah, along with angels, humans, animals and plants. Less exalted than angels, jinn rank above humans in some respects, and below them in others. As a result, jinn are often mentioned in the Qur'an in conjunction with humans – Allah addresses or acts upon both men and jinn. The word 'jinn' and its variants occur at least 29 times in the Qur'an, and the word 'shaytan' and its plural occur 88 times, as does the word 'angels' (*mala'ika*). By comparison, the word 'land' (*barr*) appears 13 times in the Qur'an and the word 'sea' (*bahr*) 33 times.

The jinn of Islam enjoy supernatural powers but they also have some human qualities, including intelligence, emotions and free will. Jinn who choose Islam are generically considered good jinn. Those who reject the one God are regarded as evil or demons. Those who choose revealed religions other than Islam, such as Christianity or Judaism, often have a more ambiguous status.

Evil jinn generally have free rein in the world of men, except during the holy fasting month of Ramadan, when they are prevented from troublemaking. Ramadan is a time when Muslims refrain from all food and drink during daylight hours and ideally spend their freetime reading the Qur'an and contemplating their faith. Allah makes this easier by keeping the evil jinn at bay.

Al-Tirmidhi explains in his collection of hadiths, 'When the first night of Ramadan comes, the devils and rebellious jinns are put in chains and the doors of hell are closed, none of them remains open. The doors of heaven are open and none of them remains closed. And a caller calls, "O seeker of goodness, come forward, and O seeker of evil, desist. And Allah has many (in this month) who will be freed from Hell." This announcement is made every night.'[26]

Good jinn, who accept Allah, are not restrained during this period.

According to Islam, evil jinn are classed among the three categories of evil spirits (demons) that will be cast into Hell after the Last Judgement:[27]

1. fallen angels (*shayatin* or 'satans')
2. unbelievers among the jinn (i.e., jinn that do not accept Islam), and
3. pagan deities (such as Pazuzu, the wind deity of ancient Babylon).

Islamic tradition says Allah created the jinn before the creation of Adam. Both jinn and men were created in heaven and lived in paradise. As God relates in the Qur'an: 'We created man from sounding clay, from mud moulded into shape; and the jinn race, We had created before, from the fire of a scorching wind' (Qur'an, 15:26–27). No one knows how much time elapsed between the creation of jinn and man. Some scholars, including thirteenth-century encyclopedist Zakariya al-Qazwini, contended that the jinn had populated and ruled the earth before the creation of Adam, but they relinquished this role when Allah punished them for their arrogance and pride.

When we call jinn 'fire spirits', we are referring not to their current nature but rather to their origin – just as man's nature is no longer clay but blood, bone and tissue. In addition to giving the above description of the jinn's origin from fire of hot wind, Islamic scripture also describes the original substance as smokeless fire: 'And He created Jinns from fire free of smoke' (Qur'an, 55:15). Muslims sometimes call the jinn 'the people of the fire'.

As to the nature of the jinn, some early Islamic scholars – such as philosopher Abu al-Hasan al-Mawardi of Basra (972–1058, known to medieval Europe as Alboacen) – believed that jinn lacked bodies of their own and did not inhabit bodies of other creatures. However, jinn were known to have their own independent existence, so these scholars were at a loss to explain what form they took. Al-Mawardi's conviction that jinn were totally incorporeal was a minority view. Many other scholars, including Abu'l-Faraj ibn al-Jawzi (d.1201) and Taqi al-Din ibn Taymiyyah (1263–1328 AD), believed that jinn did have bodies which were either defined, with density, or subtle, so fine that human vision cannot detect them. The Qur'an states that Satan and his jinn followers cannot be detected by humans: 'he and his tribe watch you from a position where ye cannot see them' (Qur'an, 7:27). One opinion circulating among Islamic scholars of the Middle Ages was that jinn had weight and density equivalent to those of air.

The conventional Muslim belief is that jinn die, just as humans do. Jinn also share emotions with humans. One of these is envy. The evil eye is the magical manifestation of envy – one who looks covetously on another's possessions or loved ones can magically inflict harm in the process. Many Muslims believe two types of evil eye exist: human and jinn. To defend against both kinds, Muslims recite various Arabic protective phrases, such as '*audhu billah*' (I seek refuge in God). In the case of other emotions that jinn share with humans, such as love, hatred, resentment, fear, and the like, one can expect magical or non-magical manifestations, some of them quite familiar to our species, and others less so. These types of emotional displays are frequently the bread-and-butter of jinn lore, and we shall encounter them again and again as this book unfolds.

Islamic authorities are divided over whether jinn and humans can interbreed or intermarry – not to mention whether they *should* do so. There have been many opinions over the centuries, based on interpretations of the clues found in the Qur'an and the hadiths. Syrian Islamic scholar Muhammad Amin ibn Abdin (d.1836), of the Hanafi[28] Sunni school, believed it was lawful to prohibit the marriage of a man to another man, to a hermaphrodite, to a polytheist woman, to a close relative, or to a female jinn. To him, marriage of a female human to a male jinn was simply inconceivable. Ibn Taymiyyah, a scholar held in high regard by many conservative Muslims today, believed that it was theoretically possible for humans and jinn to intermarry and have children. As far back as the seventh century, a prominent Islamic theologian named al-Hasan al-Basri decided that marrying a jinn was possible but impermissible. Some 14 centuries later the debate continues among Muslims, with most sentiment opposed to intermarriage with jinn. We shall return to this theme later, in our discussions of jinn behaviour.

Early Legends

Building on primordial interpretations of the jinn and the Islamic context that came to envelop much of this form of spirit belief, the peoples of Arabia and the greater Middle East developed a wealth of legends that sought to explain in detail this mysterious and significant phenomenon.

One of these old legends tells us about the original home, or homeland, of the jinn – a homeland that in a geographical sense is said to surround us yet; in fact, it may never be located. Just as Zeus and his fellow Greek gods had Mount Olympus, the fairies of Britain had the island of Avalon, and the Norse divinities called Asgard their home, the ancestral home of the jinn was Qaf, sometimes called the Qaf Mountains and sometimes simply Mount Qaf (in Arabic Jabal al-Qaf). Standing at the edge of the world, the slopes of Mount Qaf were the homeland of jinn tribes as well as of the elusive, eternal phoenix bird (*'anqa*), which had retreated to these remote peaks to live a life of isolation.[29]

The Qaf range is a mysterious chain of high mountains, fashioned out of emerald by Allah, which circle the known world and are very difficult to reach. Although not explicitly mentioned in the Qur'an, these mountains are described in hadiths and in numerous tales of the pre-Islamic prophets, including the collection by Muhammad al-Kisa'i (d.804).[30] The Qaf Mountains are believed to take their name from the Arabic letter *qaf*, which is also the name of the fiftieth sura of the Qur'an (Al-Qaf). Some scholars, among them the Persian geographer Mustawfi (died after 1340), asserted that the fiftieth sura was named after the Qaf Mountain, though this remains uncertain.[31]

As late as the fourteenth century, Qaf was included in standard geographical works produced in the Islamic world. Geographer-historian Ibn Fadl Allah al-'Umari of Damascus (1301–1349), in his encyclopaedia *Masalik al-Absar fi Mamalik al-Amsar* (*Pathways of Vision in the Realms of the Metropolises*), wrote: 'All mountains are branches of the range which encircles most of the inhabited world. It is called Jabal al-Qaf, and is the mother of the mountains, for they all stem from it.'[32]

Qaf was the loftiest of the mountain ranges created by Allah to support the earth and was the parent of all other earthly mountains, to which it was linked by subterranean ranges. The range is separated from the world of men by the oceans that surround the known world. In some Islamic cosmologies, the Qaf Mountains held the world and its oceans together like the rim of great bowl. A surviving manuscript of al-Qazwini's well-known geography, *'Aja'ib al-Makhluqat* (The Wonders of Creation), has an illustration that shows a disk-like earth with the surrounding range of Qaf Mountains resting on the back of a giant bull (al-Rayyan), which in turn stands on a vast fish (Behemoth) held up by an angel. This type of visualisation of the structure of the universe was not unusual in the thirteenth century.[33]

In that era, earth tremors were sometimes attributed to the Qaf Mountains or to the bull and fish. Even as late as the sixteenth century, Egyptian theologian Jalaluddin al-Sayuti and other Islamic scholars were describing earthquakes as punishments from Allah, transmitted via subterranean connections with the Qaf range or with the cosmic bull and fish.

A detailed description of the mountains of Qaf appears in the Persian romance of Hatim Tai,[34] where the region is called the home of the jinn and of their Persian equivalents, the *pari's* (or *peris*) and *divs* (or *devs*). From this Persian epic, says nineteenth-century Irish mythologist Thomas Keightley, 'it would seem that this mountain-range was regarded as, like that of the ancient Greek cosmology, surrounding the flat circular earth like a ring, or rather like the bulwarks of a ship, outside of which flowed the ocean; while some Arab authorities make it to lie beyond, and to enclose the ocean as well as the earth'.

According to Hatim Tai's account, the Qaf Mountains were said to be composed of green peridot or chrysolite, whose reflection gave a greenish tint to the sky – echoing older accounts that the mountains were made of emerald.

As for the kingdoms of the Qaf range, Keightley observes: 'Jinnestan is the common appellation of the whole of this ideal region ... Its respective empires were divided into many kingdoms, containing numerous provinces and cities. Thus in the Peri-realms we meet with the luxuriant province of Shad-u-kam [Pleasure and Delight], with its magnificent capital Juherabad [Jewel-city], whose two kings solicited the aid of Caherman against the Deevs and also the stately Amberabad [Amber-city], and others equally splendid. The metropolis of the Deev-empire is named Ahermanabad [Aherman's city]; and imagination has lavished its stores in the description of the enchanted castle, palace, and gallery of the Deev monarch, Arzshenk.'[35]

Al-Tabari relates a fascinating story of a conversation between the Prophet and his son-in-law, Ali ibn Abi Talib, about two strange cities that were linked to the mountains of Qaf.[36]

The cities – Jabulqa[37] in the east and Jabulsa in the west (called Djaboulqa and Djaboulsa in a well-known French translation of al-Tabari's history) – were said to be made of emerald and were impossibly large, each measuring some 12,000 parasangs (at least 36,000 miles) long and 12,000 parasangs wide.

Ali asked the Prophet whether these cities existed in the same world that humans inhabit. Muhammad replied enigmatically: 'The two cities are situated in darkness and contiguous to the mountain Qaf.'

The Prophet said that each city was guarded by fortresses, and in each fortress there was a garrison of 1,000 men who stood guard each night. The guards' tour of duty lasted a year. The cities required such garrisons because they contained enormous quantities of gems which had been captured from enemy peoples called Tharis and Taqil. These peoples warred against Jabulqa and Jabulsa unceasingly, day and night.

According to the Prophet, the inhabitants of Jabulqa and Jabulsa knew neither Adam nor Iblis. They had no experience with either sunlight or moonlight and did not know that Allah had created the sun and the moon. The light that shone on them came from Mount Qaf itself, and from the stones and the walls and the very dust on the ground. The Prophet said the people of these cities ate herbs that grew on the ground and wore no clothing.

'So they are angels,' Ali said. 'No, but their obedience to Allah is similar to the angels,' Muhammad said. The people of Jabulqa and Jabulsa were all males, the Prophet added. There were no women or children in these cities. The Prophet revealed that he had visited Jabulqa and Jabulsa during his Night Journey[38] and that the inhabitants had accepted his message and embraced Islam. He tried to do the same at Tharis and Taqil and towards the people of Yajuj and Majuj (Gog and Magog), but 'they were infidels and did not accept Islam'.

The Prophet said it was impossible for most people to travel to Jabulqa and Jabulsa, because they would have to walk for four months in utter darkness. In ancient times, in the days of the 'Ad people (to be discussed later), three men who had accepted the pre-Islamic prophet Hud and his monotheistic message fled from their own people and travelled to Jabulqa and Jabulsa. Since those days, no one had done it. Dhu al-Qarnain (He of Two Horns), a legendary figure identified with Alexander the Great,[39] had tried to reach the cities but he gave up halfway, after walking for two full months in darkness.

In Arabic literature, Qaf, as the primeval mountain, came to symbolise the cosmic mountain where the natural and supernatural met and the link between the terrestrial and celestial worlds was established.

Opinions varied as to what lay beyond the mountains of Qaf. One medieval account describes the regions beyond as two ranges of mountains stretching over 500 years' travel. The first ranges are forever blanketed in snow and beyond them are ranges lashed with eternal blinding hail. Some believed that but for the snow and hail, these countries would have been melted by the burning fires of hell.

In another old legend, the regions beyond Mount Qaf are inhabited by different races of angels. They stretch for forty days' travelling and consist of meadows and plains so white that they shine like silver.

Beyond these plains lie a land of gold, then seventy lands of silver and finally a land of musk.[40]

Although it is known that jinn have kingdoms in the Qaf Mountains and elsewhere, details about them are hard to find. There is a brief medieval reference to a jinn kingdom in the writings of the Ikhwan al-Safa' (Brethren of Purity), a rather mysterious literary and scientific brotherhood based in Basra, Iraq, in the tenth and eleventh centuries:

> The years went by, and [the Prophet] Muhammad was sent, God bless and keep him and all his House. He called men and jinn to God and to Islam. One party of jinn answered his call and became good Muslims.
>
> In the course of time a king arose over the jinn, Biwarasp the Wise, known as King Heroic. The seat of his kingdom was an island called Balasaghun in the midst of the Green Sea, which lies near the equator. There the air and soil were good. There were sweet rivers, bubbling springs, ample fields, and sheltered resting places, varieties of trees and fruit, lush meadows, herbs, and flowers.[41]

From the lands of the jinn, we move now to the first interactions between jinn and mankind. Among the oldest of the jinn legends is one tightly intertwined with the Judaeo-Christian tradition: the origin of the Devil or Satan – known as Iblis or Eblis to the Muslims – and his role in the creation and fall of Adam and Eve.

In the Islamic faith, Iblis is generally regarded as a jinn who was elevated to the status of an angel, presumably because of his intelligence and leadership qualities. As we have seen, angels were originally created by Allah from light, and jinn from smokeless fire. A few Muslim scholars suggest that Iblis was of angelic origin and others say he was created separately by God. But the Qur'an states clearly that he was a jinn, even if elevated to the rank of angel: 'Iblis ... was one of the jinns, and he broke the command of his Lord' (Qur'an 18:50).

According to an old Muslim legend, related in part by al-Qazwini and popular among the Egyptians,[42] the first jinn to be created by Allah from the *simmum*, or hot scorching desert wind, was Asoom bin Jan-Tarnushi. He and his descendants were given dominion over the earth, and they followed certain rules laid down for them by Allah. In this pre-Adamite world, inhabited by jinn-ancestors of great power, as many as 72 kings held sway, each of them bearing the royal title Sulaiman (Solomon). The last of these Sulaimans was Jann ibn Jann. From him the collective name for all jinn races, 'jann', is said to derive, and some believe it is an older form of today's word 'jinn'.

After 25,000 years, the jinn became proud and arrogant and began to disobey the divine rules. Allah sent legions of angels to punish the jinn, and many of the wrongdoers were destroyed. The rest were dispersed to distant islands – all except for Iblis, an impressive jinn who was captured and brought to heaven. There he was educated and raised to the ranks of the angels. Because of his eloquence, he became a teacher of the younger angels.

Meanwhile, the scattered jinn on the earth came together again and formed a nation on an island in the Southern Ocean. Iblis saw this development and was drawn by the lure of power. He left heaven and descended to the island, where he persuaded the jinn to accept him as their king. He then took a second name: Azazil.[43] He maintained his links with heaven, however, as we shall see.

As defined in Islamic theology, angels , unlike humans and jinn, have no free will and have no choice but to obey Allah. The Qur'an (66:6) describes angels as 'stern [and] severe, who flinch not [from executing] the commands they receive from Allah, but do [precisely] what they are commanded'. Iblis was able to exercise free choice and reject a command by Allah. When Allah created man, Iblis/Azazil refused to bow down before Adam, as commanded by his Lord. He did so, he said, because he, Iblis, was made from fire and man was made from clay, and thus he was superior to Adam.[44] Iblis was also able to compel the obedience of some rebel angels, who fell from grace with him and will suffer in Hell with him after the Day of Judgement. (This apparent inconsistency, given that angels have no choice but to obey Allah, has not been satisfactorily explained.)

Iblis figures prominently in the Islamic version of the Genesis story of the creation of man and woman (Adam and Eve, or in Arabic, Adam and Hawa), their temptation by the Devil and their subsequent fall from grace. Professor Gordon Darnell Newby of Emory University in Atlanta presents the Islamic account in his reconstruction of a celebrated work of early Islam, the eighth-century biography or *sîrah* of the Prophet Muhammad by Ibn Ishaq.[45]

Ibn Ishaq accepted the truth of the Iblis legend and described the jinn on earth before the creation of man: 'Before Iblis fomented rebellion among the angels, his name was Azazil. He dwelt on earth and was the most diligent and the most knowledgeable of the angels. That is what led to his pride. He was of a race called the Jinn.'

When Allah decided to create Adam, according to Ibn Ishaq's sirah, he did so as a test of the obedience not only of man but also of the angels and indeed of all of creation. He brought together the angels of earth and heaven and said, 'I will create a viceregent on earth' (Qur'an 2:30). Allah also told the angels, 'I am about to create man from clay. When I have fashioned him [in due proportion] and breathed into him of My spirit, fall ye down in obeisance unto him' (Qur'an 38:71–72). All the angels agreed to obey Allah except Iblis. Overcome with envy, covetousness and pride, he kept silent.

When the newly created Adam got to his feet, the angels fell down, prostrating themselves before him, as Allah had ordered. Iblis refused to do so. Allah said, 'O Iblis! What prevents thee from prostrating thyself to one whom I have created with My hands? ... I will certainly fill Hell with thee and those who follow thee – every one' (Qur'an 38:76–86). Iblis persisted in his refusal, so Allah cursed him and drove him from the Garden of Eden, condemning him and his followers to Hell, but according to the Qur'an, he also granted them 'a stay of execution' until the Day of Judgement.[46] In the meantime, Iblis and his followers inhabit what can best be described as a 'parallel universe', from which they are able to pass over into the mortal world and where they devise sinful temptations for humankind.

The ultimate domain of Iblis, when he is not abroad upon the earth working mischief and promoting evil, is at the lowermost level of Hell. Eleventh-century historian Abdul Malik al-Tha'alibi, in his *Qisas al-Anbiya'* (Stories of the Prophets), relates a tradition that divides our planet into seven realms which correspond to the seven stages of Hell, with the abode of Iblis at the very bottom. The lowest level has two distinct environments: *As-Saqar*, or the place of burning, and *Athara*, the place of damp and great cold. The latter, al-Tha'alibi relates, is the home of Iblis, who is chained in the midst of the rebel angels, his hands fastened – one in front of him and the other behind, except when set free by God to chastise his fiends. Meanwhile, Allah set about creating Eve.[47]

Citing Christian and Jewish as well as Islamic traditions, the sirah of Ibn Ishaq relates that Allah made the newly created Adam fall asleep. He then removed one of Adam's ribs from an opening in his left side and healed him while he slept. Allah then created Eve from this rib as a mate for Adam.

While this was happening, Iblis approached the animals of the world to see which one would bear him into the Garden of Eden so that he could speak with Adam and his wife and tempt them towards evil. All of the animals refused except the serpent. He told her: 'I will protect you from the children of Adam; you will be under my protection if you get me into the Garden.' She placed him between her two fangs. They entered the Garden and they both spoke from her mouth. In Ishaq's sirah, the serpent is depicted as a graceful animal that walked on four legs, but as a result of her collaboration with Iblis, Allah punished her and condemned her to travel on her belly.

Adam, in a conversation with his mate, expressed a wish that he and Eve could live forever. When Iblis overheard this, he realised this was Adam's weakness, and he came to Adam, hiding in the serpent's mouth, and offered him eternal life. Iblis began to weep uncontrollably, and when Adam and Eve heard him, they asked, 'Why are you weeping?' Iblis said, 'I'm weeping for the two of you, because you will die and leave the pleasure and honour you are in.' That moved them deeply. Then Iblis whispered in Adam's ear something that eventually would become a verse in the Qur'an: 'Shall I lead thee to the Tree of Eternity and to a kingdom that never decays?' (Qur'an 20:120). Iblis also befriended Eve in similar fashion. Both Adam and Eve ate of the fruit of the Tree of Eternity, which was the only tree forbidden to them by Allah. Unlike the Judaeo-Christian version of this story, which blames Eve for first eating the fruit and persuading Adam to do likewise, the Qur'an assigns responsibility equally to Adam and Eve. The Islamic version also rejects the Christian concept of 'original sin' and asserts that Adam and Eve were forgiven for their transgression after they repented.

The early Shi'ite scholar Ibn Babuya al-Qummi (d.991) records the view that the Garden of Eden was not entirely earthly, and that Adam and Eve were sent down to mountain peaks outside Mecca. Adam landed on Safa, and Eve on Marwa. Jewish tradition relates that Adam fell down in India on a mountain called Wasim in a valley called Bahil, between the lands of al-Dahnaj and al-Mandal. Eve fell to Jeddah in the land of Mecca. (Adam eventually travelled to Mecca and rejoined Eve.)

According to Ibn Ishaq, after Iblis was expelled from the Garden of Eden, he married the serpent whose mouth he had entered when he spoke to Adam, and they had offspring.[48] At various times, Iblis also mated with other beings to produce a number of demons. One of these mates was Lilith or the Qarinah, who, as we shall see later, bore numerous jinn offspring.

Five sons of Iblis are noted among the most celebrated of the evil jinn: Ṭīr (Bird), who causes disaster, injury and loss; al-A'war (the One-Eyed), who promotes lewd and lascivious behaviour; Sūt, consummate liar and the father of lies; Dāsim, who ruins marriages by generating hostility between husband and wife; and Zalambūr, who presides over dishonesty, thievery and fraud in the business world.[49]

An interesting branch of the Adam legend with rich jinn connections involves Lilith, a she-demon of great antiquity whose important role in Semitic lore received its richest embellishment in the late Middle Ages in Jewish Kabbalistic mystical writings particularly prevalent in Spain. Lilith – who became something of a feminist symbol in the late twentieth century for her reputed declaration of sexual independence – is regarded by many as a Jewish figure, but, in fact, her origins can be traced back to Sumerian and Babylonian legend. She first appeared as Lilitu, one of a class of wind or storm demons in Sumer, in about 4000 BC. She later became identified with the Qarinah, a female jinn who acts as a woman's 'shadow' and wreaks havoc with the woman's relationship with her husband. Lilith is also regarded by long-standing Semitic tradition as the mother of the jinn.

In a study of these traditions, American anthropologist Raphael Patai declares: 'No she-demon has ever achieved as fantastic a career as Lilith, who started out from the lowliest of origins, was a failure as Adam's intended wife, became the paramour of lascivious spirits, rose to be the bride of Samael the Demon King,[50] ruled as

Queen of Zemargad and Sheba, and ended up as the consort of God himself.'

The main features of Lilith's mythical biography first appear in Sumerian culture about the middle of the third millennium BC. What she meant for the biblical Hebrews can only be surmised, but by the Talmudic period (second to fifth centuries AD) she appears in rabbinic writings as a fully developed she-demon.[51]

The earliest known mention of a female demon of similar name appears in the Sumerian King List – an ancient manuscript recording the kings and dynasties of Sumer dating from about 2400 BC. This document asserts that the father of the Sumerian hero Gilgamesh was a Lillu-demon. The Lillu was one of four demons belonging to a class of vampires or incubi-succubi.[52] The other three were Lilitu (Lilith), the she-demon; Ardat Lilli (or Lilith's handmaid), who visited men at night and bore them ghostly children; and Irdu Lilli (apparently Ardat Lilli's male counterpart), who would visit women at night and make them pregnant. Originally these were members of a class of wind and storm demons – nature spirits that came out of the desert to terrify settled populations and were, as we have seen, forerunners of the jinn.

This early Lilith was believed to be beautiful but sexually promiscuous and a vampire. Once she chose a lover, she would keep him captive without ever giving him true satisfaction. She was unable to bear children and had no milk in her breasts.

The 4,000-year-old Sumerian epic poem *Gilgamesh* describes Lilith (there called Lillake) as building a house in a *huluppu* or willow tree that had grown on the banks of the Euphrates River since the days of Creation. The tree had been cultivated by the mother-goddess Inanna (or Ishtar), who wanted to make herself a throne and a bed from its wood. However, to her dismay, a dragon had nested at the base of the tree, and a Zu-bird (another Sumerian storm demon) had placed its young in the highest branches. Lilith had made her home in between the other two creatures. The hero Gilgamesh, seeking to rescue the tree for the goddess, slew the dragon with a bronze axe, whereupon the Zu-bird fled with its young into the mountains, and a terrified Lilith tore down her house and escaped into the desert.

Lilith is also possibly portrayed in a Babylonian terra-cotta relief[53] that dates from about the same period as Gilgamesh. A beautiful nude with wings and the feet of an owl, she stands upon two lions which face away from each other and is flanked by owls. She is wearing a headdress with several sets of horns, a common Mesopotamian motif signifying her divine status.

By the seventh century BC, as shown by a tablet found at Arslan Tash in northern Syria, Lilith had morphed into a winged sphinx. On her body is this Phoenician-Canaanite inscription:

O Flyer in a dark chamber,
Go away at once, O Lili!

These lines are from an incantation used to protect women from adversity in childbirth. They show us that by the seventh century BC, the myth of Lilith had all the major features of a baby killer, which were fleshed out in detail 2,000 years later by Kabbalistic Judaism.

'Evidently, Lilith was a well-known she-demon in Israel of the eighth century BC, whose name had only to be mentioned to conjure up the beliefs current about her,' says Patai. 'That she is said to find a place of rest in the desert seems to tie in with the episode recorded in the Sumerian Gilgamesh fragment: after Lilith fled into the desert, she evidently found repose there.'

The medieval Kabbalistic legends present Lilith as the first sexual partner of Adam. In Genesis, there is an unspecified period of time between the creation of Adam and that of Eve. During that period, God (called Yahweh by the ancient Hebrews) created the Garden of Eden, settled Adam there and created animals and birds to help him. 'But no helper suitable for the man was found for him' (Genesis 2:20). The Kabbalists asserted that during this time, Lilith was created for Adam out of the same clay used to create the man, but she proved unsuitable as a wife. At that point, Eve was created from Adam's own rib. The Lilith story is perhaps best told in the *Alphabet of Ben Sira*, an anonymous, quasi-religious text of Aramaic and Hebrew proverbs and haggadic commentaries compiled between the eighth and eleventh centuries and attributed to Jesus Ben Sira (Sirach).[54] The relevant passage is in the fifth of Ben Sira's responses to Nebuchadnezzar, king of the Babylonians. The king's son is ill, and Ben Sira writes God's name and that of three angels on an amulet for the boy. When Nebuchadnezzar asks for an explanation, Ben Sira tells the story of Lilith.

In this account, Lilith is described as refusing to assume the 'missionary position' during sexual intercourse with Adam and consequently leaving him: 'She said, "I will not lie below," and he said, "I will not lie beneath you, but only on top. For you are fit only to be in the bottom position, while I am to be the superior one."'[55] According to this account, Lilith uttered the name of God (a sign of great power), took flight in the air and left the Garden of Eden, flying to the Red Sea coast, which she made her new home.

Lilith then went on to mate with various demons that she encountered beside the Red Sea, creating countless *lilin* or succubus demons. According the *Alphabet of Ben Sira*, Adam urged God to bring Lilith back, so three angels were dispatched after her. The angels – named Senoy, Sansenoy and Semangelof – threatened to kill one hundred of Lilith's demonic children for each day she stayed away. But Lilith replied that she would prey eternally upon the descendants of Adam. 'I was created only to cause sickness to infants,' she told the angels. 'If the infant is male, I have dominion over him for eight days after his birth, and if female, for twenty days.' But she agreed that children could be rescued from her clutches by invoking the names of the three angels. For this reason, parents in Ben Sira's day wrote the names of these angels on amulets worn by their children. Lilith never returned to Adam. She spent her time seeking out men to seduce in their sleep, and finding newborns and other children to slay in their beds.

Palestinian and Syrian legends tell of an evil spirit-creature called the Qarinah who is a jinn identical to Lilith. Swiss theologian Ernst Zbinden describes the Qarinah in his definitive 1953 work on jinn lore, *Die Jinn des Islam und der Altorientalische Geisterglaube* (The Jinn of Islam and Ancient Eastern Spirit Belief): 'As in Egypt, every man is supposed to have an evil demon that pursues him. Among men, it is called *Qarîn* [i.e., companion], among women, *Qarînah*. However, only the female demon plays a role in superstition. The Qarînah is also called *tâbi'ah* [pursuer] or *ukht* or *shaqîqah* [both mean "sister"]. Christians and Jews also believe in this evil being' – a reference to Lilith.

The Qarin and Qarinah concept is at bottom that of the 'spirit double'. This concept is very ancient, most probably going back to the 'ka' (personal life-force or double) of ancient Egyptian religion, as well as to certain animistic beliefs found in Egypt and Arabia at the time of the Prophet. The Qarin can be a person's double, his companion, his mate, or his familiar demon. The spirit double is generally understood to be a jinn, particularly a shaitan, born at the time the person is born and his constant companion throughout life. The Qarin or Qarinah's task is to try to turn the person towards evil. Jesus and Muhammad had Qarins, according to tradition, but their spirit doubles were good, not evil. Muhammad's Qarin was the angel Gabriel (Jibril), according to al-Tha'alibi.

In the case of the Qarinah legend, a female spirit double was elevated to mythic proportions. Popular Arab tradition relates that the Qarinah mated with Iblis to beget the jinn and was at the beginning Adam's first wife – that is, Lilith. The Hebrew legends surrounding Lilith, as we have seen, were written down between the eighth and eleventh centuries but doubtless circulated much earlier. Lilith was a familiar figure to Arabs in areas where Jews tended to settle, such as Palestine and the cities of northwestern Arabia, just as the Qarinah was familiar to Jews. The identities of Lilith and the Qarinah appeared to merge in the early centuries of Islam. Because Lilith/Qarinah was rejected by Adam, she came to hate human beings.

Zbinden states: 'The Qarînah destroys a pregnant woman's baby in the womb. She pursues children, so that they fall sick and die. Or she causes the father to be impotent. As the enemy of children, this being is also euphemistically called Umm el-Sibyân, i.e., Mother of Children, or el-Jiddah, the Grandmother. Other euphemistic names for her include Umm el-Lêl, i.e., Mother of Night [Lilith], el-Shahhâqah, i.e., the Sobber, and el-Khunfusah, i.e., the Female Scarab or Dung-Beetle. The Qarînah is subject to the jinn king Murrah, who rules over Monday.'[56]

English chaplain and folklorist James E. Hanauer,[57] who spent most of his adult life in nineteenth-century Palestine, observed about the Qarinah: 'She is the deadly enemy of all women, especially such as have recently become mothers. These must be carefully nursed and watched, and, together with their new-born babes, fenced round with charms and holy amulets, and so forth, lest the Karineh strangle them in her jealous fury, or frighten the mother into madness. European doctors, who pretend to know everything, do not know the dreadful dangers to which they expose women in childbed when they forbid other women to visit and amuse them.'[58]

The Qarinah's – Lilith's – 'jealous fury' is pure hatred for humanity and its progeny, and it dates back to her dispute with Adam, which cost her the role of 'mother of humankind', the title bestowed on Eve. Instead, Lilith/Qarinah became known as the 'mother of the jinn' and inspired fear instead of affection among the various peoples of the Middle East.

Another early legend closely linked to jinn lore is that of King Solomon, son of David, monarch of the Israelites, who probably ruled in the tenth century BC. Muslims revere the main figures of the Old and New Testaments as prophets – including Adam, Noah, Abraham, Joseph, Moses, Solomon, David, Jesus and others. They often call Solomon by his Arabic name, 'Sulaiman'. Although historical ancient Israel was a small realm by most standards, Islamic traditions held that Solomon ruled an extensive kingdom which extended south from Palestine into the Arabian Peninsula as far as Yemen. He was uncommonly wise and understood the language of birds, animals and insects. He also possessed the power to command strict obedience from the jinn. This power derived from a sealing ring that Solomon wore which had magical powers and properties. The ring, commonly known as 'the Seal of Solomon', is said to have carried 'the most great name of Allah' and the Star of David. Some accounts say that the ring was partly brass and partly iron; that with the brass the king stamped his written commands to the good jinn, and with the iron those to the evil ones. Over both types of jinn, he was said to have unlimited power, as he also had over the birds, the winds and the wild beasts.[59] Other accounts say the ring featured a large diamond or sapphire set in gold.

Details of Solomon's sovereignty over the animal kingdom can be found in biblical verses such as 1 Kings 5:13 – 'He spoke also of beasts and of fowl and of creeping things and of fishes' – but belief about his dominion over jinn and other spirit creatures derived in part from Hebrew rabbinical commentaries on interpretations of biblical verses such as 1 Chronicles 29:23 – 'Solomon sat on the throne of the Lord'[60] – as well as Ecclesiastes 2:8, where Solomon recalls how he accumulated *shiddah veshiddot*, an obscure phrase that rabbinical commentaries identified with the Hebrew word for demon, *shed*. As we have seen earlier, the *sheddim* are the Jewish equivalent of jinn. The Qur'an explicitly says that Solomon was given control of the winds and the evil jinn – the shayatin or devils – by Allah, in order that they might serve him: 'Then We subjected the Wind to his power, to flow gently to his order, whithersoever he willed – as also the evil ones [shayatin], including every kind of builder and diver' (Qur'an 38:36–38). The spirit beings called shayatin here are called 'jinn' elsewhere in the Qur'an (such as 34:12–13). They included 'builders' of palaces, fortresses and temples, and 'divers' for precious pearls. Allah told Solomon that these servants were his to command or to place in the service of others, as he wished, without accountability: 'Such are Our Bounties: whether thou bestow them on others or withhold them, no account will be asked' (Qur'an 38:39).

The Arabic literary encyclopedist Ibn al-Nadim, writing in his *Fihrist*, a catalogue of the tenth century, says King Solomon was attended by seventy jinn. One day, Solomon called the chief of the jinn, named Fuqtus (or Quftus), to review these demonic servants. Fuqtus taught Solomon the name of each jinn and its capabilities with regard to humans. The king made all of the jinn swear a pledge of loyalty to him. They did so, and then they departed. Ibn al-Nadim identified these jinn by name: Fuqtus, 'Mrd, Kywan, Shimr'al, Firuz, Mhaqal, Zaynab, Syduk, Jndrb, Siyyar, Zanbur, al-Da'hs, Kawkab, Hamran, Dahir, Qarun, Shidad, Sa'sa'ah, Baktan, Harthamah, Takallum, Furuq, Hurmiz, Hamhamah, 'Ayzar, Mazahim, Murrah, Fatrah, al-Haym, Arhbh, Khyth', Khyfth, Rayah, Zuhal, Zawba'ah, Mhtukara, Hayshab, Tq'ytan, Wqas, Qdmnh, Mufarrish, Ayra'il, Nizar, Shftil, Dywyd, Ankara, Khatufah, Tnkyush, Misalqar, Qadim, Ashja', Nawdar, Tythamah, 'Usar, Thu'ban, Naman, Nmudrky, Tyabur, Sahitun, 'Udhafir, Mirdas, Shytub, Za'rush, Sakhr, al-'Aramram, Khashram, Shadhan, al-Harith, al-Hurth, 'Udhrah ('Adhirah) and Faqruf.

Ibn al-Nadim went on to say that all of these jinn were the offspring of seven other jinn who may have been jinn kings and were each identified with a day of the week: 'The first was Danhash, the first day; [then] Shakhba, the second day; Marbaya, the third day; 'Abara, the fourth day; Mismar, the fifth day; Namudarki, the sixth day; Bakhtash, the seventh day.'[61]

Through his power over the winds, Solomon could make them carry him wherever he wished; early Muslim religious storytellers, such as Wahb ibn Munabbih (654–729 AD), say that he used the winds to travel from place to place in what amounted to a portable palace, complete with his entire entourage, kitchens and stables. As Wahb describes it, 'He commanded the wind to carry his throne (*'arsh*) and he ordered it to carry the chairs (*karasi*) of his companions. Then he sat on his throne. He seated the men on his right and left, and he placed the jinn behind him in this way – some sitting, some standing. Then he said to the wind, "Carry us", and to the birds, "Shade us". Then the wind carried him and the birds shaded him and his companions among men and jinn from the sun.'

The Bible credits Solomon with building the First Temple of Jerusalem and many other public works and fortifications but does not describe the workforce he employed. The Qur'an records that Solomon harnessed the power of the jinn for his ambitious and demanding construction projects: 'They worked for him as he desired, making Arches, Images, Basins, as large as Reservoirs, and [cooking] Cauldrons fixed in their places' (Qur'an 34:13). Jinn servants participated in the building of the First Temple. Not all jinn were subjected to involuntary servitude under Solomon; as the Qur'an points out, those forced to do the king's bidding were evil jinn and were being punished for their misdeeds. If any of these jinn refused to obey Solomon's orders, Allah made him 'taste of the Penalty of the Blazing Fire' (34:12), that is, the flames of hell. Other jinn served Solomon freely, for example, joining his army and marching as warriors alongside men. As the Qur'an relates, 'before Solomon were marshalled his hosts – of Jinns and men and birds, and they were all kept in order and ranks' (Qur'an 27:17).

Solomon's powers over the jinn are detailed in the 'Testament of Solomon', one of the falsely attributed Greek works called the Pseudepigrapha, dating from about 200 AD. The Testament describes how Solomon built his Temple by compelling the jinn into service.[62]

One of the 'evil jinn' mentioned in the context of King Solomon is Ashmedai or Asmodeus, sometimes called the 'King of the Demons' but actually only a lieutenant of the greatest demon, Iblis. Ashmedai/Asmodeus appears in the Bible, in the Hebrew Talmud and in traditional Arabic folklore. Of eastern Iranian origin and probably initially a demon of wrath, Asmodeus evolved into a demon of lust. The story of Solomon and Ashmedai appears in *The Arabian Nights*. In 'The Tale of the Fisherman and the Jinn', Ashmedai was confined in a jar by Solomon, who 'sent his minister ... to seize me, and this vizier had me bound and brought against my will to stand before the prophet [Solomon] as a suppliant'. Ashmedai, described in the Burton translation of the *Nights* as a *marid* (extremely powerful jinn), was accused by the king of being an unbeliever. When the jinn stubbornly refused to proclaim his faith in God, Solomon had Ashmedai imprisoned in the jar, which was sealed with lead, stamped with the Seal of Solomon inscribed with God's name and cast into the sea. Hundreds of years later, the jar was recovered by a fisherman, who frees the *marid* and hears his story.

This Arab folktale has many elements in common with a tale from the Hebrew Haggadah[63] in which Solomon sends his chief minister Benaiah ben Jehoiada to capture Ashmedai to assist in the building of the First Temple of Jerusalem. Solomon held Ashmedai in chains with the help of a magic ring marked with the name of God. Although the tale does not explicitly say so, we must assume that this magic ring was the celebrated Seal of Solomon. Because it was by tricking Solomon into lending him the magic ring that Ashmedai was able to depose Solomon, only after taking back that ring was Solomon (according to one version of the story) able to return to power.[64]

Another jinn-related figure that surfaces in the Solomonic legends is Lilith, the putative mother of the jinn. The Testament of Solomon, a pseudepigraphical work ascribed to King Solomon but written in Greek between the first and fifth centuries AD, relates an encounter between Solomon and Lilith. In the Testament, Lilith calls herself 'Obizuth',[65] another name of that well-known ancient female demon of the Middle East that was blamed for miscarriages and infant mortality. The Testament of Solomon, which is believed to be a Christian text, is said to be based on Judaeo-Hellenistic magic, such as was practised in Alexandria in the early Christian era, and contains the earliest known example of the use of an amulet to ward off Lilith. Solomon, in this text, receives his magical ring, the Seal of Solomon, from the archangel Michael (other traditions say Jibril/Gabriel), and he proceeds to summon and conquer a variety of demons from Greek, Arabic, Jewish, Christian and other traditions. The work shows how different religions, magical traditions and legends were closely intertwined in the Mediterranean region of the first to fifth centuries.

The relevant passage begins as follows: 'And I [King Solomon] adored the Lord God of Israel and bade another demon present himself. And there came before me a spirit in woman's form that had a head without any limbs, and her hair was dishevelled. And I said to her, "Who art thou?" But she answered, "Nay, who art thou? And why dost thou want to hear concerning me? But as thou wouldst learn, here I stand before thy face. Go then into thy royal storehouses and wash thy hands. Then sit down afresh before thy tribunal and ask me questions, and thou shalt learn, O king, who I am."'

Solomon did as she asked, so that he might learn of her deeds, understand them and share them with others. He sat down and said to the demon, 'Who are thou?' Lilith replied, 'I am called among men Obizuth, and by night I sleep not, but go my rounds over all the world and visit women in childbirth. And divining the hour I take my stand, and if I am lucky I strangle the child. But if not, I retire to another place, for I cannot a single night retire unsuccessful. For I am a fierce spirit of myriad names and many shapes. And now hither, now thither, I roam. And to westering parts I go my rounds. But as it now is, though thou hast sealed me round with the ring of God, thou has done nothing. I am not standing before thee, and thou wilt not be able to command me. For I have no work other than the destruction of children and the making of their ears to be deaf, and the working of evil to their eyes, and the binding their mouths with a bond, and the ruin of their minds, and paining of their bodies.'[66]

Solomon listened and marvelled at her appearance. Her body was entirely cloaked in darkness and her limbs invisible, but he could see her eyes, 'altogether bright and cheery', and her hair was 'tossed wildly like a dragon's'. Her voice was very clear.

'Tell me by what angel thou are frustrated, O Evil Spirit?' Solomon said, seeking to outwit her by identifying her nemesis. 'By the angel of God called Afarof', she replied, 'which is interpreted Raphael, by whom I am frustrated now and for all time. His name, if any man know it, and write the same on a woman in childbirth, then I shall not be able to enter her. Of this name the number is 640.'

Having heard this, King Solomon, exercising control through the power of his ring, ordered Lilith's hair to be bound, thereby curtailing her seductive power, and declared that she should be hung up in front of the Temple, so that all the people could see the she-demon for themselves and understand that God had given him the strength, by means of the Seal of Solomon, to restrain her and prevent her from doing evil. So went the encounter of two of the most compelling figures of early, jinn-related legend, one of them good and wise, the other spiteful and evil.

A very popular story – in fact, love story – from the Solomonic tradition involves a queen reputed to be of partial jinn descent. Bilqis, the Queen of Sheba (a kingdom in Yemen also known as Saba), who visited King Solomon in Jerusalem, was reputed by Arab legend to have been the daughter of a human father (the Himyarite ruler Hadhad ibn Sharhabil) and a jinn mother (Umaya).

The story of Bilqis and Solomon includes both Jewish and Arab elements; their relationship is chronicled in the Old and New Testaments and in the Qur'an. With contributions from Wahb ibn Munabbih and Muhammad al-Kisa'i, a compelling version of the tale emerges:[67] One day the angel Gabriel gave King Solomon a ring that shone so brightly he could barely look at it. The ring gave Solomon the power to control the four winds, who spoke to him with one voice in a single breath, 'O prophet of God, God has subdued us for you, so ride us to any place you desire.'

As we have seen, the ring gave Solomon power over the beasts and birds, allowing him to converse with them and – significantly, in the context of this story – made him king of the jinn. Gabriel rounded up the evil jinn who had been designated for service under Solomon, driving them as a shepherd drives his flock; they poured into Jerusalem from every direction. The jinn came in every shape and size, some with hooves, with long tails and flapping ears; some with bodiless heads and headless bodies.

Solomon ordered the male jinn to construct an immense palace for the king's use. The palace was supported by a thousand marble pillars affixed with maps of gold. Diving deep into the sea, jinn brought back dazzling white pearls to decorate the onyx halls of the palace. Meanwhile female jinn cooked in the kitchens, setting out meals on tables for a mile – enough to feed all the jinn and all the children of Israel.

One day, a hoopoe bird arrived from Saba and brought Solomon word of the beautiful and powerful Bilqis. Intrigued by descriptions of her, he invited her to travel to Jerusalem, and she accepted the invitation.

Bilqis journeyed to the country of the famed Solomon and decided to stay for some time in order to learn more about the wise king and his all-powerful God. The king and the queen found each other fascinating and gradually began to fall in love. This worried the captive jinn, who feared that if Solomon and Bilqis married and had a son, the jinn would be forced to continue in service for another generation, and perhaps much longer, never again tasting freedom. A jinn named Zabwa warned Solomon: 'O prophet of God, a son by this woman will be cruel, sharp, and hot in body and soul.' Zabwa and his fellow jinn spread rumours that Bilqis was one of their own – which indeed was partly true – and as such had a jinn's tell-tale hairy legs and donkey feet.

Solomon was troubled by the rumours that Sheba had jinn blood coursing through her veins. To find out if the rumours were true, Solomon devised a test for Bilqis. In his private quarters he had an expansive glass floor constructed, with water and fish beneath it. Waiting on the far side of the glass floor, he beckoned to Bilqis to cross the room and join him. Mistaking the glass for a fish pond, the queen lifted her skirts to walk through the water. The king saw her legs and looked away. He finally confessed to Bilqis: 'Lo! It is a floor, made of smooth glass.'

What exactly did Solomon see? The sources are unclear. Most agree that Bilqis's feet were not hooved but that her legs were quite hairy. Solomon was alarmed by this discovery. His jinn rejoiced, but only for a brief moment, for the king commanded them to prepare a lotion of slaked lime and ash to remove the queen's leg hair. At this point Bilqis said, 'O my Lord! I have indeed wronged my soul: I do [now] submit [in Islam], with Solomon, to the Lord of the Worlds' (Qur'an 27:44).

Accepting monotheism, Bilqis married Solomon and bore him a son called Rehoboam, whose arms were said to reach down to his knees – a sure sign of leadership, according to the belief of the time. Bilqis remained with Solomon for seven years and seven months and then died. Solomon buried her beneath the walls of Palmyra in Syria.[68]

Why Palmyra? This ancient Syrian city, as we have seen, has traditional jinn connections and according to ancient Arab legend was also said to have been constructed by the jinn on orders of King Solomon. This belief may have been passed to the Arabs by Palmyra's Jewish population. Charles Lyall refers to the legend in his *Translations of Ancient Arabian Poetry* (1930):

> The germ, if nothing more, of the stories about Solomon's power over the Jinn, of which the Thousand and One Nights are full, was current before al-Islam, since [the Arab poet] an-Nabighah, who died before the Kur'an was revealed (though he was well acquainted with Christianity both at al-Hirah and in Syria), speaks of the authority granted him [Solomon] by God over them, and the building by them for him of Tadmor in the Wilderness 'with slabs and pillars'.

A variant of this legend portrays Palmyra as much older than Solomon but rebuilt by the jinn on his orders. This version was related in the late nineteenth century to Lady Anne Blunt, the first European woman to explore Central Arabia, by an Arab informant born in Palmyra.[69] According to this account, Queen Bilqis is anachronistically described as a Christian.[70]As Lady Anne tells it: 'This Christian lady wished to have a house between Damascus and Irak [Babylonia], because the air of the desert was good, but no such house could be found. Then Solomon, who was king of the birds as well as king of men, sent for all the birds of the air to tell him where he should look for the place Belkis desired, and they all answered his summons but one, Nissr [the eagle], who did not come.'

Nissr was busy tending his father, an old eagle whose health was failing. The other birds were unable to find a good location for Bilqis's house. Solomon used a magic ointment to restore the health of Nissr's father, who repaid the monarch by telling him the best location for the queen's house: 'It is Tudmur, the city that lies beneath the sands.' And he showed them the site.

King Solomon ordered the jinn who served him to clear away the sand, and when they had done so, Tudmur or Palmyra was revealed 'with its beautiful ruins and columns'. The city was then rehabilitated by the jinn to suit Bilqis's requirements. Lady Anne's informant told her that 'ghosts' (afrits) continued to haunt the ruins of Palmyra in the late nineteenth century. Also bizarre things happened to people who lived in the area. For example, 'there is a man at Tudmur more than a hundred years old, and ... when he reached his hundredth year, he cut a completely new set of teeth, and is now able to eat like a young man'. Lady Anne observed: 'I have since been told by dentists that the fact of a third set of teeth being cut in old age is not unknown to science.'[71]

In another version of the Bilqis and Solomon story, the queen did not spend the rest of her life in Jerusalem with the king. Medieval Yemeni historian al-Hasan al-Hamdani (c. 893–945) says she was eventually sent back to Yemen by Solomon.[72] The king dispatched a troop of his servant jinn with her, and they built a number of castles for Bilqis in Yemen.

Al-Hamdani says that according to Muhammad ibn Khalid, grandson of a companion of the Prophet, one of these castle-building jinn wrote a book that listed the palaces, fortresses and strongholds dotting the Yemeni landscape. Al-Hamdani quotes from the jinn's book: 'We built Salhin, working on it continually seven and seventy autumns. Ghumdan, we built in Azal, and also with dextrous hands we raised Baynun. As a place for joy Sirwah was erected. [We also built] Hind, Hunaydah, Tulfum, Raymah, and seven of the fortresses therein.'

Many of these named structures still exist in Yemen. 'Even to-day', writes German historian Oswald Spengler, 'the country is full of innumerable relics of mighty castles, which in Islamic times were popularly attributed to supernatural builders. The stronghold of Gomdan [Ghumdan] is a work of twenty tiers.'[73]

Note that Muhammad ibn Khalid's account says that the immense fortification at Ghumdan was one of the castles built by Solomon's servant jinn. Al-Hamdani points out that Muhammad ibn Khalid related elsewhere that the castle of Ghumdan was built by Ili-Sharha and Sha'irum Awtar, both human rulers.[74] Al-Hamdani, a serious scholar, voices doubts that jinn were involved in the construction. But he is careful to leave open the possibility:

> Inasmuch as the narratives have varied especially with regard to this particular tradition, discerning men have shown that the demons [servant jinn] had nothing to do with the building of any of these

> eight palaces. Nevertheless, they do not categorically deny its possibility because of the antiquity of the jinn's participation in such crafts which is evident in the words of God – may he be exalted and magnified – concerning the jinn attending Solomon, 'They made for him what he pleased of fortresses and bowls [large] as watering-troughs and cooking-pots that will not move from their places' [(Qur'an, 34:12a)]. A number of the kings of al-Yaman have been ministered to by the jinn in services other than construction. They also used to bring for [their masters] fresh fruits from India.

When it comes to writing about what the jinn did or did not do in the course of history, it is very difficult to rule out anything.

We have barely touched the surface of the complex, multi-level legend of King Solomon and his jinn. We shall see flashes and glints emerging from this treasure trove time and again as we sample the jinn beliefs of many peoples and countries. On one level, the tale comes to an end with the death of Solomon, which in itself is not as simple and clear-cut as one would assume.

Rabbinic legends say that Solomon was punished by God for excessive pride by being dethroned and replaced with an impersonation by the jinn king Ashmedai (who, as we have seen, was one of Solomon's jinn servants involved in the construction of the First Temple in Jerusalem). In what some have called a 'Prince and the Pauper' fable, the real King Solomon was forced to wander the world as a beggar until nothing remained of his former majesty but the simple wooden staff in his hand. One version of this Midrashic tradition states that Solomon never regained his throne and died in abject poverty – a belief supported by some interpretations of Ecclesiastes 2:10: 'and this [i.e., only what I am now holding in my hand] was my portion of all my labor'. A more popular rabbinical version says Solomon returned to Jerusalem, ousted Ashmedai and regained his throne. But to the end of his days, he lived in terror of demons and till his death maintained a company of 60 of his most valiant warriors standing guard around his bed.[75]

Solomon did not live a particularly long life. He is said to have assumed the throne at about 20 years of age and died four decades later, at about age 60. The Qu'ran and Arab tradition relate that when the king died he was leaning on his staff, watching his jinn working on his construction projects in Jerusalem. He died silently but did not fall over, and the jinn assumed he was still alive, so they kept working. Eventually, a worm gnawed through the wood of his staff and his body toppled over. Says the Qur'an: 'Then, when we decreed [Solomon's] death, nothing showed them his death except a little worm of the earth, which kept [slowly] gnawing away at his staff: so when he fell down, the Jinns saw plainly that if they had known the unseen, they would not have tarried in the humiliating Penalty [of their Task]' (34:14).

When Solomon died, Muhammad ibn Khalid relates, a jinn travelled down to Yemen, the southern reaches of Solomon's realm, and informed his fellow castle-builders there about the king's death, saying, 'Shake off the dust of labour and go your way.'[76] Not only King Solomon himself but also his vast construction projects had at last come to an end.

A postscript to this story: Many have speculated about the fate of the celebrated Seal of Solomon, the enchanted ring with which he commanded the enslaved jinn. One legend is that it ended up as part of a buried treasure on an island in a lake east of the Egyptian oasis of Siwa. This account is related by Prussian traveller Heinrich von Minutoli, who visited Siwa in 1820. He writes of a tradition that the ring, sword and crown of King Solomon are buried on an island in nearby Lake El Arashi (or Arachie). Europeans who sought to sail to the island were discouraged or threatened by local residents, who felt they would lose their prosperity and independence if 'Christian sorcerers' made off with the treasure.[77] As best can be determined, the alleged treasure has never been found.

Chapter Two

Historical Encounters

[Pope Sylvester II] was accused of gross immorality, blasphemy, magical incantations, the invocation of demons. It was whispered that goblins of fantastic dress and repulsive aspect attended him at midnight during the celebration of impious orgies and profane sacrifices. The diligent propagation of these scandals prepared the way for the punishment meted out in that age to all daring reformers, and especially to those who presumed to interfere with the prerogatives and emoluments of the clergy.

– Samuel P. Scott, historian

Al-Andalus

The Muslim conquest of Spain in the early eighth century AD introduced to the southwest corner of Europe the full panoply of Arab and Islamic custom and belief. Jinn lore and legend flooded into the peninsula and the jinn themselves began appearing there. Fascinating references to the rich folklore of Islamic Spain, or al-Andalus, can be found in the history of ninth-century Cordoban scholar Abdul Malik ibn Habib.[1] Ibn Habib's *Ta'rikh* (History) is the earliest known Arabic chronicle of the first days of al-Andalus after the Arab conquest.

Soon after the conquest of most of Spain, cycles of legends and romances started to develop about how the victory came about. King

Roderic (Ludhariq) was the ruler of Hispania, the former Roman colony and now Visigothic kingdom that encompassed all of present-day Spain and Portugal. According to one of the most popular tales, Roderic violated tradition by opening a padlocked enchanted tower in his capital Toledo, which held a painting that predicted his own downfall and the end of his kingdom at the hands of the Arabs.[2] One of the earliest sources for these romances was Ibn Habib's history. This work, a mixture of historical records and legendary tales, was probably written towards the end of the ninth century, and additions were made to it later.

In the seventh century, Arab armies had swept out of Arabia and conquered all of North Africa. The governor of the northwest part of this territory, the Maghrib, ruling on behalf of the Umayyad dynasty in Damascus,[3] was a military commander named Musa ibn Nusair. According to Ibn Habib, Musa ibn Nusair was also an astrologer who had read in the stars that al-Andalus would be conquered for Islam. He later dispatched and eventually led Arab and Berber forces in their conquest of Spain. The initial Arab landing in Spain on April 29, 711 AD, was led by Musa's deputy, a young Berber general named Tariq ibn Ziyad, after whom 'Jabal Tariq' (Tariq's Mountain) or Gibraltar was named. Tariq's modest force of some 20 Arab officers and about 7,000 Berber cavalry routed the Spanish king's army of more than 30,000 soldiers at the Battle of Guadalete on July 19 of the same year. A larger Arab (primarily Yemeni) force, led by Musa, then made the crossing into Spain. According to a tale told by Ibn Habib, Musa and Tariq, after defeating the Visigoths, marched to a land on the Atlantic coast. They passed over a bridge guarded by a copper talisman armed with bow and arrows. According legend, they besieged and captured a city made of copper and gained possession of a collection of coffers filled with jinn. As Ibn Habib told it, these imprisoned jinn were said to be evil jinn who had disobeyed Solomon many hundreds of years before and had been banished in coffers to the copper city. For his part, Musa was happy to get rid of the jinn-filled coffers, which troubled him and his men and contributed nothing to the progress of the conquest. He sent the coffers on to the Umayyad ruler, or caliph, in Damascus; unfortunately, we learn nothing more of their fate.

This tale, in greatly embellished form, became part of *The Arabian Nights* ('The Story of the City of Brass', Nights 566–578). Here brass was substituted for copper, as is often done in Arabic (where *nuhas* means 'copper', and *nuhas asfar* – 'yellow copper' – means 'brass'). We will return to this tale later and see how a jinn-linked legend from far-off al-Andalus became an integral part of the storytelling tradition of the Arab East.

The Umayyad dynasty of Damascus was ousted in the year 750 by another branch of the Prophet's extended family, the Abbasids, who established their rule at Baghdad. Abdul Rahman, an Umayyad prince, escaped from Damascus and fled to al-Andalus, where he began a new branch of the Umayyad dynasty at Cordoba. Under Umayyad rule, Cordoba became one of the great cities of the world, and al-Andalus flourished economically and socially, becoming known for its tolerance, prosperity and sophistication.

Sufism, or Islamic mysticism, thrived in the open, multicultural environment of al-Andalus under the Umayyads and continued to prosper there for centuries. The Sufis of Islamic Spain, like those elsewhere, were particularly receptive towards jinn.[4] One of the most famous Sufi mystics of the Middle Ages was Ibn 'Arabi, who was born in Murcia in southeastern Spain in 1165. He was initiated into the Sufi Way in Seville while in his early twenties and studied with many of the great Andalusian Sufi sheikhs of his day, such as Abu Ja'far al-'Uryani and Yusuf al-Shubarbuli. He mastered Sufi metaphysical doctrines and reportedly developed 'supersensory' abilities, such as visions, foresight, spiritual communication with the living and dead and powers of healing.

Late in life, Ibn 'Arabi wrote memoirs of his spiritual growth, and these included short biographies of the prominent Andalusian Sufis who had influenced him throughout his life. Some of these Sufis consorted regularly with the jinn – a common practice among Sufi masters.

One such master was Abu Ja'far al-'Uryani, who arrived in Seville around the time when Ibn 'Arabi was beginning to acquire his knowledge of the Sufi Way. Ibn 'Arabi would often visit al-'Uryani, as did many other Sufi students. Al-'Uryani was well known for being able to engage in *dhikr,* or the constant invocation of sacred names, whether awake or asleep. Ibn 'Arabi said he would often watch the master's tongue moving in *dhikr* while he was asleep. Al-'Uryani's spiritual states were so intense and perhaps shocking in their manifestation that the local people of his hometown – 'Ulya, now Loulé, in Portugal – grew hostile towards him. Instigated by a prominent citizen, the community decided to expel him and he journeyed to Seville.

Ibn 'Arabi said Allah punished the people of 'Ulya for this deed by sending a jinn, named Khalaf, to the town. Khalaf occupied the house of the prominent citizen who had prompted the expulsion of al-'Uryani. After taking up residence there, Khalaf summoned the people of the town to gather round the house, which they did. They heard the voice of the jinn asking one of the townspeople whether anything had been stolen from the prominent citizen's house and whether he suspected anyone of taking it. The townsman answered yes to both questions. Khalaf then told the man that he was wrong in his suspicions and instead named another man who was the real culprit, who had fallen in love with the prominent citizen's wife and had committed adultery with her. Khalaf then told the townsman to go and see for himself and he learnt that everything the jinn had told him was true.

Khalaf continued in this manner to expose the hidden evils and vices of the townspeople, driving them, as Ibn 'Arabi put it, to the brink of despair. They begged Khalaf to stop exposing their flaws and weaknesses, but he refused. Khalaf said that he had been inflicted upon them by Abu Ja'far al-'Uryani. The jinn stayed in 'Ulya for six months. Finally the townsfolk went to al-'Uryani and begged him to return, asking forgiveness for what they had done. Al-'Uryani relented and returned to 'Ulya, thereby freeing the people from the torment of Khalaf. The affair, said Ibn 'Arabi, became famous throughout Seville.

Another Sufi master greatly respected by Ibn 'Arabi was Abu al-Hajjaj Yusuf al-Shubarbuli, who came from Shubarbul, a village in the Aljarafe region, about six miles from Seville. He spent most of his time out in the wilderness, Ibn 'Arabi said, adding: 'I myself have witnessed many evidences of his spiritual grace. He was one of those who could walk on water.'

Al-Shubarbuli was accompanied at all times by a righteous jinn who had accepted Islam. One day Ibn 'Arabi went to visit al-Shubarbuli, bringing along with him Sheikh Abu Muhammad al-Mawruri, one of the companions of Abu Madyan, another renowned Sufi. When they arrived, Ibn 'Arabi told al-Shubarbuli that he had brought one of Abu Madyan's companions to see him. At this the Sufi master smiled and said, 'How amazing! Only yesterday Abu Madyan was with me.' Strangely, Abu Madyan was known to be at Bugia at the time – forty-five days' journey away. Thus, as Ibn 'Arabi put it, the visit of Abu Madyan to al-Shubarbuli had been 'of a subtle kind'. Ibn 'Arabi added: 'Indeed, Abu Madyan had long since ceased to travel in the ordinary way.' Ibn 'Arabi asserted that the same sort of thing happened frequently between him and Abu Ya'qub, another great Sufi whom he held in awe.

One night burglars broke into al-Shubarbuli's house while the sheikh was at home and stole some of his belongings. While the robbery was in progress, al-Shubarbuli was in another room, sitting on his prayer rug, too absorbed in his devotions to notice the presence of the thieves. When the burglars tried to leave the house, they could find no exit and the wall around the house seemed to grow higher before their eyes. Terrified, they returned the things they had stolen and after they had done so, the door suddenly appeared before them. Immediately, the leader of the thieves stood by the door and ordered the others to go back inside and get the things they had originally taken. Once again, with the stolen goods in their arms, they could not find the door. The thieves turned to their leader in panic. Even though he had not left his place, he could no longer see the door. After several more attempts to escape with al-Shubarbuli's possessions, the thieves finally realised what was happening. They put back the stolen goods for the last time and left the house humbled and repentant. Ibn 'Arabi said he heard this story from one of the thieves. Here, as in the story of Khalaf, jinn characters become part of a morality tale or fable designed to teach a lesson about right and wrong. Like the stories of Nasruddin or Aesop's fables, these episodes recounted by Sufi master Ibn 'Arabi provide proper guidance on how to live one's life.

Not all of Ibn 'Arabi's jinn stories are morality tales. Some are simply compelling narratives. For example, he described his encounters with a female Sufi adept, Nunah Fatimah bint Ibn al-Muthanna, who also lived in Seville. When Ibn 'Arabi first met her, she was in her nineties. Her only food was the scraps people left at their doors. 'Although she was so old and ate so little,' Ibn 'Arabi says, 'I was almost ashamed to look at her face when I sat with her, it was so rosy and soft.'

Nunha's devotion to Allah was profound. To those who looked at her superficially, she might have seemed like a simpleton – but she believed that anyone who did not know Allah was the real simpleton.

Some of the jinn who had accepted Islam used to sit with her, seeking her companionship. But Nunah, without explanation, would refuse them and ask them to remain hidden. She would remind them of what the Prophet had said the night he captured a big jinn-demon (ifrit) who had tried to interrupt his prayers: 'I remembered the words of my brother [King] Solomon and used them on it.'[5] Solomon had asked Allah only for wisdom, and because of that, Allah had rewarded him with many other gifts as well, including the ability to control jinn-demons. Nunah reminded the jinn around her, just as the Prophet had reminded the jinn he captured, that their supernatural powers were nothing compared with the might of Allah.

Ibn 'Arabi decided to build a hut of palm branches for Nunah, where she could perform her devotions. The first night in her new hut, the oil in her lamp ran out, something that had never happened to her before. 'She got up to open the door to ask me to bring her some more oil and, in the darkness, plunged her hand into some water in the bucket underneath her,' Ibn 'Arabi wrote. 'At this she cursed and the water was immediately changed into oil. She then took the jug and filled it with the oil, lit the lamp and came back to see from where the oil had come. When she saw no further trace of oil she realised that it had been a provision from Allah.'

The wondrous or miraculous did not seem so to Nunah, who calmly accepted the bounty of Allah's universe. This was the way of the Sufis of al-Andalus. For them, the jinn simply came with the territory.

Spirits of the Middle Ages

In the Middle Ages, from about 900 to 1300 AD, the bulk of the world's great achievements in science and philosophy were recorded in Arab capitals such as Cordoba, Cairo, Damascus and Baghdad. The great works of Arabic knowledge, erected, as we have seen, on a foundation built by the Greeks, were subsequently translated into Latin and other languages and shared with the budding universities of Europe, such as Bologna, Paris and Oxford. Particularly under the Abbasids, who ruled Baghdad from 762 to 1258, Arabic was the international language of scholarship. Al-Biruni was one of the finest scholars to work in that language.

Abu Rayhan al-Biruni of Khwarizm in Central Asia (973–1048 AD) was an acclaimed Persian scientist and historian. He was a polymath, an expert in many disciplines, including astronomy, mathematics, physics, pharmacology, geodesy, geography, history and even psychology. George Sarton, a pioneer in the history of science, called al-Biruni 'one of the very greatest scientists of Islam, and, all considered, one of the greatest of all times'. Al-Biruni is perhaps best known for his *Chronology of Ancient Nations* (also called *Vestiges of the Past*), published in 1000 AD. This work, written in Arabic, is notable for containing a defence of the reality of the jinn, nestled in a chapter on the public festivals of the Khwarizmians.

The defence occurs in a discussion of a festival called Nimkhad, which took place on the eleventh day of the month of Rimazhd. In asserting the reality of spirit beings, al-Biruni declares that the Greek philosopher Aristotle, who was greatly revered by the Arabs of the eleventh century, was a believer in jinn and devils.

Al-Biruni relates that the festival of Nimkhad was an occasion for the people of Khwarizm to use perfumes and incense as a means of warding off evil beings: 'They make the smells rise up from the dishes which they lay out for the purpose of keeping off all the injuries of the demons and evil spirits.'

Al-Biruni explains that 'this proceeding is necessary, by way of careful precaution, if some spiritual matters are connected with it'. He notes that the 'most distinguished philosophers', including the great Greek physician Galen[6] and others like him, have acknowledged the effectiveness of such 'precautions' against evil spirits, including charms, incantations and prayers. Al-Biruni observes, 'We cannot help take notice of those who try to prove that all such precaution is futile and false by no other arguments but by mockery, derision, and sneers.'

He declares, 'The existence of jinns and demons has been acknowledged by the most famous philosophers and scholars, *e.g.* by Aristotle, when he describes them as beings of air and fire and calls them "*human beings*".'

Al-Biruni also points out that the Egyptian Christian bishop Yahya Grammaticus[7] and others acknowledged the existence of jinn, describing them as 'the impure parts of the erring souls, after they have been separated from their bodies, who [the souls] are prevented from reaching their primal origin, because they did not find the knowledge of the truth, but were living in confusion and stupefaction'. According to al-Biruni, Mani (210–276 AD), the Persian founder of Manichaeism, expressed a similar view in his books, 'although his indications are expressed in subtle words and phrases'.[8] Al-Biruni (like Ibn al-Nadim) asserts that Mani allegedly received a revelation from a 'Twin' or *Syzygos*, a 'protective double' reminiscent of the Qarin or spirit double. This double was said to have taught Mani truths that he fashioned into a religion. Manichaeism, one of the Iranian Gnostic religions, thrived from the third to the seventh centuries, its popularity blunted by the arrival of Islam.

Another prominent figure of the Middle Ages who wrote about jinn was the blind Syrian poet and philosopher Abu al-'Ala al-Ma'arri (973–1057). It may surprise some that an Arab rationalist such as al-Ma'arri would devote attention to this topic; he was known as a sceptic on various matters of religion and was a firm opponent of superstition. He has often been characterised as a 'freethinker'. One of the issues he raised has been hotly debated since the earliest days of the faith: whether jinn who are believers of Islam can attain Paradise. Al-Ma'arri may not have believed in jinn at all, but he wrote beautifully about good jinn in Paradise in his classic work *Risalat al-Ghufran*, (The Epistle of Forgiveness), which has been described as a kind of Arab *Divine Comedy*.[9]

Al-Ma'arri's imaginative account begins in Paradise, with a new arrival named Sheikh Ibn Mansur who is determined to visit the jinn – 'the people of the Fire', as he calls them – who reside there.[10] So he mounts on the back of one of the horses of Paradise and rides off on his quest.

After a while, 'he beheld cities crowned with no lovely light, but full of catacombs and dark passes'. An angel informed him that this was the garden of those ifrits who believed in the Prophet and were mentioned in two suras of the Qur'an, al-Ahkaf and al-Jinn. An old man was seated at the mouth of a cave. The sheikh greeted him and received a courteous reply. 'I have come,' said he, 'seeking knowledge of Paradise and what may perchance exist among you of the poetry of the Marids'.

'Surely,' said the greybeard, 'you have hit upon one acquainted with the bottom of the matter, one like the moon of the halo, not like him who burns the skin by filling it with hot butter. Ask what you please.'

'What is your name?'

'I am Khaishafudh, one of the Banu Sha'saban: we do not belong to the race of Iblis, but to the Jinn who inhabited the earth before the children of Adam.'

The sheikh said, 'Inform me about the poetry of the Jinn: a writer known as al-Marzubani has collected a good deal of it.'

'All this is untrustworthy nonsense,' replied the old man. 'What do men know of poetry, save as cattle know about astronomy and the dimensions of the earth? They have only fifteen kinds of metre, and this number is seldom exceeded by the poets, whereas we have thousands that your littérateur never heard of.'

This whetted the sheikh's curiosity and his love of literature. He said to the old man, 'Will you dictate to me some of this poetry? In the transitory world I occupied myself with amassing scholarship, and gained nothing by it except admittance to the great. From them, indeed, I gained pigeon's milk in plenty, for I was pulling at a she-camel whose dugs were tied ... What is your *kunya*, that I may honour you therewith?'

'Abu Hadrash,' said he, 'I have begotten of children what God willed.'

'O Abu Hadrash,' cried the sheikh, 'how is it that you have white hair, while the folk of Paradise enjoy perpetual youth?'

'In the past world,' he said, 'we received the power of transformation, and one of us might, as he wished, become a speckled snake or a sparrow or a dove, but in the next world we are deprived of this faculty, while men are clothed in beautiful forms. Hence the saying, "Man has the gift of *hila* [stratagem]and the Jinn that of *haula* [power]." I have suffered evil from men, and they from me.'

Abu Hadrash the jinn then related how he afflicted a young girl with epilepsy. 'Her friends gathered from every quarter and summoned magicians and physicians and lavished their delicacies, and left no charm untried, and the leeches plied her with medicines, but all the time I never budged,' he said. 'And when she died I sought out another, and so on like this, until Allah caused me to repent and refrain from sin, and to Him I render praise for ever.'

Then the old man went on to recite a poem describing his past life.

This image of a repentant jinn happily ensconced in Paradise did not please all of the great thinkers of the Middle Ages. Some Arab scholars – among them the great al-Ghazali himself – asserted that the jinn, believers or not, could not enter Paradise, and that believing jinn instead resided in a kind of limbo between heaven and earth.

The Qur'an (7:44–46) speaks of a curtain (*al-a'raf*) that separates the blessed from the wicked. The word *al-a'raf* means 'the top part of a curtain or veil'. It is also used to denote the mane of a horse, a rooster's crest or the highest or most prominent part of anything. In a broader sense it is applied to any border or boundary between things. Thus, it is similar to the classical *limbus* ('border' or 'fringe'); but, whereas *limbus* did not acquire the meaning of a region beyond the grave until about the thirteenth century, the Arabic word had this meaning, in addition to its ordinary meaning, as early as the time of Muhammad in the sixth century.

Miguel Asín Palacios, a Spanish Arabist, wrote in the early twentieth century about similarities between Muslim descriptions of the afterlife and Dante's *Divine Comedy.* He found that medieval Arabic legends describe the Islamic limbo in various ways: as a pleasant valley studded with fruit trees; as a valley nestled behind a high mountain; as a loft turret, with battlements and a gate, rising between heaven and hell; or simply as a rise or mount in the landscape.[11] Asín declared that these concepts, grouped together, present a picture not unlike that of Dante's limbo, especially if the picture is completed with the description, recurrent in the Prophet's 'Night Journey' (*Miraj*), of the Garden of Abraham and the entrance to the Muslim hell, which, like the castle that forms the antechamber of Dante's hell, also has seven gates. 'Again', Asín wrote, 'this castle, surrounded as it is by seven walls with seven gates, is an almost exact reproduction of the Islamic castle of the garden of paradise, which is surrounded by eight walls with eight gates; as if Dante, in blending the Moslem designs of heaven and hell, had sought to symbolise the neutral nature of the souls dwelling in the limbo'.[12]

The Islamic version of limbo, according to al-Ghazali, has been shown to be the abode of those that lived neither in virtue nor in vice. In keeping with this doctrine, Islamic tradition specifies that certain groups are consigned to limbo, including angels of the male sex and jinn that believe in the Prophet Muhammad.[13] Other residents of Islamic limbo: the infant children of Muslims and unbelievers, men of learning whose vanity has canceled out their merit, and, perhaps most interestingly, martyrs of *jihad* (or war for the faith) who are denied the reward of Paradise because they disobeyed their parents.

According to Asín Palacios, these groups correspond rather well to the groups relegated to Dante's Christian limbo: unbaptised children and the heroes, poets and philosophers whose virtues and talents were neutralised by their lack of faith. There is no Christian counterpart to the believing jinn who fail to achieve Paradise despite their faith. As to the angels of male sex, they seem as puzzling as Dante's neuter angels.

According to the Qur'an and to Islamic theologians, the only suffering that is inflicted on the inhabitants of limbo is a vain longing to enter Paradise: 'They cannot enter for all their longing' (Qur'an 7:46). Their good deeds are balanced by their sins, so they neither sink into hell nor rise to Paradise. Instead they remain suspended between the two. From their position in limbo, they can see and converse with both the blessed and the damned.

Whether the 'good jinn' attain the rewards of Paradise or are relegated to this in-between world is a matter that will doubtless remain on the table and subject to debate by Islamic theologians.

Jinn in the Fihrist

The *Kitab al-Fihrist* (catalogue) of Abu al-Faraj Muhammad ibn Ishaq, known as Ibn al-Nadim, is a unique compilation of Arabic literature from tenth-century Baghdad. Some historians think Ibn al-Nadim was a Persian, in part because of his choice of the unusual Persian word *fihrist* (or *pehrest*) to describe a collection of Arabic literature. But he lived in Baghdad most of his life, apart from a short stay in Mosul. Ibn al-Nadim was a bookseller and calligrapher. He completed the *Fihrist* in about 990. The work records and describes books written in Arabic up to that time by Muslims, Christians and Jews, among others. One chapter covers 'accounts of the exorcists, jugglers, magicians, and those who use incantations, tricks, and talismans' and refers frequently to the jinn. 'The exorcists and magicians assert that the devils, jinn, and spirits obey and serve them, being directed by their command and prohibition,' Ibn al-Nadim says. 'The exorcists, who pretend to observe the sacred laws, claim that this is because of obedience to Allah, may His name be magnified.'

By invoking Allah's name, by observing religious practices and avoiding sin, these 'licit' magicians claim they can secure the obedience of the jinn. The spirits are in effect subjugated by the power of Allah's holy names. Then there are the 'illicit' magicians, who claim they enslave evil jinn through offerings and forbidden acts. These magicians argue that the demon jinn are pleased by the committing of forbidden acts – that is, acts prohibited by Allah. 'Thus the perpetrating of things such as abandoning prayer and fasting, permitting blood, marrying forbidden women, and other kinds of evil actions is also pleasing,' Ibn al-Nadim says. He observes that this type of illicit magic is common practice in Egypt, which he calls the 'Babylon of the magicians', and in nearby regions. Many books of magic have been written in Egypt, he adds, and quotes an eyewitness as saying that that land has both men and women magicians, all of whom use seals, paper charms, sandalwood, incense and other tools for their arts.

Ibn al-Nadim also wrote that King Solomon was the first person in history to enslave the jinn and use them as servants. The Persians, however, he pointed out, believed that their king – King Jamshid, son of Tahmurath – was the first person to make slaves of the jinn.[14]

Ibn al-Nadim was a Shi'ite, an advocate of religious tolerance and an admirer of Aristotle and Greek science as well as the Persian and Indian science of ancient times that had preceded the Greek. Judging from his comments in the Fihrist, he was rather sceptical of the works of magicians, soothsayers and the like, but accepting of the reality of jinn. Aristotle, as we have seen, had made room for demons in his universe, and Ibn al-Nadim was no doubt aware of this.

Genius or Jinn-Master?

Pope Sylvester II, who reigned for just four years, from 999 to 1003, was one of the greatest scholars ever to head the Roman Catholic Church.

A Frenchman, born Gerbert d'Aurillac, he studied the Arabic scientific classics in Spain and later taught them to students in France and Italy, in the process transferring a wealth of scientific knowledge from the Arab-Muslim world to Europe. He pioneered the use of Arabic numerals in Europe and is said to have reintroduced the use of the abacus and the armillary sphere to Europe, the knowledge of which had been lost for centuries. He became the teacher of Otto III, the Holy Roman Emperor, and of Pope Gregory V, whom he succeeded. Pope Sylvester was revered by scholars and scientists for his great learning but was feared and hated by many others. Sylvester was a vigorous opponent of simony and corruption in the Church and had made many enemies among the clergy and Church bureaucracy. His opponents launched a smear campaign against him, accusing him of being a sorcerer, consorting with demons and jinn.

Gerbert d'Aurillac was quick to recognise the value of Arabic scholarship – which radiated into Europe from Baghdad and Cordoba, the capital of Arab Spain. As a young man, he had been a student at the University of Cordoba. He remained there for several formative years and later established schools in France and Italy. He imported books of science and philosophy from every quarter of the world, particularly from Spain, and taught thousands of students, who then spread throughout Europe, carrying his theories and precepts to ever wider audiences.[15]

During his academic career, Gerbert taught geography and astronomy using globes and astrolabes manufactured in Cordoba. He observed the motions of the planets and determined the elevation of the pole through diopters. 'The results of the mechanical ingenuity which amused his leisure moments awakened the horror of his ignorant and pious contemporaries,' observes historian Samuel P. Scott. He also invented a steam or hydraulic organ; a clock with a mechanism largely composed of wheels and pinions; and automatons, whose mysterious movements served to heighten the suspicion among the uneducated that he had diabolical powers.

Gerbert became quite famous in his day, well before rising to the papacy, and as a result he attracted the envy of some of his fellow monks. Perhaps at the instigation of his rivals, marauders plundered his abbey at Bobbio, in Italy in the early 980s. His library was torched, his scientific instruments smashed and his students dispersed. But Gerbert's reputation for wisdom continued to grow. Hugh Capet, king of France and the German emperor Otto III were both his patrons and supporters, helping him to become archbishop of Rheims in 991 and of Ravenna in 998. With Otto's support, in 999 he was named to succeed Otto's cousin, Gregory V, as pope.

'Even in that exalted position, the relentless spirit of ecclesiastical malice did not permit him to rest,' Scott says in his history of the Moors in Europe.

> His attempts to reform clerical abuses brought down upon him the vengeance of the corrupt and rapacious ministers of the papal court. The most absurd fables were invented to account for the results of his scientific experiments, otherwise incomprehensible by mediæval ignorance. He was accused of gross immorality, blasphemy, magical incantations, the invocation of demons. It was whispered that goblins of fantastic dress and repulsive aspect attended him at midnight during the celebration of impious orgies and profane sacrifices. The diligent propagation of these scandals prepared the way for the punishment meted out in that age to all daring reformers, and especially to those who presumed to interfere with the prerogatives and emoluments of the clergy.[16]

Due to the fact that Sylvester had spent many years studying in the Arab world and had then contributed to the spread of Arabic knowledge and science, the 'demons' and 'goblins' that he supposedly commanded were perceived as dark servants of Arabic magic – evil jinn. Most likely a victim of slow poison, Sylvester II reigned as pope for less than four years. After his death, because of his alleged association with demons and magic, his name was anathematised, his doctrines condemned as heresy and his writings banned as contrary to the canons of the Church. Many centuries would pass before Sylvester II was finally recognised as a legitimate pope and acknowledged as the great scholar and scientist that he was.

Sylvester was the only Pope to have his name closely linked with jinn. This linkage, though negative, actually showed the effectiveness of Gerbert d'Aurillac's efforts to introduce Arab knowledge into Europe. The effect of this scholar's efforts, and those of others, such as Archbishop

Raimundo of Toledo and the English translator/scientist Adelard of Bath, was to furnish Europe with the breakthrough knowledge that sparked the Renaissance of the fourteenth to seventeenth centuries.

The jinn continued to influence European thought into the Renaissance period. Paracelsus, the famous sixteenth-century physician and alchemist, was said to have possessed a sword that had great powers and was linked to the jinn.[17] Perhaps as a result, the sword has become a kind of Aladdin's lamp in Paracelsian legend. Born and educated in Switzerland, Paracelsus – whose proper name was Theophrastus Philippus Aureolus Bombastus von Hohenheim – pioneered the use of chemicals in medicine to the extent that he is sometimes called the 'father of pharmacology', and he publicised the rich legacy of medieval Islamic alchemy in Europe. Paracelsus has been credited with being the first systematic botanist. He gave the metal zinc its name, calling it 'zink' (from the German *zinke*, pointed) because of the pointed appearance of its crystals after smelting. He was the first scientist to develop the opium derivative laudanum, a popular painkiller for centuries.

'Paracelsus' was a title perhaps bestowed on him by friends and eventually adopted as his name; it suggested that his work went 'beyond' (Greek: *para*) that of the authoritative Roman medical encyclopedist Celsus (ca. 25 BC–50 AD). Paracelsus was born in a village near Zurich in 1493. As a boy he served as an apprentice at the Fueger mines, where he first worked with chemicals; later he wrote a book on miners' diseases. Between 1513 and 1516 he studied medicine in Italy, gaining his doctorate at the University of Ferrara. He travelled widely, working for a time as an army surgeon. He journeyed to Egypt, Palestine, Asia Minor and even Central Asia in pursuit of esoteric knowledge and alchemical secrets. Restless by nature, he spent much of his life moving from one European town to another, lecturing, writing and engaging in private medical practice. He died of natural causes at the relatively young age of 48 in Salzburg in 1541.

Paracelsus owned a massive longsword that he called Azoth (in fact, its name was engraved on its pommel). The weapon was said to remain by his side at all times, even when he slept. Sufis say that encapsulated in its hilt was a jinn that served him in all matters, such as bringing him a handful of gold crowns when he ran short of funds.[18] Others agree the hilt contained something marvellous – a 'miracle material' – but its nature remains a mystery.[19]

'Azoth' is the transliteration of a Persian and Arabic Sufi term for 'essence' (from *az-za'uq*, meaning literally mercury or quicksilver), an inner quality capable of transforming the nature of man. This inner quality is hidden, secret and forbidden. 'Hidden, forbidden' comes from the same Arabic consonantal root as 'stone': h-j-r. (Interestingly, as we have seen, the Arabic word *jinn* also means 'hidden or concealed'.)

So, according to a Sufi tradition, Paracelsus' 'Azoth' equals the hidden transformative substance in man; a substance which is equated with the 'Philosopher's Stone' – a mysterious substance that alchemists believed was capable of transforming lead and other base metals into gold and in some cases rejuvenating individuals, possibly even assuring immortality.

The Sufi connection of jinn with Paracelsus is not so far-fetched when we realise that he conceived of the universe and all the objects in it as endowed with life. He believed that the intermediate state between the material and the immaterial was populated with a variety of jinn-like beings, each consisting of a body and a spirit but, in his view, no soul: among them were the gnomes of the earth, the sylphs of the air, the nymphs (or undines) of water and the salamanders of fire.[20] Paracelsus believed that these creatures – which he called 'elementals' because they were spirits of the elements – could marry human beings and produce offspring with souls. Paracelsus doubtless encountered a wealth of jinn lore during his travels in the Middle East, and this knowledge was assimilated in various ways into his alchemical and philosophical studies. Paracelsus recognised seven categories of spirits in the universe, and jinn could qualify for at least four of these: fiery beings residing in the upper air below the sphere of the moon and known as Pennates and Salamanders; aerial spirits in the middle and lower regions of the air; aquatic spirits; and earthly/subterranean spirits.[21] In the chapters ahead, we shall encounter numerous examples of these kinds of spirits in a wide variety of cultural settings.

Chapter Three

By Their Deeds: Jinn Behaviour

It might be a good idea for medical authorities to consider whether jinn cause certain types of cancer, since cancer is an unordered and diseased growth in the body that we describe as a kind of cellular anarchy. Maybe some jinn have settled in that part of the body and are destroying its cellular structure.

– Fethullah Gülen, Islamic scholar

The title of this section refers to a well-known quote from the Gospel According to Matthew: 'By their deeds shall you know them' (7:16). The evangelist was not referring to jinn here – though he does mention demons (or evil jinn) on other occasions[1] – but his turn of phrase is very applicable to jinn behaviour. Jinn are known by their actions, which are generally easy to identify. Among other things, they are reputed to haunt houses, abandoned buildings and all places dark, dank and deep. They guard hidden treasures and lost cities. They shapeshift into animal forms and back again. They vanish into thin air and reappear just as easily. They possess the bodies of living human beings, speaking and acting through them and afflicting them with diseases, both physical and mental.

Some jinn behaviours, such as guarding ruins or shifting shapes, are common to both good and evil jinn. Other actions, such as terrorising humans or subjecting them to disease, are performed by the notorious evil categories of fire spirits: shaitans, ifrits and marids, as well as some of the more specialised jinn types, such as ghuls. This chapter delves into many of these behaviours as well as the motivations behind them.

Amid Ancient Ruins

Jinn are often associated with crumbling castles, hidden treasure hoards and lost cities. They haunt old, abandoned buildings and serve as guardians for any treasures that lie concealed in their ruins.

An ancient Arabian legend tells of jinn who guard an immense treasure hidden in the Hejaz region of present-day Saudi Arabia. British explorer Charles Doughty – reputed to be the first European to visit the Nabataean ruins of Medain Salih (Cities of Salih, a pre-Islamic prophet), also called al-Hijr (the Stony Place), in the Hejaz region in the late nineteenth century – referred specifically to this legend:

> Upon the landmark rock El-Howwara in the plain of Medain Salih lies a great treasure (in the opinion of the Moors of the Kella) sealed in a turret-like stone chamber, in the keeping of an Afrit (evil genius loci, a word spoken of the spirits of wicked men departed, which as flies to the dunghill haunt eternally about their places of burial). Fatal, they say, were the taking up of that treasure, 'the kings of the world should strive together, the Aarab tribes should destroy one another. In that day a man will not spare his friend, nor his brother, the son of his father and his mother': thus Haj Nejm. I have looked upon the Howwara cliff from the Harra, and can affirm that the head of it is plain, a black platform of lava; the sandstone precipices all around are a hundred fathoms in height.[2]

Even the Prophet carefully avoided contact with the jinn who haunted the ruins of al-Hijr. In the words of Sir Richard Burton: 'It is related that when the Apostle of Allah passed through the demon-haunted defile [of Medain Salih], he veiled his head, muffled his face, and hurried his pace on account of the Jinns and Ghúls which infest it, forbidding his followers to halt there either for food or drink.'[3] Another reason to hurry through this area: the ancient people of Medain Salih were punished by God for their impiety, and the tribes thought it best to avoid a locale thus stained with a history of sin.

Al-Hijr is Saudi Arabia's first World Heritage site, so designated in 2008 by UNESCO. It was home to the Thamud people and the Nabataeans. According to the Qur'an, the people of al-Hijr rejected the message of God, as conveyed to them by the prophet Salih and other messengers, and as a result they were destroyed by a 'Great Blast' from heaven. Archaeologists say the people of al-Hijr disappeared in about 400–600 AD. With the people gone, it was perhaps natural that the jinn would take over. Throughout pre-Islamic history, we hear of instances such as this, where arrogance and pride leads to destruction of a magnificent city, and the ruins subsequently revert to the custody of jinn. We shall see this time and again as our story unfolds.

The Saudi government today encourages tourism at Medain Salih – the archaeological site, with its majestic rock-cut tombs and other structures, is the Saudi version of the more famous Nabataean ruins of Petra to the north in Jordan. Nevertheless, some Saudis still fear the ruins are jinn-haunted or cursed and will not visit the area. This is particularly true of farmers and villagers who have little contact with the outside world and feel the power of venerable local jinn traditions.

Another legendary treasure trove was situated in the lost city of Ubar, or Iram of the Pillars, which belonged to the ancient tribe of 'Ad. An opulent city in a fertile oasis, Ubar and its inhabitants were destroyed by Allah in punishment for their sins. Early Arab histories said that jinn haunted the ruins of Ubar and protected its buried riches. But where the lost city might be found was seriously disputed. Some Arab chroniclers thought it would be found on the southwestern edge of the Empty Quarter, in or near Yemen.[4] Others believed it was located close to Oman, in the eastern Rub' al-Khali. A decade ago, Los Angeles filmmaker Nicholas Clapp told the world that he and a team of fellow explorers had discovered this lost city on the southeastern edge of the Empty Quarter. Clapp and his team did not actually discover Ubar – but they did find the ruins of an old caravanserai and fort near the village of Shisur on the fringes of the desert in Oman.[5] They called it 'Ubar', but no treasures or signs of opulence were found, and so the search for the legendary city will doubtless continue.[6]

Ubar is one of many names for this ancient Arabian city, which is said to have vanished beneath the sands of the desert. The city was reputedly a major trading emporium at the intersection of trade routes in the Empty Quarter. It was said to have existed from about 3000 BC until the first century AD. Other names include 'Ad, Wabar, Wibar, Wubar, Irem, Iram, and Iram dhat al-'Imad (Iram of the Pillars). This last name is explicitly mentioned in the Qur'an: 'Seest thou not how thy Lord dealt with the 'Ad (people) – of the (city of) Iram with lofty pillars, the like of which were not produced in (all) the land?' (Qur'an 89:7).

Early Arab chronicles said the city was built by a powerful king named Shaddad, son of 'Ad. Modelling the city on his vision of Paradise, Shaddad ordered it constructed of gold and silver in place of stones. Its walls were studded with jewels. Ubar featured a hundred thousand palaces, supported by great pillars made of ruby and aquamarine. The city was filled with orchards and gardens, to complete the picture of Paradise.

Shaddad's arrogance in trying to re-create Paradise was his undoing. On his way to inspect his new city, a great sandstorm overcame him and his entourage as well as the king and the new city were swallowed up by the sands, never to be inhabited or seen again.

According to legend, the jinn took possession of the land where Ubar had stood. Strange jinn creatures called the *nisnas* (half-persons) roamed the land, beings with only half a head, one eye, one hand, and one leg. No man would dare enter this land, and the *nisnas* destroyed all the crops that had previously grown there.[7] The *nisnas* were alternatively described as a special type of jinn or as the former inhabitants of Ubar who were punished by Allah by being transformed into monstrosities. Incidentally, the camels of the Mahra tribe of eastern Yemen and western Oman are said to have descended from the camels of the jinn who took possession of the ruins of Ubar.[8]

According to British Orientalist and *Arabian Nights* translator Edward Lane, *nisnas* were also found in the forests of Yemen. In the ninth century one was captured, he said, and brought alive to the Abbasid caliph al-Mutawakkil in Baghdad; the *nisnas* was said to resemble a man in form, except that it had only half a face, which was embedded in its chest, and a tail like a sheep.[9] Lane said the people of the Yemeni region of Hadramaut hunted and ate the *nisnas*, and they reported its flesh was sweet. The creature was said to be found only in that country. Lane tells of an unidentified man, probably British, who visited Yemen and affirmed that he personally saw a captured *nisnas*, 'which cried out for mercy, conjuring him by God and by himself'.

Strange stories still emerge from this region. Several years ago, a group of Saudi oil wildcatters were camping in the Rub' al-Khali. There are no villages in this part of the vast sand desert, and Bedouins only rarely pass through it. One of the oil workers claimed that at twilight the team saw a woman moving alone along the crest of a nearby dune. She was draped in black, apparently wearing an abaya like many Saudi women, and was hopping along, appearing to have only one leg. She disappeared over the dune. Several of the team members went up the dune to find her, but she had vanished, seemingly into thin air. If no humans live in this part of the desert, one of the remotest and most inhospitable in the world, that may not apply to jinn.

The location of Ubar/Iram remains a mystery. Early explorers of Arabia, such as T.E. Lawrence, H. St. John Philby and Bertram Thomas, became captivated by the legend of Ubar and all of them searched for the lost city during their journeys through the Arabian Peninsula. Philby reported that in 1917, south of Saih – the main town of the Aflaj oasis (on the northern edge of the Rub' al-Khali) – he spotted the ruins of an ancient building that he thought could be associated with Ubar. His Bedouin companions told him that the structure was called Qusairat 'Ad (Palace of 'Ad), named after the legendary 'Ad people who built Ubar under the leadership of King Shaddad.

Philby gave the location of this site as 22° 10' north latitude, 46° 20' east longitude. He later wrote that Qusairat 'Ad could not be as old as the fabled lost city and probably dated from the Middle Ages.[10] His Bedouin guides said the capital of Ubar was actually located far to the south, across the Rub' al-Khali, near the frontier of Yemen's Hadramaut region – where the *nisnas* were found.[11] Philby travelled all over Arabia, and as he did so he kept his eye peeled for signs of the lost city. He never found them. (As we shall see later, Philby also heard reports of another lost city in the dunes called Jahura, but it is not known if he ever searched for it.)

Bedouin guides for Bertram Thomas insisted that Ubar lay buried in the southeastern reaches of the Empty Quarter, in or near Oman. Said one, 'It's a great city, our fathers have told us, that existed of old; a city rich in treasure, with date gardens and a fort of red silver (Thomas wondered if this might be gold). It now lies buried beneath the sands in the Ramlat Shu'ait' in northwestern Dhofar, Oman.[12] One day his guides showed him well-worn tracks, about a hundred yards wide, cut into the plain. The path led to Ubar, Thomas was told. The tracks bore 325°, approximately 18° 45' north latitude, 52° 30' east longitude, on the edge of the sands – about where the borders of Saudi Arabia, Yemen and Oman converge.

T.E. Lawrence – 'Lawrence of Arabia' – developed an interest in the lost city of Ubar in the 1930s, and it was he who first dubbed it 'Atlantis of the Sands', a name later adopted by Clapp and Fiennes for their books on the discovery.[13] Lawrence considered launching an expedition to search for Ubar in the days before his fatal motorcycle accident in 1935.

Some Saudis today claim that the ruins of Ubar lie beneath the sand in the area where the aptly named Wabar meteorite was discovered, in the north-central Rub' al-Khali, some 550 kilometres by air southeast of Riyadh. The two-ton iron meteorite was found in an ancient impact crater field in the desert area known to the Arabs as al-Hadida (Piece of Iron). It was rescued from the sands by Aramco oil workers in 1966 and is now on display in Riyadh. The crater itself was long known to local Bedouins, but its later discovery was credited to Philby in 1937. *Aramco World*, a cultural periodical of the Saudi oil company, describes it as follows:

> For 14 years he [Philby] had 'worked and waited' for a chance to verify a strange Bedouin story he had heard in 1918 from his guide, Jabir ibn Farraj: that somewhere out in that forbidding desert lay a ruined city called Wabar. According to Bedouin legend, Wabar had been levelled by a destructive wind because its wicked and lustful ruler, 'Ad, had ignored the warnings of his brother, Hud – generally identified with the biblical Heber. Legend also said that near this lost site lay a block of iron 'as big as a camel's hump'. Since tribesmen called the place 'al-Hadida', and since *hadida* in Arabic means a piece of iron, Philby presumed that there were iron artefacts in the city, perhaps of great value ... .
>
> For Philby, the first sight of Wabar was ... disappointing ... : instead of a find to match Petra or Tutankhamen's tomb, he found himself gazing down, not at the ruins of a city, but into the mouth of what he took to be an extinct volcano with twin craters side by side. Surprised and deeply disappointed, he wrote in his diary: 'I knew not whether to laugh or cry ... '
>
> Nevertheless, Philby was also fascinated by the scene. Rationalizing that the two great sand-filled craters, encircled by a rim, did bear an absurd resemblance to the tumbled remnants

> of man-made castles, he described a structure 'whose black walls stood up gauntly above the encroaching sand like battlements and bastions of some great castles'. But all his hopes faded when, after four straight days of searching, he uncovered one 'silly little fragment of iron about the size of a rabbit', instead of the iron mass as big as a camel's hump.[14]

The 'camel's hump', then covered by sand, was finally revealed in 1966 as the Wabar meteorite. Philby's extinct volcano with twin craters turned out to be two – perhaps three – astroblemes, impact craters of meteorite chunks that had entered the earth's atmosphere.

Despite the scientific explanations, some Bedouins in Saudi Arabia's Eastern Province are still convinced that the lost city of Iram lies beneath the sands near al-Hadida. By one account told to me, the sands had shifted not long ago in that area, uncovering a glimpse of the buried ruins of buildings. But such claims are difficult to confirm. Al-Hadida is deep in the trackless desert, many hours by four-wheel-drive from the nearest town. Most importantly, what the sands reveal one day they may conceal the next.

If jinn have served for millennia as the guardians of the lost city of Ubar, they have certainly played a similar role for the 'lost treasuries of Yemen'. Al-Hamdani has preserved for us a list of these treasuries – legendary locales associated with ancient fortresses or lost cities (in many cases built by jinn as well) where great quantities of gold, silver, precious gems and other treasures were kept under the protection of spirit guardians. Not surprisingly, Ubar was first on his list. Notice that he places the lost city in Yemen – not in Oman as Clapp located it, or in Saudi Arabia, where Philby hoped to find it. Ubar was followed by Dhakhir, a mountain in the Ma'afir region regarded as God's depository on earth. Next was Khuta, 'the stronghold of the Pharaohs'; this may have a trading emporium, but its location is unknown today. Khuta was followed by Zafar, stronghold of the Tubba's, a title taken by Himyar kings, and home of the celebrated fortress Husn Raydan. The next treasury was Silhin Palace in Ma'rib, capital city of Saba (Sheba), Bilqis's kingdom. Then came the lofty mountain of Shibam Haraz, northwest of Sanaa, with its massive stone fortifications; Ghumdan, the immense fairy-tale palace of the kings of Sanaa; and the mountain village of al-Hamra' in the Yafa' highlands of Hadramaut.[15]

In addition to these eight, al-Hamdani mentions another lost treasury: Dhu Ru'ayn in Baynun, which he called the greatest of the Himyar treasuries, citing a member of the 'Abs tribe who spoke on the authority of his forbears. While most of the sites named by al-Hamdani are known today, none of the treasure troves identified with them has ever been found.

In a prophecy-like statement, al-Hamdani says of the lost treasuries:

> The first to be discovered will be that of Shibam. It will be uncovered by animals and fire. The next will be that of Ma'rib, which will be uncovered by the jinn. It is a treasure which was buried by the young maiden Bilqis [Queen of Sheba]. The third, which will be brought to light by an earthquake, will be that of Ghumdan Sanaa. The fourth, which the water will reveal, will be that of Zafar. The fifth will be that of Dhakhir, which will be uncovered by a quake between Dhakhir and Sabir, the two mountains of al-Ma'afir. The sixth will be discovered in Khuta by a native of the place. The seventh will be exposed in al-Hamra' by hurricanes and panic-stricken, frightened beasts of burden. The eighth will be unearthed by ants in Iram [Ubar]. This will take place when despots are gone and the tyrannous pharaohs are no more. Then will the people prey on its spoils. At that time many in Mahit in Tamam will be transformed into monkeys. This, however, is a tradition lacking authority, and since we received it without any chain of ascriptions, we have narrated it without them.

Yet another jinn-haunted ruin was described by Czech explorer Alois Musil during an expedition in the Jordanian desert in 1908–09. Some fifty miles east of Amman, he reported that

> the sun, just rising, flooded [nearby mountains] yellow slopes with its rays and made them appear as if they were sprinkled with gold. Before them to the northwest showed the ruin of al-Khawrana (or al-Kharani, as it is called by the Beni Sakhr), resembling a fabulous castle. From all its sides and corners sparks seemed to blaze forth, surrounding the entire structure with rosy light, which caused it to contrast sharply with the blue of the sky. Suddenly the apparition faded away and a cloud enveloped the castle, for the spirit [jinn] who inhabited it would not brook the gaze of the sons of Adam.

But this was only the curtain-raiser, for Musil and his party soon glimpsed another ruin in a deep depression to the east, a structure which he called 'grotesque'. This was the famous eighth-century Umayyad castle, Qusair 'Amra (or Qasr 'Amra), now a protected UNESCO World Heritage Site. Qusair 'Amra was said to be inhabited by a ghula, or female ghoul. 'Veiled in thin vapours,' the structure, he said, 'appeared and reappeared as the breeze rent and rejoined the shifting mists. But how melancholy the castle looked from a distance! Standing deep in the lowland enclosed on all sides by high, grey, desolate slopes, it appeared to be part of the hillside ... .The castle stood as gloomy as if it were forsaken by heaven itself. No wonder the Arabs attribute such a place to none but the ghoul [ghola].'[16]

Today the site is a familiar tourist attraction, with no sign of the ghoul that graced it in Musil's day. Built of limestone and basalt, Qusair 'Amra is an exceptionally well-preserved desert castle that served as both a fortress with a garrison and a residence for the Umayyad caliphs. The most impressive features of this small pleasure palace are its reception hall and its *hammam* (bath house), both stunningly decorated with figurative murals that reflect the secular art of the period.

Other early Arab histories are replete with accounts of lost cities and hidden treasures, which invariably have passed into the custody of jinn guardians. This function is reminiscent of the role of guardian spirits in the folklore of many other cultures. Such spirits are considered by some folklorists to be projections of the belief that valuable troves are protected by a spirit or power which may be helpful if approached properly but can be dangerous if approached recklessly. Various forms of such spirit guardians can be found as far afield as China, Scandinavia, Tibet and Ireland. So the jinn are not alone in having to play watchmen for the abandoned castles, cities and treasure troves of mankind.

Human Possession and Exorcism

In the Islamic world the belief is fairly widespread that jinn can possess humans, speak through them and direct their behaviour. Like their demon analogues in Christianity, they can also be exorcised through rituals.

A common term in Arabic for spirit possession is *sara'*– a word that is also applied to epilepsy and epileptic fits. A possessed person is called *masru'*. Another word for possession is *mass*, from the verb *massa* meaning 'to touch or feel'. Massa can mean the madness of diabolical possession.[17]

In Arabic, a insane person is called *majnun*, which is from the same root as the word *jinn*; traditionally, insanity was linked to jinn possession.

Many of the great Islamic theologians believed in the reality of jinn possession. Ahmad ibn Hanbal (780–855 AD), founder of the Hanbali school of Islam, affirmed that jinn could enter human beings and speak through their tongues. The great Islamic thinker Ibn Taymiyyah, who was both a theologian and a Sufi, expressed the views of the majority of Muslim scholars of his day when he said, 'The existence of the jinn is an established fact according to the book [Qur'an], the Sunnah and the agreement of the early scholars. Likewise the penetration of the jinnee into the human body is also an established fact, according to the consensus of leading Sunni scholars ... the jinnee enters one seized by fits and causes him to speak incomprehensible words, unknown to himself, if one seized by fits is struck with a blow enough to kill a camel, he does not feel it.'[18]

Even some of the leading scholars of the Mutazilites – early Islamic advocates of rationalism – argued that jinn possession was a real phenomenon. Abdul Jabbar al-Hamadani (died 1024 AD), an Islamic judge best known for his extensive monograph preserving much original Mutazilite thinking, reportedly said, 'There is nothing to prevent them [the jinn] from entering our bodies.' Al-Hamadani believed that jinn possession was as much a reality as the basic tenets of Islam such as prayer, fasting, pilgrimage and alms-giving.

Ya'la ibn Murrah, one of the Prophet's companions, was present once when Muhammad performed a rare jinn exorcism:

> I saw Allah's Messenger do three things which no one before or after me saw. I went with him on a trip. On the way we passed a woman sitting at the roadside with a young boy. She called out, 'O Messenger of Allah, this boy is afflicted with trial, and for him we have also been afflicted with trial. I do not know how many times a day he is seized by fits.' He said, 'Give him to me.' So she lifted him up to the Prophet ... He then passed the boy between himself and the saddle, opened the boy's mouth and blew in it three

> times, saying, 'In the name of Allah, I am the slave of Allah, get out, enemy of Allah!' Then he gave the boy back to her and said, 'Meet us on our return at this same place and inform us how he has fared.' We then went. On our return we found her in the same place with three sheep. When he said to her, 'How has your son fared?" she replied, 'By the One who has sent you with the truth, we have not detected anything unusual in his behavior up to this time.'[19]

Ibn Taymiyyah believed that possession was sometimes caused by lust or love on the part of an individual jinn. Alternatively, the jinn could be motivated by mischief, horseplay or just plain evil. Possession, however, is most often a result of a jinn growing angry over a perceived wrong and seeking to punish the human deemed responsible. If a human accidentally urinates on a hidden jinn or spills hot water on him, for example, the jinn may think he has been deliberately harmed and may seek revenge by possessing the person's body.[20]

Today, jinn possession is taken quite seriously in a number of Arab countries, including Saudi Arabia, where Sheikh Abdul Aziz bin Baz, who was the kingdom's grand mufti until his death in 1999, wrote about his own participation in numerous exorcism rituals.[21]

The belief in the connection between mental disorders and jinn possession also continues today, with reports of incidents emerging even from small towns in America. In March 2002, Abu Kassim Jeilani, a former mental patient and Somali immigrant living in Minnesota, was shot to death by police as he walked down the street wielding a machete and a crowbar and shouting 'Allahu Akbar'.

The incident took place in the tense months following 9/11. Nevertheless, mental-health professionals in the Minneapolis-St. Paul area were quoted in the press as saying that the police never should have been involved, and that social workers or psychiatrists should have handled matters. Local imams felt the case should have been referred to them. 'The mental health professionals and the police are not the only solution,' said a local Somali-born imam, Hassan Mohamud. 'The imams must be part of the solution. We could have saved his life, I'm sure.'[22]

Jeilani was not identified as a terrorist – instead, he reportedly heard voices and suffered from psychosis. He had previously received hospital treatment and medication as well as some spiritual healing, which involved having the Qur'an recited to him – a technique designed to drive evil jinn away from a possessed person.

* * *

We travel from Minnesota to Egypt's Western Desert, in the remote Siwa Oasis, where another interesting twentieth-century account of jinn possession was reported in 1973 by Egyptian archaeologist Dr. Ahmed Fakhry.[23]

The jinn in this account were described as *ghulahs*, or female ghouls – evil jinn that have been known to devour human flesh. The people of Siwa are mostly of Berber ancestry, descended from the indigenous people of North Africa. Some of the Berber jinn beliefs predate Islam and the Arab conquest and have a distinctly North African flavour tinged with a bit of Graeco-Roman spice. In ancient times, the Siwa Oasis possessed a world-famous oracle at the temple of Amun, which was consulted by such rulers as King Croesus of Lydia and Alexander the Great. The oasis was known as a major spiritual center and quite naturally had a strong jinn presence. This ancient legacy lives on in a number of ways today.

Jinn capable of working either good or evil are said to live in the pools and springs of the Siwa Oasis. Mahmoud Mohammad 'Abdallah, who recorded the social customs of the Siwans in 1917, said, 'Those who have seen these ginns say that they appear either at night or Friday noon at the time of prayers when all is quite still. One who inhabits [a spring called] Ain Tomousay appears as a large and tall palm tree in the midst of the spring. When this tree disappears in the spring, the water boils.'[24] In this remote locale, we find a unique form of jinn possession.

Nowadays, when a man dies in Siwa, his widow is called a *ghulah*, because the entire community believes she has become possessed of a very powerful evil eye which brings misfortune to any person upon whom she gazes. The widow may be only a teenager, but regardless, she is labelled a *ghulah* as soon as her husband is buried.

Accompanied by female relatives, she must walk to the spring of Tamusi or of Tilihram where she removes her silver jewellery and clothing, bathes to cleanse herself of the jinn and puts on a white garment, a sign of mourning. From then on, according to Dr. Fakhry, she is required to live in total seclusion, for as long as four months and ten days in past generations and forty days in the present. She subsists on a vegetarian diet, brought to her by an elderly woman who has been assigned as the only person permitted to visit her personally during this period.

The widow, in her isolation, is allowed to speak through the door only to female relatives and to close male relatives such as her father, brothers or uncles. She is forbidden to change her white garment, bathe, fix her hair, use make-up or wear jewellery during this time.

When her period of seclusion is over, a town crier goes from street to street in Siwa, accompanied by a boy beating a drum, and announces that the *ghulah* will reappear the next day.

The following day her seclusion ends, but people still fear that some of the evil may yet remain. They believe that even now if she looks at people, she will bring them bad luck. So she must wear a blindfold whenever she is outside. She is accompanied by several relatives including children who constantly repeat a phrase in Siwan Berber: 'Avoid your misfortune, the *ghulah* comes to you.' This warning is usually not needed, because the men who live nearby have long since disappeared into their gardens and the women and children have shut themselves up in their rooms. One year after her husband's death, the widow is once again considered human and is free to marry.

Dr. Fakhry laments: 'This cruel custom is completely unknown anywhere else in Egypt, for it is in no way representative of the spirit and usage of the Muslim people, or the ancient Egyptians. However, it reminds us of other traditionally severe treatment of widows in some Asiatic and African communities. I wonder whence the Siwans inherited it, since no Berber or Arab community observes any custom of this kind nowadays.'

Egypt is known nowadays as a main center for a type of jinn-possession ceremony called the 'Zar',[25] a ritual normally involving only women. The Zar is not Islamic, though it often includes some Islamic elements. It is believed to derive ultimately from early African animist religions and to have developed its current form in East Africa several centuries ago. The Zar, sometimes called a 'healing cult', is particularly common in southern Egypt and northern Sudan. It has also become popular in Saudi Arabia, other Arab Gulf states and even southern Iran. The ritual, conducted in a large room or rented house, involves music, drums, 'séance dancing' and trances. It often concludes with an animal sacrifice and a sacrificial meal. The object of the rituals is not to exorcise the possessing jinn, but to appease and propitiate them, allowing them to remain inside their victims. The ceremonies also have a powerful supportive role, providing an emotional and social outlet for women in patriarchal societies.[26]

Dr. Ahmad Al-Safi, a Sudanese physician who has studied the Zar and similar rituals in Sudan, agrees that these ceremonies, which he calls 'parties', go far beyond therapy for jinn possession: 'The *zar* parties, in addition to being therapeutic in nature, are believed to serve social functions as well. The *zar* parties provide women with music, dancing, food and a relaxed atmosphere in which they can let off steam. Indeed, the relaxation women attain in these ceremonies sometimes amounts to moral slackness. Access to this type of life is a real privilege in the conservative male-dominated society of the Sudan.'[27]

In Egypt, the Zar is led and, in fact, 'stage-managed' by a woman called a *Kodia* (in Sudan, she is the *Sheikha*), who herself becomes possessed by the jinn during the ceremony and thereby is able to speak with the jinn and intercede on behalf of the victim or victims. The possessing spirits are usually male and the possessed are almost always females. The Zar leader is a prestigious position in Egypt and is often passed from mother to daughter.

These examples only touch the surface of the complex phenomenon of jinn possession, which we shall deal with in many contexts as we survey jinn beliefs in various lands. Possession is classic jinn behaviour, ancient in its origins but still quite vigorous in the opening years of the twenty-first century.

Jinn Hauntings

The jinn sometimes take possession of a building or a locale, just as they take possession of an individual person. In the West, haunting is a phenomenon attributed to ghosts, or the spirits of the dead. In the Muslim world, haunting is a practice of the jinn.

In Saudi Arabia, where jinn are taken very seriously, people are careful to avoid houses and other buildings said to be haunted by them.

Sometimes these buildings are left completely abandoned. During the construction of the kingdom's subterranean facilities for petroleum-product storage in the Riyadh area in the late 1990s, workers asked for extra pay on the grounds that the underground chambers were haunted by the jinn (their request was denied).

In 2000, newspapers in Saudi Arabia reported the haunting of the al-Fikriyah Institute of Education, a functioning girls' school in the Red Sea port city of Jeddah, in an incident with unusual psycho-social overtones. A number of teachers at the school were reportedly subjected to fits and epileptic-like seizures, supposedly as a result of the haunting. One fit struck a pregnant teacher, leading to a miscarriage.

Sceptics said that the fits, witnessed by school administrators sent to investigate, were a result of 'mass hysteria' due to depression and job dissatisfaction. The school's teachers vowed not to return to the school as long as it was haunted and applied for work at other schools.

However not all the investigators were doubtful that haunting was responsible. According to the *Arab News* newspaper, Sheikh Abdul Aziz al-Hamdan, a Saudi cleric who was asked by authorities to look into the matter, confirmed in a written report to the Presidency of Girls Education, a government body, that 'the school was inhabited by jinns'.[28] The sheikh's report is not available for inspection, but his views on jinn haunting – or what we know of them – are not unusual among the more conservative sectors of Saudi religious thought. We have already noted how seriously Sheikh Bin Baz, grand mufti of Saudi Arabia, took disruptive jinn behaviours in the kingdom.

In India – particularly but not exclusively among the Muslim population – jinn hauntings have also been reported. In 2006, a wire service report appeared in a number of Indian newspapers about the haunting of various mosques in Bhopal (a city whose name is easily recognizable to many due to the tragic chemical plant disaster of 1984 in which thousands died).[29] One of those mosques, which is 200 years old, is called Djinnaton Wali Masjid (Mosque of the Jinn). The imam, Ashu Mian, who had been at the mosque for many years and died in 2005, prayed constantly to rid the mosque of the jinn, according to his wife, Shahnaz Apu. She said that the jinn would appear in the form of snakes – not only in the mosque but also in their house.

'Ashu Mian would pray all night. The djinns eventually stopped harassing us,' she said, according to the wire report. 'Like humans, there are good and bad djinns. While the good ones are helpful, the bad ones often harass people.'

The neighbourhood where the mosque is located is called Ginnauri, and it is all said to be haunted. The area includes a men's college that until 2005 had been a women's college, but the college buildings that lie inside the 'haunted zone' are unoccupied, according to the wire service.

'There's a tree on the campus beyond which girls were not encouraged to go,' said a former student of the college identified only as 'Fatịma', who is now a grandmother. 'Many girls who ventured into the haunted territory fainted.'

Bhopal's old city is dotted with a number of haunted mosques. The spirit associations with these houses of worship go back many years and long predate the grim industrial disaster that struck the city in 1984.

Another of these mosques is Heera Masjid, located in an old, French-designed palace called Shaukat Mahal. The structure, built in 1890, is made of stunning white marble. And yet, 'Only the very gutsy step into this mosque,' said Syed Jamal, a lecturer in mass communications.

Part of the palace is also used for residential apartments. That section is not inhabited by jinn, but it has other problems. 'Half of the palace is entangled in a legal wrangle, and the other half is haunted,' said Triq Mirza, one of the palace residents. 'They say there is a treasure hidden in a portion of the palace, adjacent to the mosque,' he added. 'One of the inheritors of the palace died digging ... for the treasure. He would see blood splashed on the walls and the spirits haunted him till the day he died. Very few people offer *namaz* [prayers] in this mosque. It is believed that djinns like to pray here.'

Side-by-side on the banks of the Upper Lake on the west-central side of Bhopal are two more mosques said to be haunted: Masjid Maji Kurud Sahab and, on its right, Masjid Maji Kalan Sahab. During Ramadan, very few of the faithful have the courage to go to either mosque for *iftar* (breaking of the fast) or *taravih* (special Ramadan prayers), according to the wire report.

It is not known for certain why Bhopal has so many haunted mosques. The hauntings may be somehow related to the city's rich Muslim history, and the fact that Bhopal was one of the last of the princely Muslim states to join modern India by signing the Instrument of Accession in 1949, two years after India achieved its independence.

As well as occupying empty or old buildings, jinn haunt trees, bushes and even man-made statues.

The belief in the haunting of statues predates Islam and can be traced back at least as far as ancient Byzantium, for example, early Christian chroniclers reported the expulsion of a demon or jinn from a statue of Aphrodite in the Palestinian city of Gaza in 402 AD. The incident involved Porphyry, the bishop known for 'Christianising' the pagan city of Gaza in the fifth century and being canonised a saint for his accomplishment. Accompanied by Christians bearing crosses, Bishop Porphyry approached the statue in question. 'The demon who inhabited the statue, being unable to contemplate the terrible sign [of the cross], departed from the marble with great tumult, and, as he did so, he threw the statue down and broke it into many pieces,' one chronicler said.[30] Historian Cyril Mango has observed on the subject of ancient statuary: 'We must also remember that, whereas some Christian thinkers rightly believed that the idols were inanimate, the general opinion prevalent at the time – as we have seen from the incident at Gaza – was that they were inhabited by maleficent demons.'

This belief led Byzantine churchmen of those times to demand immediate action – that is, the destruction of all pagan statuary. But many statues survived nevertheless, and the demons within them underwent a gradual change of personality – from being actively maleficent to being vaguely sinister. People believed that the best thing to do was to leave them alone, and thus many ancient statues survived.

Jinn haunting is a frequently observed behavioural phenomenon that is taken seriously by traditionally oriented people in many Muslim counties. It is markedly distinct from ghost haunting, found in the West and other areas, which involves spirits of the dead. The jinn who inhabit abandoned buildings and the like are very much alive. But interestingly, their behaviour is very similar to that of ghosts – often attempting to frighten humans and drive them away from a locale they have claimed as their own. In some cases, the phenomenon may show signs of cultural overlap; over the passage of centuries, what began as a case of ghost haunting may become a case of jinn exercising their 'territorial' claims.

Jinn and Illness

According to Islamic traditions, jinn are capable of causing physical illness in humans as well as possessing and haunting them. To deal with jinn-caused illness, Qur'anic medicine is invoked, including the recitation of appropriate suras and the application of herbal and other physical remedies recommended by the Prophet or others in Islamic tradition, such as Muhammad al-Razi (known to the West as Rhazes), Abu al-Qasim al-Zahrawi (Albucasis), Ibn Sina (Avicenna) and Ibn al-Nafis. The belief in jinn-produced ailments remains strong in the Arab and Muslim worlds even today. Saudi scholar and author Dr. Abu'l-Mundhir Khaleel ibn Ibraaheem Ameen, in his recent book *The Jinn and Human Sickness*, is said by his translator to take 'a balanced view of sicknesses that are commonly attributed to the jinn, and makes a wise plea for Muslim doctors to work hand in hand with the practitioners of the Qur'anic medicine, pointing out that recitation of the Qur'an over a sick person can never do any harm'.[31]

The types of 'sickness and harm' attributed to the jinn, according to Dr. Ameen, include intense fear as well as psychological and nervous diseases such as insanity, depression, tension, anxiety, epilepsy, personality disorders and something called *waswas* (which he describes as whisperings from the devil, or 'temptation'). Jinn may also bring on physical illness that modern medicine cannot treat and for which there seems to be no medical cause. They may be responsible for hallucinations and for social strife such as hatred between couples, business partners, friends and relatives. Female diseases such as menstrual irregularities, heavy bleeding, infections and infertility are blamed on the fire spirits. Male sexual problems are also their fault, including impotence and premature ejaculation.

Turkish Islamic scholar Fethullah Gülen, known for his efforts to promote dialogue between Islam and the West, writes in an article on jinn in the modern world:

> Jinn can penetrate a body even deeper than X-rays. They can reach into a being's veins and the central points of the brain. They seem to be like lasers, which are used in everything from computers to nuclear weaponry, from medicine to communication and police investigations, and to removing obstructions in our veins and arteries. So, when we consider that Satan and all jinn are created from

> smokeless fire that penetrates deep into the body, like radiation or radioactive energy, we can understand the meaning of the Prophetic Tradition: Satan moves where the blood moves.

If we assume that the jinn can harm the body and cause physical and psychological illnesses, then Gülen suggests that 'It might be a good idea for medical authorities to consider whether jinn cause certain types of cancer, since cancer is an unordered and diseased growth in the body that we describe as a kind of cellular anarchy. Maybe some jinn have settled in that part of the body and are destroying its cellular structure.' Gülen heads an international movement that practises a modernised, moderate version of Sunni Hanafi Islam, with some conservative overtones. His views on jinn and disease are part of that effort to bridge old and new.

As we have seen, the jinn are seen as responsible for some psychological ailments. Dr. Ameen of Saudi Arabia suggests Muslim scientists consider the possibility that evil spirits play some part in illnesses such as schizophrenia. 'We constantly hear of cases that those who suffer from mental illness, epilepsy, or even cancer recover by reciting certain prayers,' he adds. 'Such cases are serious and significant, and should not be denied or dismissed by attributing them to "suggestion" or "auto-suggestion". When science breaks the thick shell in which it has confined itself and accepts the existence of the metaphysical realm and the influence of metaphysical forces, its practitioners will be able to remove many obstructions, make far greater advances, and make fewer mistakes.'

Dr. Ameen comes from a much more conservative tradition than Gülen, but both are on the same page, it seems, when it comes to incorporating jinn therapy into modern medicine and psychiatry.

'The Condemned System'

Jinn behaviour and the millennia-old practice of magic in the Islamic world have always been closely connected. Arab interest in magic derives from Greek, Babylonian, Hebrew and Chaldaean/Nabataean traditions and predates Islam by many centuries.

Arab tradition makes a clear distinction between licit and illicit magic, as we have seen previously. Licit magic invokes the name of

Allah and prevents evil activity by spirits or jinn. Forbidden magic, conversely, invokes evil spirits or jinn and enslaves them to do one's bidding. The *Fihrist* of Ibn al-Nadim gives us a glimpse of forbidden medieval magic as practised among the Arabs. It involves the summoning of Bidhukh (or Bayduk), a female jinn-demon believed to represent the pagan goddess Venus or Aphrodite:[32]

> This system which is condemned [shameful] is the system of the magicians. Those informed about it claim that Bidhukh is the daughter of the Devil [Iblis], or it is also said of the Devil's son, and that she had a throne on the water. If he who seeks this affair comes to her after doing for her what she wishes, she makes a servant of whomever he desires and fulfils his purposes. He is not isolated from her nor from anyone who makes offerings to her from among humans and animals, if he renounces the ordinances [of religion] and employs that which is repugnant to the mind.
>
> It is also said that Bidhukh is the Devil himself. Another person has stated that Bidhukh is seated on her throne, and that whoever seeks to obey her is brought to her and worships her. Almighty is Allah and sanctified are His names!
>
> One of them [the magicians] told me that while asleep he saw her with an appearance as when awake, and that he saw around her a group resembling the Nabataeans, black, barefoot, with cloven heels. He said to me, 'I saw in their group Ibn Mundhiryani, who was one of the greatest workers of magic, [living] near to our time. His [real] name was Ahmad ibn Ja'far and he was an apprentice of Ibn Zurayq.'[33] He, moreover, spoke from under a basin.[34]

The Nabataeans mentioned here were an ancient Arabian tribal group, perhaps of Iraqi origin, with a deep magical tradition. In the Roman period they were known as a prosperous merchant people, involved in the trans-Arabian caravan trade as well as nautical commerce, and were identified primarily with the dramatic, carved stone cities of Petra (now in Jordan) and Medain Salih (in present-day Saudi Arabia). Ibn Wahshiya, born near Kufa in the ninth century, was an important advocate of Nabataean culture as it survived into the Islamic period in Mesopotamia and wrote much about their magical traditions. His works, including the *Nabataean Agriculture* and the *Book on Poisons*, are said by scholars to derive from Chaldaean/Babylonian lore. It is the

Nabataeans of magic, rather than the Nabataeans of commerce, who are referenced in Ibn al-Nadim's writings.

Ibn al-Nadim's description of a magician's vivid dream – 'as when awake' – includes a sinister portrayal of the Nabataean-like 'magicians' around Bidhukh, daughter of Iblis, that captures the flavour of a swarm of demons: 'black, barefoot, with cloven heels'. The description reflects Ibn al-Nadim's view that no good could come from this type of magic.

Seals and talismans are an important component of Arab and Islamic magic – that is, in both 'the condemned system' handed down from pagan times and the religiously approved Qur'anic magic. Many of these objects are used to protect against or control jinn.

Magical seals, used to impress wax and other substances, are inscribed with reverse images of symbols, numbers, magic squares or obscure inscriptions. The same symbols, letters and scripts can be found engraved in positive on amulets. These inscriptions are also found in all sorts of different contexts from magic bowls to letters or tombstones.[35] Dr. Venetia Porter of the British Museum, an expert on Islamic seals, cites a story about the use of seals in magic in the *Ghayat al-Hakim*, a medieval text on magical practice translated into Latin and known in the West as the *Picatrix.*[36] According to the tale from Egypt's Tulunid dynasty, a person in the court of Emir Khumarawayh (who reigned from 884 to 896) witnessed a young man make use of seals to assist someone complaining about a scorpion sting. The young man took out a cloth containing a collection of seals (*tawabi'*) made from a substance resembling incense, chose one of these seals and ordered that it should be pulverised and given to the injured man to consume. This was done and the man then quietened down. 'Wanting to find out more about this', said the courtier,

> I looked carefully at the seals and I found that on each one was the likeness of a scorpion. He [the young man] then took out a gold ring, its seal a bezoar stone[37] on which appeared the scorpion. I asked him about the secret of the seal and how it was made. He told me that it was engraved while the moon was in the second face of Scorpion [Scorpio]. I went ahead and made one and started sealing with it. I would alter the material that I stamped the signet onto fearing that it was the material [i.e., the incense] that was having the effect. Afterwards with seals and seal impressions I did wonderful things before all the world.[38]

According to Ibn al-Nadim, licit magicians constrained the spirits by obeying and supplicating God, while illicit magicians enslaved the spirits through offerings and evil deeds. 'All the exorcists and magicians [in other words licit and illicit magicians] assert that they have seals, charms, paper, ... sandalwood and other things used for their arts,' Ibn al-Nadim said. 'One group of philosophers and servants of the stars assert that they have talismans based on astronomical observations for all things desired in connection with wonderful actions ... They also have designs on stones, stringed beads and signet stones'.[39]

In addition to the inscriptions, the stones themselves had particular properties. The mineral chalcedony, for example, was used for rings and seals since ancient Greek times; it was believed to protect from the evil eye and to give a person a peaceful disposition. Cowrie shells, originating in the Indian Ocean but widely disseminated by trade, were also thought to have talismanic properties and are even today frequently found sewn into clothing in a number of countries, particularly in African countries such as Nigeria and the Democratic Republic of the Congo.

Another category of magical seals, according to Porter, are inscriptions which draw on the power of individual letters and the so-called Ninety-Nine Names of Allah. This is a major theme of Ahmad ibn Ali al-Buni's thirteenth-century classic, *Shams al-Ma'arif al-Kubra* (The Sun of Great Knowledge), the most popular treatise of its day on magic, occult practice and talismans. In this category of seals there are magic squares with individual letters or numbers or linear compositions of mixed numbers and letters. As we have seen, King Solomon controlled evil jinn by virtue of a talismanic ring engraved with 'the most great name of God'.

Since the days of ancient Egypt and Babylon, talismans have been influential instruments of protection in the Middle East. To this day, they are used by Muslims, Christians and Jews in the Arab world. Modern talismans are not so very different from ancient ones. They are (and were) inscriptions – often beautifully executed and frequently with undecipherable markings – on metal, stone, wood, paper and an array of other substances. Coins inscribed with professions of faith (e.g., 'there is no god but Allah' in Arabic) and metal cases or cylinders that hold Qur'anic or other religious writings on pieces of paper from holy texts are also examples of talismans. Some talismans are carried on the body, others are hung on the wall of one's home or buried under the lintel of the front door. Some talismans are sacred writings washed from a sheet of paper with ritually clean water and drunk as a liquid. The texts of talismans can be sentences, single words, letters and numbers, or signs and figures. Strange non-Arabic expressions or mystical letter combinations are often found on talismans. Many of these are corrupted Hebrew, Syriac or Greek words

Some talismans, again both ancient and modern, are inscribed with the name of a powerful evil jinn or demon, who is ordered to obey the accompanying instructions or commands. The jinn-demons most often mentioned are kings of the jinn, of whom there are seven in the following example, each identified with a day of the week:[40]

- AL-MUDHIB, also known as Abu 'Abdallah Sa'id, rules over Sunday;
- MURRAH al-Abyad Abu al-Harith (Abu al-Nur) over Monday;
- Abu Mihriz (or Abu Ya'qub) AL-AHMAR – Tuesday;
- BARQAN Abu al-'Adja'yb – Wednesday;
- SHAMHURISH (al-Tayyar) – Thursday;
- Abu Hasan ZOBA'AH (al-Abyad) – Friday; and
- Abu Nuh MAIMUN rules over Saturday.

Generally only the names written in capitals above are mentioned in talismans. The other names appear in legends and other lore. Each of these jinn kings has many tribes of jinn subject to his rule. All the above given names are Arabic – except for Shamhurish, whose origin is unclear. Shamhurish is considered by some accounts to have been a jinn companion of the Prophet, and some believe he died long ago – in the early eighteenth century – and has been replaced by Mutawakkil. 'Abu Murrah' (Father of Bitterness) is a common alias for Iblis. 'Abu al-Harith' (Father of the Plowman) is, for reasons lost in antiquity, an old Arabic term for the African lion.

Al-Qarinah (sometimes called al-Tabi'ah) and Umm al-Subian are well-known demons whose names are also often found on talismans. Al-Ahmar is sometimes called Abu al-Tawabi', or father of the *qarins*, the male versions of al-Qarinah.

Al-Buni said four of the seven jinn kings qualified as 'archdemons', or leaders of infernal hosts: Mudhib, Maimun, Barqan and al-Ahmar. This paralleled the Muslim hierarchy for angels, where four of the seven angels were assigned to govern the days of the week – Jubra'il (Gabriel), Mika'il (Michael), Sarafa'il (or Israfa'il) and 'Uzra'il – and were elevated to the status of 'archangels'. Each of the four archdemons had for his deputy an ifrit, an evil jinn more powerful than a run-of-the-mill shaitan or devil. Mudhib had the ifrit Damriat (or Tamriat), Maimun had Man'iq (or San'iq), Barqan had Wahdelbadj (or Wahdeliadj) and al-Ahmar had Sughal. None of these ifrits' names has appeared on a talisman, according to Palestinian folklorist Tewfik Canaan, who published important writings on the translation of Arabic talismans in 1937–1938.[41]

Four mysterious but powerful beings called the 'Four Heads' or 'Four Helpers' sometimes appear on old Arabic talismans, particularly on the four sides of square seals. They are identified as: Mazar, lord of East; Kamtam, lord of West; Qasurah, lord of South; and Taykal, lord of the sea.

These beings played a very important role in talismans, Canaan said, noting that the 'Four Heads' were called upon to take revenge upon an enemy. On occasion, when the task might not require the 'power of four', one of the four names might be found alone, written along with unintelligible words or with the name of the person for whom the talisman was written. Each of the four heads had a special servant from among the seven jinn kings. Al-Ahmar served Mazar, Mudhib served Kamtam, Shamhurish (or his successor) served Qasurah, and Murrah was servant of Taykal.

Other jinn associated with talismans include F-qt-sh (vowels uncertain), physician of the jinn; Isma'il, secretary of the jinn; and Abu Dibaj, king of the *qarins*.

Seals and talismans, active magical tools even today, have a long and involved history, drawing on traditions from a number of faiths and reaching back to the dawn of civilisation. Much mystery still surrounds talismans and seals from ages past, and we have a great deal to learn about the symbols and unintelligible writings that many of them bear. These seals and symbols remind us of King Solomon's ring and his resulting ability to command the cooperation of legions of evil jinn. Today's magical symbols may be less ambitious, but the mystique surrounding them endures.

Abductions and Trials

Jinn have been accused of abducting humans – men, women and children – for centuries and throughout our areas of interest, from the Maghreb to the Far East. These alleged abductions date back to the Middle Ages, and possibly earlier. People could be abducted for a variety of reasons: for example, for marriage or sex, for trial in jinn courts or for replacing a jinn child killed by human action, deliberate or inadvertent. There are, incidentally, uncanny similarities between these kidnappings by jinn and modern accounts of abductions by alien visitors from space. If nothing else, these similarities suggest striking parallels in the ways human beings of all times and places react to unexplainable or frightening occurrences.

In seventh-century Arabia, one of the Prophet's companions – he was unidentified but was said to be a member of the Ansar or one of Muhammad's early supporters from Medina – was outside performing the evening prayer when a jinn kidnapped him. He was absent for so long that his wife remarried. Eventually he reappeared in Medina. One of the Prophet's closest companions, 'Umar ibn al-Khattab (who later went on to become the second caliph, or political successor to Muhammad), asked the man about his absence. The man replied, 'The jinn kidnapped me and I stayed among them a long time.' He was held prisoner by unbelieving jinn, he said. Eventually a band of believing (or Muslim) jinn raided the camp of the unbelievers, battled them and defeated them. 'They took captives and took me prisoner along with them. They said, "We see you are a Muslim and it is not permissible for us to take you captive." They let me choose between staying with them or returning to my own people. So I chose my people and they brought me to Medina.'

'Umar asked the man: 'What was their food?' He replied, 'Ful [brown fava beans] and everything over which the name of God is not mentioned.' 'What was their drink?' 'Umar asked. He replied, 'Jadf.' Jadf, according to al-Damiri, is the froth whipped up from water. He also said it is 'every vessel left uncovered'.[42]

Some abductions of humans are authorised by jinn leadership – that is, by the king of the jinn or a lesser tribal leader. In one case in twelfth-century Iraq, the kidnapping was resolved through the intervention of a holy man – 'Abd al-Qadir al-Jilani, a Sufi leader or *qutb* who founded the Qadiriyah order. As the story went, Bushair bin Mahfuz, a citizen of Baghdad, went to al-Jilani and explained to him that his unmarried daughter Fatima had been kidnapped from the roof of his house.

'Go to the ruins of Karkh [in western Baghdad] tonight,' said the sheikh,

> sit on the fifth hill and draw a circle around you in the dirt. As you are drawing it, say: 'In the name of God for 'Abd al-Qadir's intention.' When darkness falls, parties of jinn will pass before you in various shapes. Do not let their appearance alarm you. When it is nearly dawn, their king will pass before you amidst a great army of them and he will ask you your need. Say: ' 'Abd al-Qadir has sent me to you' ... then mention the matter of your daughter to him.[43]

Bushair went and did as the sheikh instructed. Frightening jinn began to materialise around him, but none had the power to approach the circle in which he sat. Troop upon troop of jinn passed by until finally their king arrived on horseback. He halted by the edge of the circle and called out, 'O man, what is your need?' 'Sheikh 'Abd al-Qadir has sent me to you,' Bushair said.

The jinn king dismounted, kissed the earth and sat down outside the circle. He asked the man: 'What is your business?'

Bushair explained how his daughter had been abducted. The jinn king called to his entourage, 'Bring me whoever did this!'

Eventually a marid or demon – said to be a Chinese demon – was brought forward and with him was the man's daughter.

'What drove you to snatch someone under the aegis of the *Qutb*?' the jinn king asked.

'Indeed I liked her,' the marid replied. The jinn king then ordered the demon decapitated and he returned Fatima to her father. 'I have never seen as tonight such compliance as yours to the command of Sheikh 'Abd al-Qadir!' Bushair said.

'Yes,' the jinn king answered, 'he observes from his house the demons of the jinn and although they are at the ends of the earth they would flee out of fear of him. 'When Almighty God establishes a *Qutb* he gives him power over jinn and humans.'[44] *Qutb* is the Arabic word for 'pivot' or 'axis' and designates the highest form of Sufi master. Al-Jilani was also a descendant of the Prophet, on both his mother's and father's sides, adding to the aura of sanctity surrounding him.

As well as abducting adults, jinn are known to steal human babies and leave their own offspring in their place as 'changelings'.

One such exchange was reported in 1971 by folklorist Hasan M.El-Shamy, who recorded an account of the incident as told by a 24-year-old Egyptian housemaid named Galeelah. She lived and worked in the Cairo suburb of Maadi but originally came from a village in the Nile Delta. She told El-Shamy:

> I hear stories like this every morning while I am waiting for the bus [the route cuts across an old cemetery]. Women say they take their babies [believed to be changelings] to the cemetery and leave them for fifteen or twenty minutes ... Then they return to find out whether they [the jinn] have returned the real child.

Galeelah heard this particular story from her father:

> My father said that there is a man in our village who was married and had a son; it was only forty days old. His wife had left the little boy in a room by himself and gone off to do something and left him to cry. When she returned, the little boy was sick. They took him to everybody, to no avail. They took him to doctors and sheikhs. They took him to visit [the shrine of] el-Sayyid el-Badawi and all the saints, to no avail. The boy's stomach was like an open irrigation canal. He ate everything, and nothing showed on him, neither food nor days [age].
>
> One day his father looked in his mouth and found that [the supposed] forty-day-old infant had teeth! He knew it was a *badal,* changeling. He got his cattle whip and said to it, 'Where will it hurt you [most]?' Taaakh! taaakh! taakh! (hit, hit, hit) until the baby spoke and said to him, 'I'll bring your son back.' They found their own son in the room, and the other one disappeared in the ground. Of course they [the jinn] (may God make our talk light on them) had exchanged one of their own for the boy![45]

Not all Egyptian changeling tales have happy endings. The Egyptian medical doctor 'Abd al-Rahman Isma'il, writing in the late nineteenth century, discussed grim rural 'remedies' for the problem. In Buhaira

Province and its environs, he said, 'they put the child, about sunset, inside an oven which has no fire underneath, and close the door tightly, and leave it there until the morning. When they abandon it they say, "God is between us and you; give us our son and take your own."' In Giza and Beni Suef, and surrounding districts, 'in place of the oven they choose an abandoned tomb, in which no dead person has been buried during a year at least,' Isma'il said.

He described the two methods as 'savage', noting: 'Often the child dies for want of breath inside the oven, or the tomb; or else some dangerous accident may lead to its destruction.'[46]

Changeling stories are common in many cultures. In European countries, ill-favoured or deformed infants were traditionally believed to be the offspring of fairies (in countries such as Britain, France and Italy), of subterranean dwarves or gnomes (in Germany, Scandinavia, and Slavic countries) or of demons or witches (in other parts of the world). The changeling was thought to be substituted for a normal baby before the newborn could be protected by purification rites. In these folkloric accounts, the changeling was often taken back after the parent took some drastic action, such as whipping the intruder child.

In the Middle East, changeling stories go back more than four thousand years, to the world's earliest known urban civilisation in ancient Mesopotamia. King Sharrukin, better known to us as Sargon the Great, ruler of Akkad (or Agade), who conquered the Sumerian city-states and created an impressive empire in the land of the two rivers, claimed himself to be the son of a changeling. Sargon, who ruled for 56 years, was the first of the great Semitic rulers of Mesopotamia. His empire preserved the best of ancient Sumer, including its literature, but it was Semitic in language and administration, setting the standard for the later Babylonian and Assyrian empires. Sargon's people came from the desert, where the jinn make their home. One of his inscriptions reads:

> *Sargon the Mighty King, King of Agade am I.*
> *My mother was a changeling, my father I knew not.*[47]

Thus Sargon believed himself to be at least half-jinn, similar to Bilqis, the Queen of Sheba. His mysterious background and its hint of supernatural influence may have contributed to his success as a leader.

The changeling motif is thus very old and very widespread. In the Middle East, as in most cultural settings, if the jinn perceive that the secret child swap has been discovered and has, in fact, failed, they act quickly to reverse it and take back their own offspring.

The jinn have their own judiciary, and often abductions of humans lead to trials under this system. Details on how the system is organised are elusive, but we know of its existence because of accounts that have reached us of humans being brought before such courts on matters of law. Humans may come into contact with the jinn courts by killing jinn or committing other serious crimes against them. The most common stories about jinn courts, dating back to the time of the Prophet (and perhaps even earlier), involve cases in which a jinn has taken the form of a snake and a human kills it, not realising it is a jinn. In such cases, the human may be abducted and put on trial in a jinn court. These stories are durable and popular, offering a sense of order and structure in an often chaotic and unpredictable world and so continue to circulate among Muslim communities to this day.

To avoid having to face jinn justice, Muslims are instructed that when they see a snake, they should tell it three times to leave. If it does not depart, then it is not a jinn and may be killed with impunity.

Shah Waliullah Dehlavi of India was a prominent Sunni intellectual and political theorist of the eighteenth century. He was a traditionalist Sufi of the Naqshbandi Order who sought to purge from Sufism such non-Islamic elements as Neoplatonism, Hindu Vedantism and Persian mysticism. Shah Waliullah's orthodox theories and strict interpretations of Islam provided inspiration for Muhammad ibn Abdul Wahhab, who founded the strict orthodox Saudi Wahhabi interpretation of Islam – as well as, eventually, for the Taliban of Afghanistan. According to popular belief in India, Shah Waliullah once killed a jinn that had approached him in the form of a snake. Shah Waliullah was taken to the court of the jinn and was in the process of being sentenced when an ancient Muslim jinn – a 'jinn companion' of the Prophet and convert to Islam more than a millennium earlier – intervened in the proceeding. This jinn said that he had heard the Prophet himself declare that if anyone takes the form of another creature and is killed, then the killing is forgiven, blood money need not be paid and the killer cannot be punished.

There is another such tale from the *Siyar A'lam al-Nubala* (The Lives of Noble Figures) of Muhammad ibn Ahmad al-Dhahabi, a Syrian historian and Islamic hadith expert of the thirteenth century.[48] Al-Dhahabi cites a tradition that 'Aisha bint Abi Bakr, wife of the Prophet, said she had killed a jinn that had entered her tent. She saw afterward in a dream that the jinn had been a Muslim.

'Aisha declared in the dream that if he was indeed a Muslim he would not have entered upon the wives of the Prophet. But someone pointed out that she was veiled at the time and the jinn might not have recognised her. 'Aisha awoke disturbed and ordered that 12,000 dirhams be given to charity, apparently as 'blood money', or compensation for the death of the jinn.[49] Blood money is seen as a settlement that obviates the need for a prolonged court proceeding. In this case, in a bid to achieve the same effect, 'Aisha paid the money to charity.

'Aisha bint Talha,[50] another prominent woman of early Islam, told a variation of this story, also reported by al-Dhahabi: A jinn visited the Prophet's wife 'Aisha repeatedly. She warned him a number of times, but he refused and kept appearing, so she attacked him with a knife and killed him. She then dreamt that someone said to her, 'You killed so and so,' naming a jinn who had witnessed the Prophet's victory at the Battle of Badr, and said this jinn visited her only when she was veiled, apparently only to hear stories about the Prophet.[51]

She told her father, Abu Bakr, about all this, and, according to her niece, he recommended that she pay 12,000 dirhams to charity as blood money.

In Yemen, too, there is a tradition of jinn courts, but in some cases these appear to be mental processes, rather than physical court sessions:

> Throwing hot substances and other materials in bathrooms and deserted places is believed to be harmful [to jinn]. Doers may be paralysed or become mad if they hit the invisible creatures. If a jinn is hit, a court session will be held soon inside the doer's mind until they decide to forgive. During the period of holding those sessions, the host is mad.[52]

Thus, as we go about our day-to-day lives, a parallel society operates in the jinn realm. When the jinn world and ours intersect, abductions and trials before jinn courts may be the result. Human beings are, therefore, advised to be cautious and avoid circumstances that could lead to an unexpected and potentially unpleasant outcome on the other side.

Shifting Shapes

As shapeshifters, jinn often take the form of other living creatures. These forms can be dogs (especially black ones), cats, camels, goats, lions, jackals, toads, beetles, scorpions or, of course, human beings. But snakes or serpents are the most common form assumed by the jinn. Whenever Bedouins come across snakes in the desert, they have to be mindful that the creatures could be jinn.

According to one early Islamic tradition, related in al-Damiri's *Hayat al-Hayawan* (Life of Animals), 'Amr ibn Jabir al-Jinni was the last of a company of nine jinn who had actually heard the Qur'an recited by the Prophet himself. When 'Amr died, he happened to be in the form of a snake. Some pilgrims came upon the snake writhing in its death throes near the town of al-'Arj, southwest of Medina. Not knowing that it was a jinn, one of the pilgrims wrapped the dead snake in a rag, dug a hole in the ground and buried it. They then went on to Mecca. Arriving at the great mosque, they were met by a stranger who said, 'Which of you is the friend of 'Amr ibn Jabir?' The pilgrims replied, 'We don't know him.' The stranger said, 'Which of you is the friend of the jann?' He relayed to the pilgrims a message from the jann: 'May God reward you on our behalf. Verily, he [whom you buried] was the last of the nine of the jinn who heard the Qur'an from the Prophet – blessings and peace be upon him.'[53]

The Umayyad caliph 'Umar ibn Abdul Aziz[54] is reputed to have also buried in a scrap of cloth a dead snake he found while walking in the desert. This snake too was found to be a jinn who like 'Amr was among the early accepters of Islam. According to al-Damiri, when 'Umar had completed the burial, a disembodied voice (of another jinn) informed him that the deceased was named Sariq. The Prophet, the voice said, had told Sariq when he was alive: 'You will die in a waterless land and a pious man will shroud and bury you.' The speaker said he and Sariq had been the last two of the nine to survive. That means, of course, that the disembodied voice belonged to 'Amr ibn Jabir al-Jinni.

There was in the seventeenth century a renowned holy man of Upper Egypt known to us only as Sheikh al-Haridi, who was believed to have returned after his death in the form of a large snake. People were uncertain whether al-Haridi was originally a good jinn who took the form first of a man and later of a snake, or whether he was a genuine human being who was miraculously transformed by Allah into a snake after his death. The only thing locals could be certain of was that the serpent – which took up residence in a cleft in the rocks near the holy man's small domed shrine or *kubbah* on the east bank of the Nile near Tahta – was indeed al-Haridi himself.

During his lifetime, al-Haridi was known as a famous healer, and miraculous cures were said to be effected in his name even after his death and his transformation into a snake. Al-Haridi's *baraka,* or blessing, was especially invoked in cases of barrenness or foolishness. According to one local Muslim legend, he was once a *jinni salih*, a pious jinn, who met the Prophet and sought his intercession to enter Paradise. Local Coptic Christians did not dispute the miracles, but they maintained that al-Haridi was actually Asmodeus, the demon king.[55]

Al-Haridi was reported by some travellers in past centuries to be Turkish in origin. His shrine is still considered locally to be an important pilgrimage place. Tradition certainly seems to be alive, and the snake still holds a considerable place in folk beliefs and customs of the region.[56]

One shape that jinn will not assume – in almost every country of the Islamic world – is that of the wolf because the jinn are known to have a strong aversion to, and fear of, wolves.

Folklorist Ethel S. Stephens, who collected traditional tales in Iraq after World War I, says that the wolf is the only animal jinn fear, because for some reason when a wolf is present jinn are unable to sink into the earth and so fall prey to the wolf's teeth and claws.

Women of the Shammari tribe, who today reside in both Iraq and Saudi Arabia, would traditionally lull their children to sleep at night with this lullaby:[57]

Bismillah
Ism adh-dhib
Al-khotib
'Ala galbak!

In the name of God
The wolf's name
The invoked one
Upon your heart!

The Shammari mother is convinced that this refrain frightens off evil spirits.

Among other old Iraqi beliefs, is the tradition that a wolf's teeth may help prevent coughing, and the teeth and claws are worn by girls as charms, or hung up in the house or in one's tent to keep out evil. A wolf's eye, dried and carried on one's person, protects a man against being surprised in his sleep by an enemy or by the law.

According to an Iraqi tradition recorded by Stephens, talismanic stones resulted from an encounter between a wolf and a jinn. One day, a wolf came upon a company of female jinn. They were able to escape by using sorcery and turning themselves into semi-precious stones. These stones took on the magic qualities of the female jinn, each one retaining special powers, for example, soapstone prevents heart ailments, hematite gives the wearer power, and so on. Talismanic stones are an ancient instrument of magic associated with the signs of the Zodiac, and their use dates back to the ancient Egyptians and Babylonians, perhaps even earlier. Different coloured stones are believed to confer specific properties or qualities on the wearer, such as courage, strength, health, virtue, among others. This legend linking talismanic stones to the ancient enmity between wolves and jinn (and female jinn at that) may appear on the surface to be a simple folktale, a case of Little Red Riding Hood on steroids, but given its origin in a land steeped in ancient magical lore, it probably conveys deeper symbolisms whose meanings elude us even today.

Of all living creatures, the wolf will be the last to die, the Arabs say, at the very end of the world. This belief, reported in rural Iraq, is of unknown origin and is believed to pre-date Islam.

It is also said that wolves stalk the *si'lah*, another kind of female jinn demon who is described as 'the worst of the ghouls'. The ghoul (Arabic *ghul* or the feminine form *ghulah,* pl. *ghilan*), as we shall see shortly, is a shapeshifter that eats human flesh. The *si'lah* (pl.*sa'alin*)[58] is the most wicked and most dangerous kind of ghoul. She would play games with her victim, making him caper and dance before she devoured him. When an Arabian poet of the Prophet's day wrote that 'the Jinn and the Ghouls of a land become changed to demons', he was referring to their transformation into *si'lahs,* which was another way of saying that the land had changed for the worse.[59] Al-Damiri, citing Zakariya al-Qazwini, describes the wolf's hunt of this demon:

> The wolf sometimes hunts her at night, he says, and then eats her. As he tears into her she raises her voice saying, 'Save me. The wolf is eating me.' Sometimes she will say, 'I have a thousand dinars and whoever rescues me will take it.' People know that these are the words of the *si'lah* and nobody rescues her and the wolf eats her.[60]

The only place where jinn and wolves seem compatible is in Yemen. There is a type of jinn found only in Yemen called the *'udhrut* (plural *'adharit*). The *'udhrut* normally looks like a wolf, but it can change its shape into that of a dog, cat or any other animal, or it can resemble a stone, or even a man or woman.

According to Yemeni folklore, the *'udhrut* is attracted by the blood of the dead and is known to appear at the scene of a murder. It will suddenly materialise before a person, bark or growl at him and then vanish. There is apparently no way to exorcise the 'udhrut, whose only purpose seems to be to frighten humans. They apparently do no other harm.[61]

A medieval legend recorded in Mamluk Egypt between the twelfth and sixteenth centuries describes the creation of a race of ghouls in Yemen, which are the result of the joining together of a wolf's seed, smoke from a fire, and human seed inside the body of a human woman. This strange tale appears in the Arab *sira*, or folk epic, of Sayf Ben Dhi Yazan, an adventure tale set in Yemen and in the Nile Valley (Egypt, Sudan, Ethiopia). Sayf was an actual historical figure, a sixth-century Arab king who ruled in Yemen before the advent of Islam. The hideous ghouls produced by this strange process were said to inhabit the legendary – and now lost – Valley of the Ghouls in Yemen and were eventually wiped out by King Sayf himself.[62]

The Arabs have a form of werewolf in their folklore, the *qutrub*, a corruption of the Greek *lykanthropos* or wolf-man. Edward Lane, a translator of the *Thousand and One Nights*, says the male ghoul is called by this name. In popular belief, the *qutrub* is a man or a woman who is transformed into a beast by night and who feeds upon corpses. The beast is wolf-like but not a wolf per se, because as we have learned, most jinn (apart from *the 'udhrut*) do not shapeshift into wolves.

While on the subject of shapeshifters, we should devote a bit more time to the flesh-eating ghoul, who, as was noted, is usually female. She often disguises herself as a human being to lure her prey. The ghoul lives alone in the desert or lies in wait at some place where men are destined to perish. She appears to people travelling unaccompanied at night and, seeming to be a traveller herself, lures them out of their way. She not only talks with travellers but sometimes prostitutes herself to them.

Some Arabic dictionaries define the ghoul as a sorcerer or magician among the jinn. Some say that ghouls are evil jinn that appear at night, and si'lahs are those that appear during the daytime.[63]

Imaginative tales and romances from and about the Middle East, dating back to the Middle Ages and beyond, have always featured accounts of ghouls as violators of graves. The ghouls of these tales are intent upon digging up corpses and mangling them. Says Victorian folklorist Sabine Baring-Gould, writing about such stories in the 1860s:

> Of a moonlight night weird forms are seen stealing among the tombs, and burrowing into them with their long nails, desiring to reach the bodies of the dead ere the first streak of dawn compels them to retire. These ghouls, as they are called, are supposed generally to require the flesh of the dead for incantations or magical compositions, but very often they are actuated by the sole desire of rending the sleeping corpse, and disturbing its repose.[64]

Baring-Gould – perhaps best known for composing the religious anthem 'Onward Christian Soldiers' – was an author, antiquarian and folklore expert. He wrote a definitive work on werewolf legends in 1865 and in the course of that book discussed grave violators, or ghouls. He believed that the ghouls of his time and of the medieval period were not spirit creatures or hallucinations, but human practitioners of black magic.

'There is every probability that these ghouls were no mere creations of the imagination, but were actual resurrectionists,' he asserts.

> Human fat and the hair of a corpse which has grown in the grave, form ingredients in many a necromantic receipt, and the witches

> who compounded these diabolical mixtures, would unearth corpses in order to obtain the requisite ingredients. It was the same in the middle ages, and to such an extent did the fear of ghouls extend, that it was common in Brittany for churchyards to be provided with lamps, kept burning during the night, that witches might be deterred from venturing under cover of darkness to open the graves.

In the same book, Baring-Gould relates an old legend about a ghoul in fifteenth-century Baghdad:

> In the beginning of the 15th century, there lived at Bagdad an aged merchant who had grown wealthy in his business, and who had an only son to whom he was tenderly attached. He resolved to marry him to the daughter of another merchant, a girl of considerable fortune, but without any personal attractions. Abul-Hassan, the merchant's son, on being shown the portrait of the lady, requested his father to delay the marriage till he could reconcile his mind to it. Instead, however, of doing this, he fell in love with another girl, the daughter of a sage, and he gave his father no peace till he consented to the marriage with the object of his affections. The old man stood out as long as he could, but finding that his son was bent on acquiring the hand of the fair Nadilla, and was equally resolute not to accept the rich and ugly lady, he did what most fathers, under such circumstances, are constrained to do, he acquiesced.
>
> The wedding took place with great pomp and ceremony, and a happy honeymoon ensued, which might have been happier but for one little circumstance which led to very serious consequences.
>
> Abul-Hassan noticed that his bride quitted the nuptial couch as soon as she thought her husband was asleep, and did not return to it, till an hour before dawn.
>
> Filled with curiosity, Hassan one night feigned sleep, and saw his wife rise and leave the room as usual. He followed cautiously, and saw her enter a cemetery. By the straggling moonbeams he beheld her go into a tomb; he stepped in after her.
>
> The scene within was horrible. A party of ghouls were assembled with the spoils of the graves they had violated, and were feasting on the flesh of the long-buried corpses. His own wife, who, by the way, never touched supper at home, played no inconsiderable part in the hideous banquet.
>
> As soon as he could safely escape, Abul-Hassan stole back to his bed.

He said nothing to his bride till next evening when supper was laid, and she declined to eat; then he insisted on her partaking, and when she positively refused, he exclaimed wrathfully,–'Yes, you keep your appetite for your feast with the ghouls!' Nadilla was silent; she turned pale and trembled, and without a word sought her bed. At midnight she rose, fell on her husband with her nails and teeth, tore his throat, and having opened a vein, attempted to suck his blood; but Abul-Hassan springing to his feet threw her down, and with a blow killed her. She was buried next day.

Three days after, at midnight, she re-appeared, attacked her husband again, and again attempted to suck his blood. He fled from her, and on the morrow opened her tomb, burned her to ashes, and cast them into the Tigris.[65]

This story links the ghoul with the vampire. As Baring-Gould points out in his book, the werewolf and the vampire are closely related as well. He describes a French historian's account of *lamias* harvesting the bodies of dead soldiers on a Syrian battlefield in the dark of night. *Lamias* are Greek female mythological creatures that sometimes devour human flesh (like ghouls), particularly the flesh of children, and sometimes drink human blood (like vampires). A number of these *lamias* were shot at by surviving soldiers and were found next morning to have taken on the shapes of wolves. In Baring Gould's words:

> Marcassus[66] relates that after a long war in Syria, during the night, troops of lamias, female evil spirits, appeared upon the field of battle, unearthing the hastily buried bodies of the soldiers, and devouring the flesh off their bones. They were pursued and fired upon, and some young men succeeded in killing a considerable number; but during the day they had all of them the forms of wolves or hyaenas.

Baring-Gould felt there was 'a foundation of truth in these horrible stories', and that it was indeed possible for a human being to be possessed of a depraved appetite for rending corpses.

Thus we see that shapeshifting comes in many forms and can be used by jinn quite innocently to protect them from prying eyes or, quite maliciously, to advance predatory activities against human beings. For the jinn, this amazing ability is truly 'second nature', and one of the various tools they use to assure survival. Whether this tool is used for good or ill depends on the character and nature of the jinn in question.

Jinn Living

Jinn lifestyles are sometimes remarkably similar to those of humans, but often with a slight twist or a more clearly observable difference. The average jinn is born, grows up within a family, marries, raises his own family and eventually dies. The fact that he can transform himself into a snake or vanish into thin air or fly through the skies does not change certain other more mundane aspects of his life.

The Islamic theologian Ibn Taymiyyah wrote about many aspects of jinn life and activity in a remarkable piece entitled 'Essay on the Jinn'.[67] One of the more unusual discussions in this work deals with what the jinn use for food and as feed for their animals.

Ibn Taymiyyah points out that according to Islamic tradition, the jinn asked the Prophet to provide some food for them and their animals.[68] The Prophet replied: 'Every bone on which the name of Allah is recited is your provision. The time it will fall in your hand it would be covered with flesh, and the dung of (the camels) is fodder for your animals.' The Prophet added: 'Do not clean yourselves with both of them (bones and dung) for verily they are provisions for your brothers among the jinn.'

Elsewhere in the essay, Ibn Taymiyyah reports that Salman al-Farisi (the Persian), a companion of the Prophet, was once asked mockingly by a polytheist unbeliever: 'Your Prophet has taught you everything, even including how to use the toilet?' Salman replied, 'Yes. He forbade us from facing the direction of prayer while defecating or urinating, from cleaning ourselves with our right hands, cleaning ourselves with less than three pebbles, or from cleaning ourselves with animal droppings or bones.'

Abu Huraira,[69] a companion and member of the Prophet's inner circle, used to carry Muhammad's ritual ablution container and his effects. Once the Prophet answered a call of nature and asked Abu Huraira to bring something for cleaning himself. The Prophet said, 'I would like some stones to remove (the remains) but do not bring any bones or animal droppings.' Abu Huraira related,

> So I brought him some stones in the edge of my garment and placed them beside him and left until he had finished. I then came and asked, 'What is wrong with bones and animal droppings?' He replied, 'They are among the food of the jinn. Verily a delegation of jinns from Nasibin [or Nisibis, in northern Iraq] came to me – they

were the best of jinns – and they asked me to specify some provisions for them so I asked Allah on their behalf that whenever they pass by a bone or animal dropping they would find on it food.'[70]

Ibn Taymiyyah, commenting on these traditions, noted that the Prophet's prohibition against cleaning away feces with the food of the jinn and their animals also contains a more obvious prohibition against whatever would defile human food and that of their animals. However, the dislike and revulsion over food contaminated with excrement is natural to man, the theologian said, so it was not mentioned – which is not the case with regard to bones and animal droppings, since the food of jinn was unknown to man.

Desert sands throughout the world are occasionally said to make mysterious sounds – sometimes singing, sometimes buzzing, sometimes moaning. In Arab and Muslim countries, these haunting noises are often attributed to the jinn. Marco Polo, writing in the thirteenth century, also attributed such sounds to evil spirits. Writing about crossing the Lop Desert in Muslim Eastern Turkestan, he relates:

> Beasts there are none; for there is nought for them to eat. But there is a marvellous thing related of this Desert, which is that when travellers are on the move by night, and one of them chances to lag behind or to fall asleep or the like, when he tries to gain his company again he will hear spirits talking, and will suppose them to be his comrades. Sometimes the spirits will call him by name; and thus shall a traveller ofttimes be led astray so that he never finds his party. And in this way many have perished. [Sometimes the stray travellers will hear as it were the tramp and hum of a great cavalcade of people away from the real line of road, and taking this to be their own company they will follow the sound; and when day breaks they find that a cheat has been put on them and that they are in an ill plight ... Even in the day-time one hears those spirits talking. And sometimes you shall hear the sound of a variety of musical instruments, and still more commonly the sound of drums. [Hence in making this journey 'tis customary for travellers to keep close together. All the animals too have bells at their necks, so that they cannot easily get astray. And at sleeping-time a signal is put up to show the direction of the next march.][71]

H. St. John Philby, who travelled across Arabia early in the twentieth century, related certain Bedouin stories about drumming and moaning sands in the heart of the Rub' al-Khali or Empty Quarter. He linked these reports to a lost city called Jahura, said to be hidden in the dunes about 100 miles south of al-Hadida, the field of meteorite craters. Jinn, of course, are reputed to inhabit such desert ruins. Philby told Lord Curzon that he never heard the phenomenon himself, but that it was often mentioned to him by Bedouins, particularly in relation to Jahura, which was said to lie buried in the dunes and had never been seen by a European.

At this site, 'the sounds of drumming and moaning are regularly heard at night by passing travellers, by whom they are of course attributed to jinns or ghosts, persons of weak intellect having even been known to lose their reason,' Lord Curzon said. 'This, however, may be a case of merely imaginary haunting, the product of superstition.'[72]

According to pre-Islamic belief in Arabia, the jinn made sounds in the desert at night to reveal their presence to other jinn or to humans, depending on the circumstances. Charles J. Lyall, Arabist and translator of ancient Arabian poetry, described the sound thus:

> Belief in the Jinn, good and evil (but principally evil), existed all over Arabia long before Muhammad, through whom it has come to be embodied in the Kur'an, and an article of faith for all true believers. Certain places in the Desert were supposed to be specially haunted by them, of which a list is given in al-Hamdani's *Geography*, p. 154. Their presence is thought to be indicated by a peculiar sound,[73] heard at night, a low, faint humming or murmur; al-Asma'i says that this sound is really produced by the falling of grains of sand driven along by the wind, as they sweep over the wrinkled surface of the desert.[74]

In 2004, a team of scientists headed by physicist Bruno Andreotti of the University of Paris-Diderot headed for the Sahara Desert in southeast Morocco – one of only 35 known places where these mysterious desert sounds are heard – to try to uncover the secret behind this phenomenon.

The team attributed the 'natural music' to sand avalanches down the slopes of dunes that were of sufficient dryness. They found that the noise occurs with small dunes only in the few days in which there is no wind and no clouds, 'so that the sun can dry efficiently the slip face'. In effect, the face of the dune acts like a huge loudspeaker, with sand waves on the surface producing the sound in the air. But the team did concede that the mystery was not completely solved, since they could not explain why the cascading sand grains made a rumbling noise while tiny glass beads moving in a similar avalanche did not.[75]

Beyond producing frightening sounds, jinn are also capable of speaking the many languages of those humans with whom they come in contact. But do they speak a particular language among themselves? According to some traditions from the Maghreb, they speak Suryaniyya, or ancient Syriac, a dialect of Aramaic. As an offshoot of the ancestral language of the Semites, Syriac is a most suitable tongue for fire spirits who reached their finest articulation in the Semitic tradition.

In the twelfth century, under the Berber Muslim Almohad dynasty, an aide to secretary of the Imam Ibn Tumart, Mallul ibn Ibrahim ibn Yahya al-Sanhaji, was described as a man who knew many languages and who wrote in the Suryaniyya script, which Berbers called the language of communication with the jinn.[76] It is not known whether Mallul's job involved communicating with jinn, but it was impressive for a Berber in Morocco to read and write a language and script from the far-off Arab heartland, and this suggests he may have studied in Damascus or Baghdad.

Finnish anthropologist Edward Alexander Westermarck, in his definitive study of Moroccan rituals and beliefs, had additional insights about jinn language: 'They speak, but their language is different from that of men; when a jenn speaks through the mouth of a human being, he calls money *qshor* instead of *flus*, and excrements *jatu*; and his voice is very thin.'[77]

Some contend that the jinn are also telepathic and can communicate mentally, without an actual spoken language. This facilitates jinn possession of human beings, for it allows the spirit beings to transfer thoughts to the minds of the possessed. It also allows jinn to 'speak' among themselves without being heard. (For an example of jinn telepathy, see 'Syria: The Red King's Daughter', p.143)

As we have noted, jinn, like humans, have many faiths: Islam, Christianity, Judaism, Zoroastrianism, paganism. In the nineteenth century, Egyptian physician 'Abd al-Rahman Isma'il took note of Christian jinn in his *Old Wives' Medicine*, published in Cairo in 1892–1894.[78] He pointed out that Muslim healers in his day used images of Christian crosses to protect people against Christian jinn:

> One of the methods of 'cure' [for a headache or *suda'*] is to draw a cross on the temple of the patient with saliva ... We have even seen many fools who have tattooed crosses upon their temples to guard against the evil of *suda'*.

The logic of such treatments is unclear. Perhaps Christian jinn would be deterred from causing headaches if they saw that their potential victim was marked with a cross and thus appeared to be a Christian as well. Isma'il's translator, John Walker, accepts this explanation: 'Many Moslem women wear crosses, or hang them on their children to drive away evil spirits, or 'afarit. At first sight it appears strange that Moslems should be found wearing the Christian emblem. But it is really a case of sympathetic magic. The evil spirits are conceived as being of Christian origin and therefore unwilling to approach anyone protected by Christian symbols.'[79]

* * *

Another important aspect of jinn life is their day-to-day interaction with the natural environment. Like humans, jinn interact with various plants, bushes and trees in their environment, making use of some and avoiding others. Some plants and trees have long-standing traditional associations with the jinn – sometimes even serving as their homes.

According to Arabian lore, jinn are attracted to the **lote-tree** or *sidr* (*Ziziphus nummularia*), a wild, thorny shrub-like tree that grows in desert areas where ground water accumulates. An old legend cited in Muslim sources says that this is also the tree from which Jesus' crown of thorns was made.

Explorer Alois Musil reported in 1928 that Arabian tribes living in the northern ranges of the lote-tree – in the Najd region of central Arabia – believed that sidr thickets were haunted by jinn who 'have their gardens' there. The trees were, therefore, not used for fuel by local villagers or Bedouins.

Some Bedouins from northern Arabia regard a shrub known as ***awsaj*** (*Lycium shawii*) as another abode of jinn. Musil noted that the Rwala tribe of this area would not cut *awsaj* for fuel to avoid provoking the spirits that resided in the shrubs. In the mid-twentieth century, Harold R.P. Dickson, a former British political agent in Kuwait and later representative of the Kuwait Oil Company, said the Bedouins of Kuwait avoided cutting the plant because of its association with jinn. Dickson wrote that *awsaj* bushes in the Kuwait area were sometimes seen surrounded by stones because passing Bedouins would seek to keep the jinn at bay by tossing a stone at the bush and reciting a protective phrase, such as 'Bismallah' (In the name of God). (The longer version of the *bismallah* is 'Bismallah ar-Rahman ar-Rahim' [In the name of God the Compassionate and Merciful].)

Bedouins in Saudi Arabia's Eastern Province told botanical cataloguer James Mandaville that the *awsaj* was not used for fuel there, but Mandaville noted that its branches were not very suitable for this purpose anyway, because they were thorny and difficult to break. This suggests that tribal caveats against burning *awsaj* may have had practical reasons as well: it just did not serve the purpose. An elderly Bani Hajir tribesman told Mandaville a number of 'campfire anecdotes and folk stories' about *awsaj* bushes and the jinn. Mandaville noted that *awsaj* is frequently seen growing around ruin sites and desert burial grounds, which he said could account at least partially for the 'apparent wealth of superstition' associated with the plant.

As well as plants that attract jinn, there are also plants that jinn avoid, just as we might steer clear of poison ivy or Jimson weed.

One of these plants is **Syrian rue** (*Peganum harmala,* called *harmal* or *feyjan* in Arabic), a medicinal herb that grows throughout Southwest Asia, including the Arabian Peninsula, where it is associated with the jinn. Harmal is still highly regarded for its more supernatural properties. It is one of the *shajarat al-jinn* (plants of the jinn) and precautions should be taken when gathering it: the collector should wear a piece of iron, which repels jinn, and he should approach the plant praising God and pronouncing Qur'anic formulas. He should not come under any shade cast by the plant – the shade being particularly dangerous – nor should the plant be collected before dawn. When plucking the stem, one would traditionally say, 'I take this from you in the name of God on behalf of so-and-so,' extending a piece of iron towards the plant while picking it.

In the last century, leaves and fresh growing tips of harmal were rubbed all over the body to protect against jinn and the evil eye. The plant, though known now to contain toxic alkaloids, was sometimes boiled and the water drunk on an empty stomach to ease abdominal pains. Some of this water was also rubbed on the painful area. This treatment (though not recommended today!) was said to be particularly effective for women suffering from post-partum pains, both to relieve the discomfort and to protect the mother, who was believed to be vulnerable to evil influences at that time. Also, harmal leaves were sometimes thrown into the night fire to keep away evil and to protect sleepers.

Indian costus or *Saussurea costus* is a plant that has been cultivated for thousands of years in Kashmir and other high elevations of India and is known for its ability to repel jinn. It also happens to be an important medicinal plant still widely used in Ayurvedic medicine and other systems for the treatment of various ailments, including asthma, inflammatory diseases, ulcers and stomach problems. Recent research has shown that it may also possess anti-cancer properties.

Some Saudi religious scholars assert that nose drops made of Indian costus-root powder, mixed with olive oil, may be used to exorcise a 'stubborn' jinn who has possessed a person and is not easily expelled. This practice dates back at least to the times of the Prophet and is reported in the hadiths. Says Dr. Ameen, Saudi authority on jinn and human sickness: 'The patient should take it in through the nose, so that the costus goes straight to the brain where the jinn is located, and he will be greatly annoyed by it, so much so that he will not be able to bear it and will hasten to flee, or he will talk to the practitioner and promise to leave and not come back.'[80] It is not known what property of the plant the jinn find so distressing.

The **Easter tree** (*Holarrhena antidysenterica*), also called ivory tree or Tellicherry bark, is from India and has a seed that is light brown, elongated, brittle and nut-like. Used medicinally in the Middle East, the seed is ground and mixed with water and is used both externally and internally. Healers massage the body with the mixture to drive away pain and aches caused by devils or jinn. Used as a tonic, aphrodisiac, astringent and febrifuge, it can also cure amoebic dysentery, worms, restlessness, tremors and insomnia.

Found on Socotra Island off Yemen, the solid purple resin from the **Dragon's Blood tree** (*Dracaena cinnabari*) is mixed with other drugs, added to soup or boiled in water. Taken internally, it helps drive away jinn, treats eye disease, rids newborns of meconium, decreases crying as well as fever and treats rash, haemorrhaging, foot/ leg pain, dysentery and diarrhoea. The resin is an astringent and can be used as a tooth powder. It can also supposedly induce abortion.

The **asafoetida** plant (*Ferula*) grows in western Saudi Arabia. Often called devil's dung, its resin is sticky and has a strong odour. It is boiled; the liquid can be drunk or the resin chewed. The dry powder may be put in the nostrils of a child. It is used to treat colic. It is also used as a seasoning, perfume, laxative, expectorant, sedative for mild hysteria and anti-spasmodic. Some people wear a bag of the resin around the neck to ward off evil spirits. It can substitute for myrrh.

Mastic (*Pistacia lentiscus*) is a yellow, tear-shaped aromatic resin that grows in India, Iran and the Mediterranean. The best mastic grows in the Greek islands. An astringent, it is taken internally or externally. It can be burnt and the vapours allowed to fill the room. Combined with other herbs, it is used for fevers, as flavouring in jams and chewing gum, as temporary fillings for carious teeth and as a protective covering for wounds. It is also used to drive away jinn demons.

Grown in India and Iran, the fruit and aromatic seed of **jinn's apple** or *Cupressus* are burnt in a fire, producing vapours that are inhaled to treat whooping cough and expel worms. Also, the vapours are known to drive away demons from people.

Jinn have a particular aversion to the **citron** (*Citrus medica*), the large yellow-green fruit that was one of the first citrus varieties to be introduced to Europe from the Orient.

Al-Damiri wrote that jinn will not enter a house in which there are citrons. He cites the example of an imam named Abu al-Hasan ibn Muhammad al-Khal'i, a companion of pre-eminent Arab jurist Muhammad ibn Idris al-Shafi'i (767–820), founder of the Shafi'i school of Islam. Al-Khal'i used to serve as a *qadi* or Islamic judge for a group of jinn, even though he was human. These particular jinn for whatever reason lacked an Islamic judge in their own community and thus asked al-Khal'i to rule from the bench on their behalf. Since Islam in its essentials was the same for men and jinn, this type of temporary arrangement is conceivable. The jinn stayed away from the judge's court for a week, and when they finally came back to him, he asked why they had stayed away. The jinn replied that there was citron in his house, and they would not enter a home in which that fruit was found.

The imam, relating this story, said, 'The Prophet ... cited a comparison between the believer who recites the Qur'an and the citron, because the devil flees the heart of a believer reciting the Qur'an just as he flees a place in which there is citron. It is appropriate therefore to cite a comparison with it, in contrast to the other fruits.'[81]

Most of these jinn-repelling plants are valuable medicinal herbs in their own right that happen to treat in a purely conventional manner illnesses or complaints often attributed in olden times to jinn. Thus the plants do double duty, not only treating the given ailment chemically but also driving off the offending 'devil'.

In addition to these plants, jinn are said to hate and dread salt and iron.

Salt is noted for its ability to put jinn to flight. Edward Westermarck, in his study of Moroccan customs, noted that a little salt thrown into a crackling fire is sufficient to extinguish the ardour of the spirits that have taken possession of the fire. Moroccans will sprinkle salt under the bed of a woman who has given birth, or on a site chosen for setting up the tents of the *douar* (camp), or on heaps of grain and in grain silos. A knife blade to be used to sacrifice an animal is often passed over some salt beforehand. Some Moroccans believe that the sea is not haunted by the jinn because of the salt it contains. When a person enters the sea to bathe, there is no need to pronounce the *bismillah* – a practice that is obligatory if one bathes in sweet water or enters a water tank to clean it.[82]

Edward Lane observed that in Muslim Arab lands during the month of Ramadan, evil jinn are believed to be confined in prison; thus, on the final night of the holy month, women sometimes repeat the *bismallah* and sprinkle salt on the floors of their houses.

Jinn are also deathly afraid of iron (and sometimes steel), a characteristic they share with numerous other spirits, including the Celtic elves of the Scottish Highlands, the evil spirits that plague Sri Lanka's Sinhalese population, and the demons of West African animists.[83]

Particularly in Morocco, iron is regarded as a great protection against evil jinn. A knife with an iron blade is often placed beneath the pillow of a sick person. The jinn's fear of iron dates back to prehistory, according to Edward Westermarck. He notes that, as with salt, Moroccans have a custom of putting a worn-out sickle or old knife blade in silos to keep the jinn away from the grain. Interestingly, they also share the European custom of nailing a horseshoe over the door of a house or stable to assure good luck.

Edward Lane wrote that sometimes Arabs will seek protection from jinn that ride whirlwinds by exclaiming, 'Hadeed! Hadeed!' (Iron! Iron!), or, 'Hadeed! yá mashoom!' (Iron! Thou unlucky!), because of the jinn's terror of that metal.

This fear is recognised not only among Muslims but also among Hindus. In India, jinn and evil spirits are thought to fear iron in any form, and traditional Hindu women wear iron bracelets as wedding bands regardless of caste.[84]

Some sociological theories see this fear of iron as a symbolic rejection of modernity, of which iron and steel are key substances. Modernity is regarded as the enemy of the jinn, or at least not part of their 'comfort zone'. This would explain the widespread opposition to iron by spirit beings in many countries, and religious taboos against the use of iron in religious temples, altars and precincts of many ancient cultures, including the Greeks, Romans and Hebrews.

Despite their supernatural powers, jinn do not always have an easy life. They are not all-powerful, and over the centuries humans have discovered numerous, clever ways to keep them at bay. These protective measures often involve natural substances which counter ailments or conditions blamed on spirit intervention. At times, the protections are symbolic, representing worlds where the jinn do not feel at home. In any case, it is a great comfort to many believers to have such tools for maintaining a healthy separation of humans from jinn.

Sex and Marriage

Most Muslim scholars agree that jinn can have sexual relations and marital relationships with humans. Islamic jurists over the centuries have been divided on whether members of the two species should be allowed to marry. While most Islamic scholars appear to oppose it, some reputable authorities believe human-jinn marriages are licit.

Imad al-Din ibn Yunis, a learned scholar of Mosul in the early thirteenth century, believed that racial differences in general were an obstacle to marriage. He went beyond that, saying, 'It is not allowed that a man marry a female jinni according to the Almighty's statement, "And Allah created for you from among you spouses" [Qur'an 16:72]. The Almighty has said, "Among His wonders is that He created for you from among yourselves spouses so that you may live with them and He has made between you love and mercy" [Qur'an 30:21]. Love meaning sexual union and mercy meaning children.'

Jalaluddin al-Suyuti, a noted Egyptian religious scholar of the fifteenth century, contended that human-jinn marriages were allowed. Al-Suyuti mentioned cases from the early days of Islam when humans and jinn were reported to have married.[85] Ibn Taymiyyah similarly took note of such historical cases and said that some of these couples had borne children.

The brilliant scientist al-Jahiz of Basra[86] observed: '[Some Islamic theologians] allege that intermarriage and cross-breeding has occurred between the jinn and humans according to the Almighty's statement: "Make them partners in wealth and offspring" [Qur'an 17:64]. This is apparent since female jinn undertake to seduce human men out of passion, seeking fornication, and likewise the men of the jinn, human women. If it were not for that [among the jinn] men would seek out men and women would seek out women.'[87]

Al-Damiri asserts that the daughter of Arabic language scholar al-Nu'man al-Najariyah had an illicit sexual relationship with a jinn servant, which ended when the jinn accepted Islam. The daughter, Fatimah, was quoted as saying, 'I had a servant from among the jinn and he used to rush into the house where I was [for illicit relations]. He came to me one day, stood against the wall and did not do what he used to do. I said to him, "What's on your mind that you do not do the deed you used to do before?" "Indeed there has been sent today a prophet who forbids fornication," he answered.'

Al-Damiri called attention to a Qu'ranic verse about the houris, the virgins of Paradise: 'Neither men nor jann have deflowered them [the houris] before them [the believers in the next world]' [Qur'an 55:74]. He observed: 'If the jann did not use to deflower women and that was not in their nature, God on High would not have made this statement.'[88]

Al-Damiri used this argument to demonstrate that sexual relations between jinn and humans were theoretically possible.

A fourteenth-century Moroccan magician known as Muhammad ibn al-Hajj al-Tilimsani produced a treatise published in Cairo called *Suns of Lights and Treasuries of Secrets*, whose contents included a spell for having sex with the daughter of the White King of the jinn. Historian Robert Irwin describes the process: 'After twelve days' fasting and uttering of conjurations in the desert, first a dragon appears (which must be ignored) and then a very pale woman who approaches with an undulating walk and who is laden with gold and jewels. The trouble is, if you agree to marry her, this will make you impotent with ordinary women.'[89]

Although Muslim women are required to perform full ritual washing (*ghusl*) after having had sexual relations with men before they can perform prayers, the Hanafi legal compilation *Al-Fatawa al-Hindiyya*[90] says there is no need for the full washing after having had sex with jinn. The presumption of the Hanaji legal scholars here is that in jinn-human sexual intercourse there would be no bodily discharges requiring *ghusl*.

Jinn are believed to be sexually drawn to humans. For this reason, Muslims believe that jinn, who can render themselves invisible at will, may use this advantage to spy upon humans who are naked or in the process of undressing. How does one know whether a demon is lurking about, unseen, waiting for a man or woman to disrobe? To prevent this situation from occurring, people often recite the *bismallah* before taking off their clothes. This is expected to put any jinn with prurient intentions to flight.

Ibn al-Nadim, compiler of the *Fihrist*, in a section on stories and storytellers includes a list of tales of jinn-human romance. The names are book titles, and the stories seem to be for the most part about imaginary characters:

> The Names of the Humans in Love with the Jinn and the Jinn in Love with the Humans
>
> Da'd and al-Rabab; Rifa'ah al-'Absi and Sukr; Sa'sa and Qum'; Na'im ibn Darim, Rahimah, and *Shaytan* al-Taq; Al-Aghlab and al-Rabab; Al-Dirgham [the Lion], Jud [the Liberal], the Waqs [the Worthless]; 'Amr and Diqyanus; Al-Shammakh [the Proud] and Dam' [the Weeping]; The Tricky Khazraji and Asma'; Husn

[Modesty, Chastity] ibn Nabhan and the Female Jinni; Al-Dilfa, Her Brothers, and the Jinni; Da'd al-Fazariyah, the Jinni, and 'Amr; 'Umar ibn Sufyan al-Sulami and the Female Jinni; 'Amr ibn Makshuh and the Female Jinni; Rabi'ah ibn Qudam [Qaddam] and the Female Jinni; Sa'd ibn 'Umayr and al-Nawar [the Timid, Innocent].

Ibn al-Nadim notes that 'evening stories and fables' of such inter-species romantic encounters were popular under the rule of the Abbasid caliphs in Baghdad, especially in the time of al-Muqtadir (ruled 908–932), only a few years before the *Fihrist* was compiled. The reign of al-Muqtadir is generally described as a period of political and socio-cultural decline, though a number of great scientists, poets and historians, including al-Razi, Omar Khayyam and al-Tabari, published classics during these years. Al-Muqtadir was a weak and venal ruler, manipulated by members of the royal court. In an atmosphere of decline and corruption in Baghdad, romantic tales with a fantastic, even impossible, flavour would have exerted some appeal over the educated classes.

The belief that liaisons between humans and jinn are possible remains alive even today among farmers and villagers in modern Iraq. Speaking of a type of ghoul, the *s'iluwa*, that lives in and around Iraqi rivers and seeks human lovers, folklorist Ethel Stevens notes: 'The union of human men and women with river demons is to this day credited as possible, and the existence of *s'iluwa* is not questioned among the [uneducated] classes. Even amongst those who are semi-educated there are many who believe in her existence.'[91] Some Iraqis even believe that these unions can result in children, she observes.

Today, jinn have an enduring, very real presence in Pakistan. So readers of *The Friday Times* of Lahore were not surprised to come across a report in November 2000 about a jinn eloping with a 17-year-old girl who had been confined in a locked room in her parents' home in Phoolnagar.[92]

According to the newspaper, the lecherous jinn had been following the girl for six months. Her family considered her 'possessed' and occasionally locked her in a room while she recovered from a 'fit'.

One afternoon, her parents unlocked the door and saw that she was gone. Relatives told authorities that she and the jinn eloped.

What actually happened to the unfortunate girl, perhaps only her parents know.

Jinn behaviour is in some ways very 'human', but in others very magical and otherworldly. Motivations for jinn actions, both for and against mankind, are often similar to those of our own human world: revenge, love, anger, pity, envy and other such emotions. But the tools at their disposal are dramatically different from ours and enable them to produce amazing or horrific outcomes. In the pages to come, we shall see how these behaviours play out in widely differing cultural and social settings, in a sweeping panorama of countries.

Chapter Four

Jinn Geography

If some Muslim became possessed [in old Lahore], an amil or spirit-master was sent for to exorcise the foreign spirit. He would arrive, say his prayers, blow into the face of the possessed man or woman several times and then order the jinn in a loud voice to depart the body he had occupied otherwise he would be burnt to a cinder. If the amil had the powers he claimed, the jinn would say in the voice of the man he had possessed, 'Have mercy, I am exiting.' The amil would ask, 'Leave a sign when you depart.' The jinn would answer, 'This brass mug resting on that table will topple to the ground when I leave.' The next moment, the mug would come tumbling down and the possessed man would return to his normal self.

– A. Hameed, Pakistani novelist

Arabia: The Heartland

The Arabian Peninsula is the heartland of the jinn and, as the birthplace of Islam, the focal point of many jinn legends and beliefs. It is among the Bedouin tribes of Arabia that one finds some of the earliest articulations of jinn lore.[1] We have observed that the intensity of belief in the jinn tends to be strongest among settled populations. At the same time, many of the beliefs seem to originate in the trackless deserts and may have been brought to settled areas by nomadic tribes.

The Bedouins of North Arabia consider the jinn to be nature spirits, which usually manifest themselves in the form of animals or mixed beings – part human, part animal. These nomads believe that almost every snake conceals a shapeshifting jinn. For that reason, people spit at them and seek to kill them. In every *bûma,* or Egyptian eagle owl, dwells a jinn, as well as in the bird called *mbârake* (blessed), probably a kestrel, which nests in desert ruins. If a child sees this bird, he or she will get sick. Among the Zullam tribe of the Negev desert, the feathers of the buma are burnt as protective magic and as a medicine against childhood illnesses. According to the beliefs of the Central Arabian 'Utaibi tribe, the jinn take on the shape of snakes, hares or gazelles, which are also ridden by the jinn. The North Arabian (Palestinian) Hanajre tribe believe that the *sa'lawiya* – evil jinn, probably identical to the extreme ghouls seen earlier, the *si'lahs* – possess very long forelegs and hind feet and have a mane of ash-grey colour. As for their overall appearance, they are supposed to resemble greyhounds, making them analogues of the Bedouins' favourite canine, the slender, long-legged hunting *saluqi*. They enjoy frightening camels away from their grazing areas. There are a number of other specialised jinn types attached to certain tribes, and most of these creatures have names linked to the *si'lah*. The 'Utaibi, for example, believe in the *si'reh*, which they say is a jinn shaped like a greyhound, similar to the Hanajre's *sa'lawiya*. They also speak of the *sa'aliya*, which they describe as a mixed being, half maiden, half ass. These jinn live in the mountains and lie in wait for timorous wanderers, whom they attack and devour. The Shararat of the al-Jawf region in north-western Arabia tell us of evil jinn called the *sa'alu*, which they know to be maneaters. According to them, these jinn have glowing eyes and they shriek in the night. They also regard the *ghul* as a man-eater. To the Shararat, this monster looks like a combination of man, bird and camel: a Cyclops eye in the middle of a human-like head, to which a beak is attached, wings like a chicken's, a camel's body (which at the same time resembles an ostrich's body), and even an ass's and ostrich's foot. This demon seeks to lure people into its clutches, in order to destroy them. Other North Arabian beliefs say the *ghuls* are shaped like men, cats, horses, asses, camels and owls. Even more frequently, they are said to take on the appearance of a coloured dog. Every narrow ravine or cave has its own *ghula*, according to these tribes.

Seldom are jinn found in human form in North Arabia. Those called marids, who we saw earlier are the most powerful and most evil class of jinn, are visualised by these Bedouins as giant demons. Local legends say that whoever happens to see such a towering being is certain to lose his mind from fear. As we can conclude from the earlier assertion about the *mbârake* bird, the most common form of jinn is airy, hazy, uncertain – otherwise they could not enter into people. The Hanajre also maintain that jinn are invisible beings that cannot be tracked by man or beast. If these spirits are in the neighbourhood, a man will grow uneasy and animals will flee, as if driven mad.

A few tribal groups in Arabia are said to have descended from the jinn. William Robertson Smith, a Scottish Orientalist who studied the social customs of early Arabia in the 1880s, briefly discusses one of these, an Arabian tribal clan, called the 'Amr ibn Yarbu', who were believed to be at least partly of jinn origin:

> There is in Arabia at least one case of an historical clan that had a legend of their descent from a supernatural being. The 'Amr ibn Yarbu' are called also Banu 'l-Si'lat, 'sons of the she-demon', who according to legend became wife of their father, but disappeared suddenly on seeing a flash of lightning (Ibn Doraid, p.139). We must therefore hold that it was because Arabic tribes claimed to be the children of their tribal god that they took his name.[2]

In old Arabia, several entire tribes were said to have descended from jinn. One was the Banu Uqaish, which was described by German Semitic scholar Theodor Noeldeke as a 'mysterious' tribe considered to be a class of demons. In order to scare away Uqaishis, people would rattle a number of dry skin bottles together, according to Noeldeke.[3] The social environment of traditional Arabia included pariah tribes and outcast groups of camp followers, of which the Uqaishis may be an example. Better known pariah tribes include the Hutaim and the Sulaib, both of which have been called 'gypsy-like' by scholars such as Philby and Doughty.[4] Such discredited tribes are often branded as descendants of non-believers (the Hutaim), Christians (the Sulaib) or even Jews (the Subut). It would not be surprising to see tribes of jinn descent included in these ranks.

Totems were very much part of the early Arabian tribal experience and were deeply connected to the belief in the jinn. The word 'totem' comes from the Ojibwa American Indian word 'ototeman', meaning 'his sibling kin'. It became a household word among anthropologists and other social-science scholars thanks to the writings of folklorist-anthropologist Sir James G.Frazer, author of *The Golden Bough*, an epic study of magic and religion published in two volumes in 1890 and expanded to 12 volumes by 1915.[5]

A totem, says Frazer, is a 'class of material objects' that a simple, tribal people regards with 'superstitious respect,' believing that 'an intimate and altogether special relation' exists between that people and all members of the class. Totems are most often animals. A particular type of animal, such as the grizzly bear or the white owl, is adopted by a tribe as its special symbol and protector, a kind of religious 'mascot'.

Many Arabic tribal or clan names have totemic origins – for example, Asad ('lion'), Bakr ('young he-camel'), Tha'laba ('female fox or vixen'), 'Anaza ('she-goat'), Kalb ('dog'), Fahd ('lynx'), Ghorab ('raven') and Namir ('leopard').

Animals were not the only totems of early Arabians. There were also the jinn, according to William Robertson Smith (who wrote about the phenomenon in his *Lectures on the Religion of the Semites*, published in 1894).

'In the belief of the heathen [pre-Islamic] Arabs,' said Smith,

> nature is full of living beings of superhuman kind, the *Jinn* or demons. These *jinn* are not pure spirits but corporeal beings, more like beasts than men, for they are ordinarily represented as hairy, or have some other animal shape, as that of an ostrich or snake. Their bodies are not phantasms, for if a *jinni* is killed a solid carcase remains; but they have certain mysterious powers of appearing and disappearing, or even of changing their aspect and temporarily assuming human form, and when they are offended they can avenge themselves in a supernatural way, *e.g.* by sending disease or madness. Like the wild beasts, they have, for the most part, no friendly or stated relations with men, but are outside the pale of man's society, and frequent savage and deserted places far from the wonted tread of men.[6]

The northern Semites also believed in similar demons – hairy beings (*sĕ'īrīm*), nocturnal monsters (*līlīth/lilitu*), which haunted wastelands and desolate places, living with jackals and ostriches and other animals that avoid humankind.

In Islam, Smith argues, the ancient gods are degraded into jinn, just as the gods of the Greeks and Romans became devils to the early Christians. 'In all these cases,' he says, 'the adherents of a higher faith were not prepared to deny that the heathen gods really existed, and did the things recorded of them; the difference between gods and demons lies not in their nature and power – for the heathen themselves did not rate the power of their gods at omnipotence – but in their relations to man.'

In a totemistic system, men relate to certain classes of natural agents. The premise is that nature, like mankind, is divided into groups or societies of things, analogous to the groups or societies in the human world. The most popular such groups under totemism are animals. In such a system, man enters into permanent relations of kinship or hostility with certain types of animals, and they become the focus of his psychosocial life. Keeping these facts in mind, Smith asks us to consider the Arabian jinn.

One difference between gods and jinn is that the gods have worshippers and the jinn do not. Another difference is that the gods have individuality, and the jinn do not. In the relatively recent *Arabian Nights* one finds jinn with individual names and distinctive personalities, but in the ancient legends an individual jinn that appears before a man has 'no more a distinct personality than a beast,' Smith asserts. Such a jinn is just one of a group of beings which from a human perspective are indistinguishable from one another. These beings are regarded as making up a nation or clan of superhuman beings that inhabit a particular locality and are joined together by bonds of kinship and by such practices as the blood-feud, so that the whole jinn clan acts together in defending its haunts from intrusion or in seeking revenge against men for any harm done to one of its members.

The concept of jinn communities is virtually the same as primitive man's concept of animal communities. In this view, each type of animal is viewed as an organised community, bound together by blood ties and blood revenge, and thus presenting a united front whenever a human attacks any one of its members. It is this solidarity among all the members of one species – be it jinn or animal – that makes the species an object of superstitious terror.

Jinn, as we have noted, usually appear to men in animal form, though they can also take the shape of men. This last feature, however, cannot be regarded as constituting a fundamental distinction between them and ordinary animals in the mind of the Arabs, who believed that there were whole tribes of men who had the power of assuming animal form. The supernatural powers of the jinn do not differ substantially from those which primitives, under totemism, ascribe to wild beasts. The jinn appear and disappear mysteriously and are linked to supernatural voices and warnings, and to unexplained sickness or death, just as totemic animals are. Jinn also occasionally enter into friendly relations or even marriages with humans, but animals do the same in the legends of primitive peoples. Finally, a madman is believed possessed by the jinn (*majnūn*), just as among primitives there are many examples of the soul of a beast entering into a man.

Says Smith:

> The accounts of the *jinn* which we possess have come to us from an age when the Arabs were no longer pure savages, and had ceased to ascribe demoniac attributes to most animals; and our narrators, when they repeat tales about animals endowed with speech or supernatural gifts, assume as a matter of course that they are not ordinary animals but a special class of beings. But the stories themselves are just such as savages tell about real animals; the blood-feud between the Banu Sahm and the *jinn* of Dhu Tawa is simply a war between men and all creeping things, which, as in the Old Testament, have a common name and are regarded as a single species or kindred; and the 'wild beast of the wild beasts of the *jinn*', which Taabbata Sharran slew in a night encounter and carried home under his arm, was as concrete an animal as one can well imagine.[7]

Ta'abbata Sharran's encounter is described in detail in his classic pre-Islamic poem (see 'How I Met the Ghul', p. 216).

The 'normal' appearance of a jinn seems to be that of some type of lower animal, or a monster made up of various animal forms. But humans who have moved beyond the early tribal stage find it hard to resist giving human shape to creatures that can reason and speak. Just as animal gods are usually converted into anthropomorphic gods shown riding on animals or otherwise associated with them, the jinn gradually began to be conceived as manlike in form, and the supernatural animals of their original appearance are seen as the beasts on which they ride.[8]

Ultimately the only animals to remain directly and constantly identified with the jinn were snakes and other creeping creatures. The sayings of the Prophet played a role in this limitation. But Smith notes that 'it is natural enough that these creatures, of which men everywhere have a peculiar horror and which continue to haunt and molest men's habitations after wild beasts have been driven out into the desert, should be the last to be stripped of their superstitious character'.[9]

Even in modern accounts jinn and animals are often closely associated, while in the older legends they are practically identified with each other. Smith finds that 'nothing is told of the *jinn* which savages do not tell of animals'. Given this, the Scottish philologist is confident that 'the *jinn*, with all their mysterious powers, are mainly nothing else than more or less modernised representatives of animal kinds, clothed with the supernatural attributes inseparable from the savage conception of animate nature'. He concludes, 'A species of jinn allied by kinship with a tribe of men would be indistinguishable from a totem kind, and instead of calling the *jinn* gods without worshippers, we may, with greater precision, speak of them as potential totems without human kinsfolk.'[10]

The Arabian experience with jinn, particularly in the western part of the peninsula, is very well illustrated by nineteenth-century English explorer Charles Montagu Doughty in his masterpiece *Travels in Arabia Deserta*.[11] Doughty describes the jinn traditions of the people of the Holy City of Medina (originally called Yathrib), where the Prophet and his allies took refuge during the Hegira (migration) from Mecca, in 622. A Christian, Doughty could not visit the Muslim holy city himself, but he learnt about its jinn lore from a Medina resident, a Kurdish travelling companion he called Amm Mohammed (Uncle Mohammed).

Amm Mohammed told Doughty that 'half of the jann or jenun [or jinn], inhabiting the seven stages under the earth, are malicious heathen spirits, kuffar, or kafirun; and the other half are accounted Moslems'.[12] Mohammed recalled that when he was a youth, a chest belonging to his father and containing some embroidered clothing was stolen. His family sent for the local *mundel* (conjurer) to identify the guilty person or persons. A *mundel* serves as a kind of broker or medium between mankind and the jinn.

The *mundel* asked the family: 'Who here is sure of heart and strong?' 'Mohammed my son is a stout lad,' said Mohammed's father. The *mundel* poured water into a bowl and sat Mohammed down before it. 'Now, what do you see?' he asked the youth. Mohammed said: 'By God, I see no more than this basin and water ... yet now it's as if I saw through a casement, and a sea is under me; and beneath I see a wide plain, and now I see on the plain as if it were the haj [pilgrimage] arriving! They have pitched the pavilion of the Pasha – I can see the Pasha sitting with his friends.'

The *mundel* declared: 'Say to him, "O Sultan of the jann! Doctor so-and-so [the *mundel* named himself] salutes you, and bids you enquire, if in your company there be any jinni who was nearby when the coffer was stolen from Yelduzely Haseyn; and if he witnessed the theft, that he name the persons."' Mohammed spoke as instructed, and the sultan of the jann replied: 'I have just now enquired of all of my company; none was present, and no one has heard any news of this.' The *mundel* said: 'What do you see in the water now, young man?' Mohammed replied: 'The former company has passed by, and another similar company [of jinn] is now arriving.' 'Say, "O Sultan of the jann ... " as before.' Mohammed did so, and the sultan of the jann responded: 'I have just now asked all of my company, and there is none here who has seen anything, or heard word of it.' 'Say yet, "Is any absent?"' The sultan of the jann replied: 'There is none absent.' The *mundel* said to Mohammed: 'What do you see now?' Mohammed: 'The second company has passed from my sight; a third company [of jinn] is arriving.' 'Say, "Sultan of the jann ... " as before.'

Mohammed did as instructed, and the sultan answered, 'I have asked all of them just now, and there is none here.' The *mundel* declared: 'Ask again, "Are all of your people present?"' 'I have enquired, and there is one absent – he is in India.' The *mundel* said: 'Say, "Let him be brought here and questioned."' After much discussion, the jinn in question was finally brought – in an instant – from India. Amm Mohammed told Doughty: 'Then I saw him, led in like an old man; he was grey-headed and lame.'

The sultan of the jann questioned the jinn: 'Have you seen anything, or has anything come to your knowledge, regarding this theft?'

He answered: 'Aye, for as I lay in the likeness of a dog upon the dunghill which is in front of this house, in the middle of the night, I saw a man come with the chest upon his back. He entered the house next door, and two women followed him.' The jinn revealed the names of the persons.

The *mundel* sent for these three people – they were known in the town as troublemakers. They soon arrived; but when they were questioned, they swore upon their religion that they knew nothing about the theft. Then they departed.

The *mundel* took three water-skins, blew them up and cast them away from him. In a little while the three suspects came again, running, the man ahead of the two women, and all three of them holding their bellies, which were swollen to bursting.

'Oh me! I beseech you,' cried the man. 'Sir, I have the chest! Just release me from this pain and I will restore it immediately!' His women also pitifully acknowledged their guilt.

Then the *mundel* fingered his prayer beads backwards, to reverse the enchantment, and he said to Mohammed: 'What do you see in the water now?'

'I see only the great plain – and now, just this basin and the water in it.'

'Look up, young man! Rise and walk about, while these wicked persons bring the stolen chest and its contents.'

When Amm Mohammed told Doughty this tale, he seemed to believe every word of it. For some time afterwards, he said, he had the ability to perceive jinn, and he could see that nearly half of all those around him who seemed to be human beings were actually jinn. He noticed that many a house cat and street dog were actually jinn as well. This ability, however, gradually faded, and in time he could discern jinn no longer.

Doughty asked: 'Well, tell me, what language do your jann speak, and what kind of clothing do they wear?'

Amm Mohammed was a bit startled by these questions. He answered after a moment, with a smile: 'It is plain that they dress and speak like Moslems.'[13]

* * *

A Saudi oil worker of Bedouin descent who knows the desert extremely well told me recently about a low-lying desert area in eastern Saudi Arabia, called Jawb al-'Asal, which is said to be inhabited by jinn. The area is a *sabkhah* (salt flat) on the outskirts of the Empty Quarter, the world's largest continuous sand desert. People avoid the Jawb al-'Asal area like the plague. The Saudi oil worker knows a man, we will call him Mahmoud, who had a harrowing experience in Jawb al-'Asal about 20 years ago.

Mahmoud was a lorry driver. He drove a big Kenworth lorry between towns and cities in Saudi Arabia's vast Eastern Province. He had an assistant from India, named Mujeeb.

One day Mahmoud and Mujeeb were on their way to a destination that required them to circle around the region of Jawb al-'Asal. Mahmoud was sceptical about the jinn and decided to take a shortcut across the *sabkhah.* They left the road and drove across the salt flat. They drove for what seemed like hours. Then suddenly, in the midst of a remote part of the *sabkhah,* the Kenworth's engine cut out. No matter how they tried, they couldn't get the lorry started again. They decided that Mujeeb would walk across the desert to the nearest town, and Mahmoud would stay with his lorry. Mujeeb set off and before long was out of sight.

Eventually twilight came. Mahmoud figured he'd be spending the night there, so he climbed up on top of the lorry – to avoid the inevitable scorpions and vipers – and went to sleep. The moon was high when he awoke. He heard a voice. No, two voices – a woman and a little boy. Mahmoud climbed down from the lorry and saw them. The woman was totally covered with a black cloak that concealed her face, even her eyes. She pulled the young child to her side and addressed the lorry driver.

'Mahmoud!' she said. She knew his name! 'Mahmoud, why did you come here? Don't you know this place belongs to us? You should never come to Jawb al-'Asal! Never! This is our home! Not yours! You will pay for your sin!'

As Mahmoud stared, the woman turned her covered head swiftly to the left and to the right. Her head swivelled like a falcon's, in an unhuman way that terrified Mahmoud. She began wailing and cursing. She then strode towards him and struck him in the chest. Stunned, Mahmoud fell back and dropped to the ground. He lay there, frozen in terror, against one of the lorry's tyres, staring at the woman and her boy. He tried to speak, but his voice was gone. He trembled uncontrollably. The woman strode back and forth, condemning him for his transgression. Mahmoud went into shock and lost consciousness.

When he awoke next morning, the woman and her boy were gone. And so was Mahmoud's voice. When Mujeeb finally came with help, the lorry driver could say nothing about his experience. In fact, it was many weeks before he could speak again.

He never forgot his encounter with the jinn-woman whose head spun like a falcon's. To this day, when people mention Jawb al-'Asal, his eyes widen and he warns sternly: 'Never go there! Never! It belongs to the jinn!'

There are other mysterious accounts of Jawb al-'Asal. One appears in a published memoir of a trip across the Rub' al-Khali by Erik A. Mandaville, son of an oil company employee, who grew up in Saudi Arabia.

In 1967, when he was four years old, Mandaville, his and another family travelled into the desert on a camping adventure. On the edge of the Empty Quarter, 'The vehicles had ventured into this area of *sabkhah* called Jawb al-'Asal – despite a Bedouin folk tale that the flats were haunted by *jinn*.' As in the case of Mahmoud, the engine of their vehicle suddenly stopped running as it approached the middle of the *sabkhah*. Mandaville said: 'My dad remembers that our Bedouin guide Hadban was not surprised. With a weak smile and a nonchalant shrug of his shoulders he said something like, "Some of these bushes are probably *jinn* in disguise, and maybe a branch of one of them got into the engine and jammed it." '[14]

* * *

In February 2001, an Internet discussion group on the jinn received an e-mail message from an individual who claimed to be a jinn of Saudi Arabia.[15] Claims of this sort are, of course, impossible to verify, but the message was interesting both for its effort at authenticity and its detail. Sceptics might scoff at the message, but others might view it as representative of the Saudi Arabian jinn tradition. What is also interesting here is the way traditional jinn beliefs continue to endure in the modern world. These concepts are not just transmitted orally around remote desert camp fires but have also found their way into the digital era and thrive in Internet chat rooms and discussion groups.

'I was born as a jinn,' the person said. 'However, I live among people like you. I am no different than the physical body you have. I can take shapes of any kind except 7 shapes. I live in Saudi Arabia, where I am a scholar of Arabic. My father is also a scholar of Arabic.'.

He said his family chose to mix among humans because their life in the world of the jinn was 'very different' and they suffered from 'limited resources'. In that world, his family lacked 'knowledge of books, food, habitation'.

'I was born in the year 1902,' he said. 'Our family struggled, as we were poor. Our homeland is in the Qaf Mountains, where we also have an equivalent government like your own. There is always turmoil between different sects. What your family possesses physically determines how rich and aristocratic you are.'

To live among humans, his father had to be granted permission by his elders, 'Once permission was granted, we were allowed to live in Taif [in the mountains of western Saudi Arabia]. We make our living through teaching. We live in an apartment, where like everyone else we have to pay rent. We eat the same foods as you. We wear the same clothing as you. We fear the same as you fear.'

He said that his 'sect' is 'that of the jann', or ordinary jinn, sometimes described as the 'least powerful' class of fire spirits.

> Yes, I can fly great distances and move great buildings. However this is only done when needed. We don't make this a selling point to show our existence. Yes, we are made from smokeless fire, but no, I won't burn you if I shake your hand. Like humans are made from clay – does this mean clay runs in your veins? It's the same for us. Fire does not run through our veins. Whilst taking human shape, we have the same characteristics as yourselves. We can even die whilst being in the human form, just like a human.

He had some observations on magical practices used to summon and bind the jinn – activities considered illegal in conservative Saudi Arabia. 'These manuscripts, procedures, talismans, etc. used to summon jinns and bind them are possible. Some of the procedures are correct. However, 90 per cent of them are fiction.

It is very painful if a jinn is summoned and bound. His entire body burns with fire while in captivity. We do not choose to capture you [humans], so I can't understand why this is done to us.'

He observed that in the world of the jinn, as in human societies,

> there is good and bad. We have bad jinns who like to cause mischief among humans. These are heavily punished if caught by our governing bodies. Human possession is not really done these days. The novelty has worn off among the mischievous. However there is the odd one who likes to experiment. Just as you have books concerning us, we have books concerning you. It takes a lot of studying and practice to possess a human being.

He sought to reassure members of the discussion group:

> I do not wish to alarm anyone. I do not wish to make anyone laugh or feel dubious. I am what I am, and [for] what I am, I need no excuses. I bet you might be saying, prove to me you are a jinn. If you need proof, then I will give it to you. Tell me what to do and I will do it within reason. However, please do not make a mockery of this.
>
> Let us all live in peace. Let us all respect each other. We are all created from the same source. Please do not make us look like horror films because we are not. I can give you a horror face if you make me angry, like when you can pull an ugly face when you are angry. Judge me for what I do, not for what I am. Fables and stories are good for entertainment. But the reality of Jinns is far from what you know. What you need to know, ask me with respect and I will answer what I am permitted to say.

Unfortunately, he posted no further messages. Whether he responded privately to questions from individual group members is not known. For all practical purposes, this jinn had simply vanished into thin air.

Iraq: 'Pandemonium'

Iraq is a complex and colourful society, woven of many ethnic and religious strands, and so it is no surprise that this 'land amidst two rivers' features a wealth of lesser-known jinn types. British folklorist Ethel Stevens explored jinn beliefs of Iraq in the decades following World War I.[16] Although Stevens acknowledged that Western readers were already familiar with the more common spirits so often cited in *The Arabian Nights* – the standard jinn and the more frightening ifrit and ghoul – she sought to shed some light on what she called the less well-known creatures of the Iraqi 'pandemonium' (or realm of demons) such as the *s'iluwa*, the *deyu*, the *dami*, the *se'ir*, the *tantal*, the *tabi'a*, the *um es-sabyan* and the *qarina*. The last three, which we have encountered with slightly variant spellings – al-Tabi'ah, Umm al-Subian and al-Qarinah respectively – are likely different manifestations of the same creature, the Lilith analogue.

The *s'iluwa* – an Iraqi variant of the creature we know as the *si'lah*, the 'worst of the ghouls'[17] – plays much the same role in Iraqi folk legend that the witch or troll does in Western fairy-tales. A water-spirit that dwells in rivers or in caves near streams, the *s'iluwa* is covered with long hair and has pendulous breasts that reach her knees. When she wishes to suckle her children, which she carries on her back, she throws her breasts over her shoulders. She is shaped like a woman but is sometimes portrayed as having a fish tail instead of two legs. She enjoys consuming human flesh, but at the same time she has a propensity towards human lovers. She is mortal like all of God's creations except angels, and as a jinn she fears iron. Stevens believed that this demon was a composite myth derived from an ancient river-goddess cult and anecdotes which African slaves who served the Abbasids told about the great apes.

Another river-demon is the curiously named *ferij aqra'a* (bald lieutenant-general) who likes to play tricks on fishermen and river-dwellers but is not as dangerous as the *s'iluwa*. Like her, he possesses either a fish tail or weak legs. He looks like an old man, but his head is red and bald and the hair of his beard is green. A Bedouin of the Shammar, a large tribe divided between Saudi Arabia and Iraq, told Stevens a story of a sheikh who, while camped beside the Euphrates, noticed that his mare, previously tireless and strong, had suddenly become weak and dispirited. Using an old folk remedy to invigorate the horse, he smeared some pitch on her back one night. The next morning they found a *ferij aqra'a* stuck on the mare's back, struggling in vain to escape after his nocturnal ride. The sheikh's people fell on the monster and killed it with their knives. A sighting of one of these demons was reported in a Baghdad newspaper as recently as August 1922.

The *dami* (bloody one), according to Stevens, is a 'half-bestial ogress' that haunts the outskirts of towns and villages. As with ancient Babylonian and Assyrian demons, its usual food is dirt, refuse and leavings of all kinds, but it is also said to enjoy eating human flesh. In Iraqi folk-tales, the *dami* often plays the role assigned in European fairy-tales to the wolf (as in, for example, Little Red Riding Hood).

The *qarina* (companion), as we have seen before, is a female jinn who attaches herself to a man, draws away his affection from his wife or betrothed and even has children by him. In Iraqi folk tradition, an unmarried man is often thought to have a *qarina* as his wife. Amorous dreams, including nocturnal emissions, are often put down to intercourse with her. The *qarina* is said to be very jealous and will hurt any human woman that her human lover may care for. She also steals or murders babies. Babylonian scholar Reginald Campbell Thompson has noted that the *qarina* of Iraq is probably the direct descendant of the Babylonian demon *ardat lili*, or Lilith.[18] This is equally true of the *qarina* as seen elsewhere in the region.

The *deyu* is a rustic demon who haunts woods and desolate places. He and his female counterpart occur frequently in the folk-tales collected by Stevens. These are likely Iraqi versions of the Persian *devs* or *divs* (jinn). The *deyus* are known to fly long distances through the air, sometimes riding horses. They can appear in single colours: for example, black *deyus*, red ones and white ones. They are also sometimes seen to have two heads, and in the folk-tales, one of these heads can be lopped off with a sword, apparently with no ill effects.

The *se'ir* was described to Stevens by a Shammari tribesman as haunting desolate places and ruins, especially Hatra near Mosul in northern Iraq, capital of the earliest known Arab kingdom. The city of Hatra was a staging point on the Silk Route to China and dates from the second or third century BC. It has been a UNESCO World Heritage Site since 1985. Prior to that, the Hatra archaeological site gained modern celebrity as the setting for the opening scenes of *The Exorcist* (1973), the popular movie about demon possession. Stevens' Shammari tribesman described the *se'ir* as a very old man with a beard to its knees, one eye, very long teeth with iron on them, and toe-nails made of iron – a very unusual appearance, given that jinn normally avoid iron. This creature devours human beings. Stevens said she has heard of this demon only from the Shammari tribe; in Baghdad and the southern marshlands it is apparently unknown. But its apparent antiquity is impressive. Campbell Thompson says in his

Semitic Magic:

> It appears from several poetical passages of the Old Testament that the Northern Semites believed in demons of a precisely similar kind – hairy beings (*se'irim*), nocturnal monsters (*lilith*), which haunted waste and desolate places in fellowship with jackals and ostriches.

Stevens suggested that the *se'ir*, as an ogre with one eye, was probably related to the Cyclops of Greek legend. In fact, one of the Iraqi tales she recorded speaks of a *se'ir* being blinded with a hot stake, as in Homer's Odyssey.

The marshes of southern Iraq also harbour special jinn. The marshes extend for some 6,000 square miles around the confluence of the Tigris and Euphrates rivers. They have been home for hundreds of years to the Ma'dan or Marsh Arabs, Shi'ite Muslims of Bedouin ancestry who live on small natural islands in the marshes and sustain themselves largely by fishing and raising water buffalo. Iraqi leader Saddam Hussein drained most of the marshes in the early 1990s, in an attempt to crush a Shi'ite rebellion in the south. Many of the Ma'dan left for the cities at that time, but the post-Saddam government of Iraq has pledged to restore the marshes, and people have been returning to the watery world they once knew. About half of the marshlands have been restored, according to recent estimates.

British explorer Wilfred Thesiger wrote about the world of the Marsh Arabs as it existed about a half century before the violence of the 1990s.[19] Thesiger, who had come to Iraq after extensive explorations of the Empty Quarter, was 'captivated by the wild, free existence of the Marshes', according to the magazine *Aramco World*. He 'wandered through this vast region off and on for seven years, staying first with this tribe, then with that, paddling his long, graceful canoe through narrow canals that curved in an eerie silence among towering reeds, hunting the huge, razor-tusked boars lurking in the reeds by the hundreds, and healing the infections and diseases of the Marsh tribesmen'.[20]

The Ma'dan he encountered believed in jinn in general and in their ability to take the form of humans or animals. But they also spoke of special, marsh-adapted jinn found nowhere else. One they called the *anfish* (wooly one?), described as a giant serpent with hairy skin. Another was the *afa* (ruin?), a giant serpent with legs. Both lived in the heart of the marshes and were said to be deadly.

The Ma'dan also told Thesiger about a mysterious place called Hufaidh, an island paradise somewhere in the marshes (its exact location was unknown, but it was believed to be in the southwestern reaches). On Hufaidh, there were palaces and palm trees and gardens of pomegranates, and huge water buffaloes – bigger than those raised by the Ma'dan. 'Anyone who sees Hufaidh is bewitched,' Thesiger's informants told him, 'and afterwards no one can understand his words.... They say the Jinns can hide the island from anyone who comes near it.'[21]

We can see that the jinn lore of Iraq has a complex ancestry, stretching back millennia and weaving together variegated strands from many sources, including the Sumerian, Babylonian, Aramaic, Hebrew, Greek and Islamic traditions. This is not surprising in a country such as Iraq, situated historically at the crossroads of many cultural and social movements, migrations and invasions.

Harran: The 'North'

The god called Shamal, or 'the North', is a rather mysterious deity worshipped long ago by the Sabians of Harran, the town in northern Mesopotamia (today, southeastern Turkey) to which Abraham, father of the Semites, migrated from Ur. The North ruled over jinn and devils, among others.

The Sabians of Harran, or Chaldaean Sabians, were a pagan community said by some to be different from the 'true Sabians' of southern Iraq (sometimes called the Mughtasilah [Those Who Wash Themselves]), who are mentioned in the Qur'an as being 'People of the Book', or adherents of the divinely inspired faiths, along with Christians and Jews. (The true Sabians, according to some scholars, were forerunners of the present-day Mandaeans, a religious minority in modern Iraq.) The Sabians of Harran may have adopted their name – and perhaps some beliefs – from the 'true Sabians' in order to win protected status under Muslim rule (specifically, under the Abbasid caliph al-Ma'mun in the ninth century). Some of the Harranian beliefs and rituals are described in the *Fihrist* of Ibn al-Nadim.

Ibn al-Nadim speaks often about the 'North', whom he calls the 'Greatest God', and 'The Chief of the Jinn, who is the Greatest Divinity'.

According to Bayard Dodge, English translator of the *Fihrist*, this god was probably the same as the ancient Semitic divinity Saphon or Zephon.[22] The deity Adon Saphon or Baal Zephon is identified as the 'Lord of the North'. The people of the ancient port city of Ugarit (at modern-day Ras Shamra in Syria) worshipped Saphon or Zeus Cassios at Mount Casius located north of the city, while the Mandaeans regarded the North as a source of light and power. The people of Harran may have identified the North with the Primal Cause, from which the cosmic existences were said to emanate. 'It is more likely, however,' Dodge says, 'that they inherited from earlier peoples the idea that, in addition to the twelve deities for whom they built shrines in their sacred enclosure, there was also a great deity called the North, who was not transcendent, but active in the universe, directing the planetary spirits, lording it over the jinn and disciplining the devils.' Like most pagan peoples, the Harranians believed in jinn and devils, whom they propitiated and attempted to control through charms and incantations.

During five months of the year, the Sabians of Harran celebrated certain feasts on fixed days that honoured the 'mystery of the North'. The exact significance of the ceremony remains unknown, but scholars believe it included sun worship, the sacrificing of animals and birds, with burnt offerings, eating and drinking, as well as a ritual known as smelling the rose (taking in the fragrance of this flower as a symbol of materialism and the transitory nature of life), which was also practised by the Mandaeans. The rituals of the mystery featured magic and efforts to win the assistance of the North in order to take control of the jinn and devils, who served the North. Women, slaves and lunatics were reportedly barred from practising this rite, for reasons unknown.

When the mystery was celebrated in conjunction with the birthday of the moon on the twenty-fourth of Kanun al-Thani (January), the Sabians burnt pine rods, apparently for magical purposes. During three days of Aylul (September), they heated water in connection with the mystery of the North and added tamarisk, wax, pine, olives, cane and caustic to it; the contents would then be boiled and allowed to cool. Just before dawn they poured this infusion over their bodies 'as the magicians do', according to Ibn al-Nadim. They also slaughtered a lamb for the North and sacrificed seven others for the sun, moon and five planets, after which each worshipper drank seven cups of wine and donated two silver coins to the treasury.

The magic of these and other rituals was apparently directed at both the gods and the demons. Most likely the deities were propitiated to win their help in controlling the evil spirits. On the eighth of Nisan (April), the Sabians held a feast in honour of the seven deities, the devils, jinn and spirits. They burnt seven lambs – for the sun, moon and five planets – and two sheep, one as an extra offering to Mars and the other for the devils.

During the month of Shubat (February), the Sabians fasted in honour of the Sun – the 'Great Lord' or the 'Lord of Well Being' – but instead of praying to him, they prayed to the North, the jinn and the demons. The Moon god, Sin, was also honoured, not just on his birthday during Kanun al-Thani, but also on the twenty-seventh day of each lunar month.

The Sabians borrowed from many cultures. They worshipped the deities associated with the known heavenly bodies, whose Greek and Roman names were familiar to them due to the various conquests by the Greek and the Roman: the Sun (al-Shams), the Moon (al-Qamar), Mercury (Hermes or 'Utarid), Venus (Aphrodite or al-Zuhara), Mars (Ares or al-Mirrikh), Jupiter (Zeus or al-Mushtari) and Saturn (Cronos or Zuhal). At a shrine known as the Cupola of al-Ujurr, Mars was worshipped on the twenty-eighth of the month of Adhar (March). Sheep, cocks and many small chickens were burnt as offerings. Then on the twenty-eighth of Nisan they held a festival at another shrine in the village of Sabta, close to one of the gates of Harran. They sacrificed a bull in honour of Hermes, nine lambs for the seven heavenly bodies, a tenth lamb for the god of the jinn and still another for the 'Lord of the Hours', who may have been the metaphysical deity of Time or Sequence. They did not burn the victims for this feast and, though it ended with eating and drinking, they did not necessarily eat the meat. In fact, as a rule they generally ate things other than the sacrificial meat.

Magic was not limited to their feasts. The Sabians used charms for just about any occasion. Some of these were made from the organs of creatures such as crows, pigs and donkeys, while others were signet stones and charred bones found in ancient tombs. They also scraped chicken wings – the left wing only – to make talismans, which they hung around the necks of young boys or the waists of pregnant women to protect them from demons and the evil eye.

The most extraordinary practice at Harran was the ritual of al-Ra's, or 'The Head'. Ibn Khaldun, al-Dimashqi and Ibn al-Nadim[23] all made mention of it. The leaders of the Sabians would search until they found a man who resembled Mercury or Hermes in both appearance and personal qualities. He was probably a young blond man with a fair complexion. After being duped and seized, he was soaked in a bath of oil and borax for a long time, until his joints became completely relaxed. Then, when the planet Mercury was at its height, the head of the man was cleanly separated from his body. Believing that Mercury caused the man's spirit to enter his separated head, the Sabians asked him questions and reportedly listened to his sage replies. Bayard Dodge speculated that the Harran priests used some trickery to make the severed head play the role of an oracle, just as the oracles did in ancient Greece.

The Sabians also celebrated many of the region's popular Semitic feasts, including one that marked the annual fruit harvest. The Jewish Feast of the Tabernacles was one such festival. But Harran's version of the harvest, celebrated by those who also took part in the rituals of the North, was horrific in the extreme. For eight days the Harranian worshippers would tread the harvested grapes to make new wine for the gods. They would also conduct a human sacrifice, putting to death a newborn infant.

As Dodge described it, 'After killing the baby, they boiled him, until his body became disintegrated. Then his flesh was kneaded with fine flour, saffron, spikenard, cloves and oil, so as to make cakes for baking in an oven. The three priests officiating at the feast burned the remains of the infant as an offering to the gods, while the cakes were distributed to members of the community, who were eligible to eat them.' While followers of Shamal, the jinn lord, were allowed to participate in this ceremony, women, slaves, lunatics, young children and foreigners were banned – clearly to keep the grim ritual as secret as possible.

This barbaric harvest tradition, practised until the coming of Islam, was doubtless of great antiquity. It was one of many aspects of Harranian belief selected and adopted from the surrounding cultures over the centuries and in some cases millennia.

Palestine: Underground

The Palestinian experience with jinn follows the general guidelines of the Arabian experience, with variations attributable to the unique cultural setting of the 'Holy Land'. Let's pick up the story in the early years of the twentieth century, about the time of the First World War, and then move to the early years of the twenty-first century, when traditional belief bumps heads with modern nationalism.

The Reverend James Edward Hanauer (1850–1938) – a Jaffa native, honorary canon of St. George's Cathedral in Jerusalem in the late nineteenth century and British chaplain at Damascus from 1908 to 1920 – was intrigued by the folklore of Palestine and the surrounding Levant. He focused in particular on jinn – whom he called 'the Jan' and 'the underground folk' – in his book *Folk-Lore of the Holy Land* (1907).[24]

The people of Palestine – Christian, Muslim and to an extent Jewish – believed in the existence of a race of beings created before Adam, which the Arabs call by the general name of Jan.[25] Hanauer became familiar with the ancient system of creation as understood by the Palestinians. The angels, he was told, dwelt in heaven, held various offices and took different forms according to their respective abodes. Those in the lowest heaven, for example, were shaped like cows; those in the second like falcons; in the third like eagles; in the fourth like horses, and so on. The Jan were said by the learned of Palestine to be created out of the fire of the *simum* (a hot wind or sandstorm), which they characterised as a fire lacking both heat and smoke. These jinn, like those we have discussed before, were said to dwell chiefly in or around the Jebel Qaf, the range of mountains which encircles the Earth. Some of the Jan were good Muslims and did not injure their human co- religionists, but Palestinians regarded most of them as unclean infidels who took up their abode in rivers, fountains, cisterns, ruined buildings, baths, cellars, ovens, caves, sewers and latrines. Some of them chose to live in cracks in the walls or under the doorsteps or thresholds of inhabited houses, making it very dangerous for people, especially females, to sit on a doorstep in the evening when these night-prowling evil spirits might do them grievous bodily harm. The Jan were believed to be capable of assuming any shape they pleased and changing it at will.

Among the peasantry, there was another story that had gained currency regarding the origin of Jan. They believed that Mother Eve, whenever she gave birth, brought forth forty children at at a time, but being unable to nurse more than half that number, she picked out the twenty best ones and threw the others away. She told Adam on each occasion that she had borne only twenty; but he did not believe her. He, therefore, asked Allah to let any children she had thrown away live underground and go abroad at night when all men sleep. Thus the Jan came into being.

The Jan were envious of men and women, always on the watch for a chance to injure; unless people said 'Bismillah' whenever beginning any work or taking anything out of storage, the jinn succeeded in robbing them. There was, in Hanauer's day, a man living at Ain Karim who had experienced this to his detriment. He had a silly, forward daughter, who, despite frequent warnings from her parents and neighbours, would not invoke Allah's name. He was a man of substance and brought home provisions in great quantities, but the blessing of Allah did not rest upon his property. At length, perplexed and discouraged, he consulted a great sheikh, who asked him, 'Whom have you in the house?'

> 'My wife and daughter,' the man said.
> 'Does your wife invoke the Name of Allah?'
> 'I would not have married her if she had not done so.'
> 'Does your daughter also "name"?'
> 'I regret to say she does not.'
> 'Then,' said the sheikh, 'don't let her touch anything about the house, and get rid of her at once!'
> The father acted on the sheikh's advice: He married off his daughter. No sooner had she left the house than the Jan stopped troubling him. But the bridegroom, who until then had been a prosperous merchant, now didn't have enough money to buy oil to keep a lamp burning through the night.[26]

Hanauer was told that not only were Jan divided into males and females like human beings, they could also – as they sometimes did – intermarry with sons and daughters of Adam, often against the will of the human partners, particularly when the latter had failed to ask for the protection of Allah. To demonstrate this point, Hanauer related an incident that occurred some years earlier.

There was a man from the village of El Isawiyen, in the valley north of the Mount of Olives, who vanished one day while harvesting his crops in the fields at Ushwan, near Artuf, and was not heard of for nine years. People believed he had been devoured by a hyaena. But eventually he reappeared and told this story:

He was sleeping one night on the threshing-floor to protect his freshly harvested store of *dhurra* (sorghum) when he was awakened at about midnight by the sound of voices approaching. Fearing it was the tax-collector and his *khayaleh* (horsemen), who rode in support of him, he lay quite still to avoid being beaten. But it turned out to be a party of jinn. Before he had originally gone to sleep, he was too tired to invoke the protection of Allah. Now terror kept him from using that simple precaution and left him at the mercy of the demons. He did not realise who they were until it was too late. All he knew at first was that a woman appeared suddenly and struck him on his forehead. The blow drained him of all willpower. She bade him follow her, and he obeyed blindly.

After travelling some distance from the threshing-floor, she informed him that she was now his wife, and that, unless he submitted to her desire, her brothers, who had watched him follow her, would kill him most horribly. Soon afterwards her brothers caught up with them, and he realised they were jinn. They told him he had been transformed into a jinn himself, and from now on he would be invisible to the eyes of men. (They were being deceptive, of course. Human beings cannot be changed into jinn, but jinn can use various tricks to make humans invisible to their own kind.)

For nine years he belonged to the Jan and took part in all their depredations. Then one day, when they were lying hidden among some ruins, he noticed how his companions kept away from one of the walls, which bore a luxuriant growth of *feyjan* (rue). Out of curiosity, he approached it. His jinn 'wife' suddenly shrieked, 'Don't go near those plants!' He ran and plucked whole handfuls from the wall. Then, looking around, he saw that the Jan had vanished and he was free to return to his human family.

Back home, the *fellahin* (peasants), his neighbours, disbelieved his story. So he asked about a local woman named 'Ayesha and was told that her husband had repudiated her because she had robbed him and given his goods to her brothers – there was no other explanation to account for the way things vanished from his house. For instance, one day he filled a large *khabieh* (mud-built bin) with barley, but when he opened it the next morning it was empty, and, in spite of his wife's denials, he believed her to be the thief. The man who had been living with the Jan explained that he had asked about 'Ayesha on purpose to prove her innocence and his own truthfulness. He had been present when the barley was carried off by the Jan, who knew that the Divine Name was not usually invoked in that house. Other things that went missing from the village while he was away had, in fact, been carried off by jinn in a similar manner. Since that time, Hanauer reported, everyone has been careful to gather handfuls of rue and keep it in the house. No good man begins a task without invoking Allah, the Merciful and Compassionate, and no respectable woman takes even a handful of flour from its receptacle without calling on the Most High.

Hanauer related that a *fellahah* (peasant woman) of El Welejeh[27] lost an eye a few years earlier under the following circumstances (The incident was narrated to him by another *fellahah*).

The woman was returning from Jerusalem; as she passed a spring called Ain El Haniyeh, she heard a frog croak. Looking around, she noticed close to the stream a female frog much advanced in pregnancy, and she thoughtlessly (but ill-naturedly) said to the creature, 'Allah grant that you may not be delivered of your child till I be called to act as your midwife.' Having uttered this unkind speech, the woman went on her way.

In the evening, the woman, who was a widow, retired to rest with her children around her. But suddenly, in the middle of the night, she awakened to find herself not in her home but in a cave surrounded by strange, angry-looking people. One of them gruffly told her that if she ventured to 'name' (i.e., to invoke the name of God) she was a dead woman.

'If we who live below,' said he, 'come to you who live aboveground, then it is a protection for you to "name"; but if, as in your case, one of you intrudes needlessly and officiously on us, "naming" will not help you. What harm had my wife done you that you should curse her as you did this afternoon?'

'I do not know, nor have I ever seen your wife,' the terrified woman replied.

'She was the pregnant frog you spoke to at Ain El Haniyeh,' he replied. 'When we who live underground want to go abroad by day-time we generally assume the form of some animal. My wife took that of the frog you saw. You cursed her and mentioned the "Name". She was in the pangs of labour but, in consequence of your cruel malediction, cannot be relieved till you assist her. I warn you, therefore, that unless she give birth to a boy, it will go hard with you.'

He then led her to where his wife lay, with females round her. The woman from El Welejeh, though almost frightened out of her wits, did her best for the jinn patient, who soon gave birth to a fine boy. When the father was informed of the happy event he handed the human mid-wife a *mukhaleh* (kohl-vessel) and told her to apply some of the contents to the infant's eyes so that they might become dark and bright.[28] While doing this she noticed that the baby's eyes, like those of the other Jan around her, differed from those of humans, in that the pupils were longitudinal and vertical.

When she applied the kohl to the infant's eyes, she took the bodkin which she had used and applied some kohl to one of her own eyes, but before she had time to put kohl on the other the female jinn, having noticed what the former was doing, angrily snatched the *mukhaleh* from her. They then had her loosen one of her long, flowing sleeves, in which, like other peasant-women, she used to carry things, and they filled it with something, though she knew not what. Next they blindfolded her and led her out of the cave. When they told her she could uncover her eyes, she did so and looked around her. She was standing alone at the spring of Ain El Haniyeh. Curious to know what the Jan had stuffed in her sleeve, she opened it and found a quantity of onion-peels, which she promptly threw away.

A few minutes later she reached her home, where she found her children still asleep. As she was preparing to lie down, something fell out of her sleeve. She picked it up and saw that it was a piece of gold. Realising the true nature of the supposed onion-peels she had thrown away, she at once hurried back to the spring, and sure enough she found the onion-peels lying untouched, but all of them transformed into gold pieces. Gathering them up eagerly, she returned home, and as there were still some hours till daylight, she lay down and went to sleep. On awakening next morning, she thought that she must have dreamt it all. But when one of her children told her that one of her eyes had kohl on it and the other did not; above all, when she saw her store of gold coins she realised she had not been dreaming and was now a wealthy woman.

According to Hanauer, this same woman, some time afterwards, went to El Kuds (Jerusalem) to *howij*, that is, to do some shopping. As she was standing near the draper's shop – the Jewish draper whose shop was just in front of the wheat-bazaar – she saw the female jinn whom she had assisted in her pregnancy, now accompanied by her baby, mingling with the crowd and pilfering as she went from shop to shop. The woman from El Welejeh went up to her, and, touching her shoulder, asked her why she was doing this. Frightened and flustered by the jinn's angry look, she stooped and kissed the baby. The people passing by thought the woman must be mad. To them, it looked like she was kissing the air; they did not have the Jan's kohl applied to their eyes, so they were unable to see what was really going on.

The jinn, however, said angrily, 'What! Are you going to disgrace us?' Straightaway poking a finger into the poor woman's eye – the eye that had the kohl applied to it – she blinded her on the spot.

Hanauer observed:

> What misfortune might have happened had she applied Jan's kohl to both eyes, Allah only knows; but this seems certain, namely, that by reason of their having such curiously-formed eyes, the Jan can see and know many things which ordinary mortals cannot; and their kohl helps them to a sort of second-sight which we do not possess. You very rarely meet people with such eyes. There is perhaps scarcely one in ten thousand, but that one sees and can do things which other people cannot, and therefore the Mugharibeh [North Africans], who by the powers of magic know where hidden treasure may be found, are always on the lookout for such persons, in hopes of obtaining their assistance.

The use of special or magic kohl to see what the jinn see is a motif in various Asian cultural beliefs, including those in India. In the epic Urdu stories of Amir Hamza, which we shall examine later, the special substance is called the 'kohl of Solomon'.[29] Hanauer refers to North African magicians because their prowess was legendary throughout the

Arab and Muslim countries. From time immemorial, these Muslim sorcerers (Arab and Berber alike) were known to travel throughout these lands, offering their services in exorcisms and other jinn-related therapies.

Fast-forward to the twenty-first century … .

The quaint charm of Rev. Hanauer's portrayal of jinn in Palestine gives way today to a much edgier, more dangerous phenomenon. As we know, jinn seem to enjoy causing trouble for humans. They have surfaced with a vengeance in the current Palestinian-Israeli conflict, as Palestinian Muslims report cases of possession by Jewish jinn. The reports are rich with political symbolism, but there is a social component as well.

Robert Robins and Jerrold Post have taken a rather unsympathetic look at the phenomenon in their book *Political Paranoia, the Psychopolitics of Hatred* (1997) and blame it on 'entrepreneurial spiritualists' who have profited from 'the Middle Eastern readiness to succumb to conspiracy thinking'.[30]

Since the Palestinian *intifada* (uprising) against Israeli occupation erupted in the occupied territories in 1987, contending with jinn has become a growing business in Gaza. Sheikh Abu Khaled, an exorcist, said that the number of possessed Muslims had more than tripled: 'I suspect that Jewish magicians send Jinns to us here in Gaza. In fact most of my patients are possessed with Jewish Jinns.' According to Robins and Post, both Jewish and Christian Jinns are reported to be black in colour, but the Jewish ones are distinguished by the horns growing from their heads.

A more in-depth look at the phenomenon of jinn possession among the Palestinians was conducted by Celia E. Rothenberg, an anthropologist who conducted 14 months (1995–1996) of fieldwork in the West Bank village of Artas.[31] Rothenberg explored how the experiences of some women and men with jinn embody the multiple dimensions of the Palestinian-Israeli conflict. The human body, in relationship with or possessed by a jinn, thus becomes a site for the enactment of this conflict in surprising and revealing ways.

In one case, a young Palestinian woman from Artas, identified as Zahia, experienced episodes of possession by a Jewish jinn after she moved to Jordan to marry her cousin. During periods of the possession, the Jewish jinn spoke Hebrew through her mouth and attempted to use her body to strangle her infant son. Back home in the West Bank, the male members of her family worked together with Jewish men building Jewish settlements. Given the nature of village social life as Zahia had experienced it, the young woman's story appears, in Rothenberg's view, to be a commentary on how Jews and her own male family members may seem to collude in shaping and constraining her life. According to Rothenberg, given that Zahia was forced by her father to marry her cousin in a relatively distant place and blocked from returning to the West Bank by both social mores and Israeli bureaucracy and that she was aware that her family's very livelihood comes from Israeli Jews, her possession by a Jewish jinn 'embodies the intimate realm of the Israeli-Palestinian conflict'.

In another case, a young Palestinian man named Muhammed, while serving time in an Israeli prison, was attacked by a Jewish female jinn. Their relationship quickly became an extended friendship, lasting throughout Muhammed's time in prison. At times, Muhammed allowed the jinn to possess him in order to entertain the other prisoners or to scare his Israeli guards. The nature of the friendship between Muhammed and the jinn was surprising, because of its setting and its sheer improbability. The Jewish female jinn initially sought a prison love affair with the Palestinian man, but she came to accept a friendship instead. This account of possession dealt with the possibilities which might emerge in relations between Jews and Palestinians in a very unlikely setting. Indeed, Rothenberg found that their relationship, realised in the experience of possession, addressed numerous layers of the Palestinian-Israeli conflict which are often overlooked. Such additional levels of conflict help compare notes on Jewish and Arab experiences of oppression and the underlying friction between similar but divergent ethnicities.

The Palestinian jinn experience has many similarities to the Arabian, but it has also been uniquely salted (if one may use that term) with other cultural influences, particularly that of modern Israel. Not only does the Palestinian-Israeli conflict intrude upon the spirit realm, but also the ancient Jewish/Hebrew traditions regarding the jinn have their effect.

Syria: The Red King's Daughter

According to some Islamic traditions, jinn are distinguished by colours. In Syria, the tradition holds that the king of the jinn is red in colour. Ernst Zbinden finds 'a very charming correspondence between old and new perceptions' in the notion that the most evil jinn are coloured red. But he was able to confirm this view only in North Africa. These general theories about jinn stem from ancient works on Arab magic, some of them handbooks or grimoires, mostly of Egyptian origin.

'Among the seven jinn princes, Egyptian, North African and Syrian folklore calls the king al-Ahmar (i.e., the Red or the Red One),' Zbinden reports. 'The red jinn are the troops belonging to him.' In the Persian epic *Shahnameh* there are also coloured demons and above all coloured demon princes, but there is no discussion in that work of red *divs* – div being the Persian equivalent of jinn – or indeed of the belief that red divs would be the most evil ones.

The Egyptian legends contain the best parallels between old and new. For red was the colour of the ancient Egyptian god Seth and was, therefore, the colour of all evil. 'The red jinn are the descendants of the troops of the god Seth,' Zbinden declares, 'and there probably hides behind the cryptic name "the red king" no one other than the evil god himself. The Red or the Red One is probably a designation for the god Seth.'[32]

Whether or not Syria's jinn king is the epitome of evil – a doubtful proposition, perhaps – he certainly is red. And the jinn of his kingdom engage in pursuits that are quite familiar to us by now, including possession.

In 2002, an article appeared on an Arabic Internet web site that purported to be an interview with a female jinn who had possessed a human being.[33] The article was written by a 'Mr. Abdalrazzak'. The interview is set in Damascus, Syria, and includes discussion of jinn kingdoms and the phenomenon of jinn possession.

The article consists of various conversations between the author and his paternal grandmother, Husna Khanum, which took place, as he put it, 'when I was quite young'. The dialogues were not literally with his grandmother, he says, but rather with the jinn that had possessed her. The spirit had taken possession of her many years before, during the French occupation of Syria in 1920, when the constantly exploding shells had caused her psychological trauma and opened her to jinn possession. The manifestations of the female jinn would come and go, depending on circumstances, over the years. At times, Husna Khanum would seem totally normal; at others, the personality of the jinn would take over.

The writer's discussions with his possessed grandmother included the following exchanges:

Q – What is your real name?
A – Our names are secret and cannot be given. We borrow names similar to your names and keep them throughout our lifetime.

Q – Where is your location in this world?
A – Our location is also secret.

Q – Do you have continents and countries as we do?
A – No, but we have many kingdoms, kings, princes and peoples.

Q – Can we know the names of some of those kingdoms?
A – We describe our kingdoms in terms of colours to bring the concept closer to your understanding, so we say the red jinn, the blue jinn and the yellow jinn, but in reality these colours are expressions of differences amongst us.

Q – Then you too are veiled from each other as per the type or colour?
A – Yes, we are veiled from seeing some among us, and we cannot see other types of jinn from other kingdoms, but there are exceptions, as is the situation now.

Q – Husna Khanum, what is your position in your world?
A – I am the daughter of the red jinn king, who still reigns over our kingdom.

Q – How old are you?
A – Twenty-seven years old.

Q – Are you married?
A – No, not married, for your grandmother [i.e., the person talking to the writer] doesn't leave me with much free time. She summons me often to come cure people and solve problems arising from jinn.

Q – I know you are a Muslim. Do you have other religions?
A – Yes we have converted to Islam along with humans and have entered into this holy religion. We have other religions and we have infidels. We are much like you in this respect.

Q – How are you able to enter our world?

A – We see and feel you because your density is higher than ours. This can be exemplified by a staircase whose steps go up from the subtle to the dense. This is as regards the physical formation; the basic structure of humans contains all the steps of this staircase, but your sciences have still not attained even a minimal knowledge of the real structure of the human being – till now we're unable to interact with you in a good way except through you, i.e., by entering your bodies.

Q – Can you explain to me how do you enter our bodies?

A – We enter the human body during one of the moments of its life, and at a certain state of it.

Q – What do you mean by a certain state?

A – I mean when the soul splits from the body for a period of time, and then we open a loophole through which we can enter.

Q – When does the soul split from the body?

A – Many are the states in which the soul splits from the body – other than death of course – i.e., temporary splitting, such as during dreams that occur in sleep. The hero of this kind of dream is the soul or the astral body that goes out and flies away.

Q – That means you enter when the human dreams?

A – No, of course not. We can't reach someone through these exitings [of the soul]. If this were the case, it would be easy to enter all human bodies.

Q – Then which state are you talking about?

A – There are many states – quite a lot of them – such as a coma resulting from shock, a fall or a crash, or those that occur due to extreme panic or terror. All such states, in addition to the psychological state of the target person, are suitable for entering a person.

Q –Are there targeted persons?

A – Yes. Due to our structure, we can see you without you being able to see us. By your normal actions you might cause us harm, either intentionally or not. In this case, the person who caused us harm becomes a target for us and we watch him closely, and when a certain entrance state occurs we take the opportunity and enter him.

Q – What languages do you speak?

A – We do not have a specific language. We communicate telepathically [with each other], but through you we speak your languages, which we learn through our interaction with you.

Q – Can you tell us about your social life?

A – Yes. It's very similar to your life [as humans], especially after you [humans] die.

Q – In reality, we don't know anything about the shape of our life after death, except through the philosophies we study.

A – When you die and remove this heavy body garment, you move to a stage which is very similar to us as regards motion, formation and relationship, especially at the lower stages of your non-material existence, when you shall live in a parallel world very similar to your world as regards places and feelings. Your physical, sensory life is but a school in which you learn, taste, hear, smell and see, and you graduate after death to a non-material world, a feelings world. You benefit from your earlier life by acquiring certain experiences that qualify you for the non-material life, and you become capable of certain conceptualisations through which you live and develop to higher and higher grades. You repeat the experience over and over again. Each time the experiences increase greatly, to reach the final form that promotes you to a higher plane. What I want to say is that you are similar to us in that first stage of the other world.

Q – If I ever became like you, what would I see?

A – You would see a transparent, misty life. No matter binds us, no physics or chemistry, but feelings and formations similar to you in appearance, i.e., general appearances, but as to the contents, we differ much from you.

Q – Do you eat and drink, or what are your energy sources?

A – We do not eat or drink. We are energies by ourselves. Programmed energies subject to higher law, we develop or degrade as per our deeds. We are also subject to the law of [divine] reward and penalty like you. Our good deeds reflect positively, providing us with the subtlety that promotes us on up the staircase of transcendence, and our evil deeds make us go back towards higher density and keep us in within the bottom layers.

Q – Why are you called inhabitants of lower-order worlds, despite the fact that you – especially the believers among you – have, as I understand it, a composition similar to angels?

A – We've been described by this term [lower-order] for an important reason. The reason is not our position [in the universe], as some would think; it is because we are below you in density. As I said before, it is a reversed staircase for us, but for you the staircase is not reversed, and here lies the secret: Had this staircase been not reversed, the jinn would have been humans in advanced stages, i.e., transcending the material state, thus becoming angels, as you said.

Q – Am I to understand that when you develop, and are promoted, you go down, or is it the opposite?

A – Not spatially, as you understand it. You humans are very much bound by matter, in addition to time and space. The gist here is that we as jinn and you as humans have free will, the ability to choose good or evil, and this is what distinguishes us both. But each [of the two species] has its direction – not spatially, as you imagine, but mentally: we develop in a certain direction and you develop in an opposite direction. We live the first stage as neighbours, and talk to each other, as if we are undergoing an examination in the same school, but each in his own class. And at the end of this test, each of us exits through a separate door. We and you are a basic condition for the existence of this school, and while we are similar to you at one stage of your transitional stages, this does not mean that we mix with you after evolving.

Q – Many times I've heard about or seen human males or females possessed by jinn who go into convulsions and break down psychologically. This leads people to claim that all those who have relations with you are mentally ill, especially in the first stages. Can you explain this?

A – Can you imagine a watermelon entering you through your nostril? What torture that would be! It isn't easy for a foreign body to enter into the structure of another body. The torture affects both parties, the host and the hosted, but in different degrees. The jinn has a different consciousness, mind and environment, etc., and enters a body that's not parallel in structure, and this is what causes torture and misery, especially in the first stages.

Q – Then why do you enter these bodies?

A – For us, these bodies are a window of relief. The jinn who enters a human is fortunate and enjoys beautiful periods of his life, giving much of his time and energies in the service of humans ...

Q – Why do cases of jinn manifestation or possession occur so frequently only in our regions, or, to use a better phrase, in underdeveloped societies? Why not in America or Europe, for example?

A – There are possession cases all over the world, but their treatment differs from one region to another. In addition, we have a greater presence in certain societies because of the prevailing manner of thinking or the cultural background which provides the right setting for our entrances. As I said before, we wait for the proper moment, and these are many among you. Also, you enrich the opportunity greatly, since your social composition is more suitable.

We have seen how Syrian jinn traditions go back thousands of years, at least as far as ancient Palmyra and its guardian jinn-gods. For many centuries, until the fall of the Ottoman empire in 1922, Syria was significantly larger than we know it today, and it included Palestine as well, so the Palestinians' jinn heritage can be considered part of the Syrian legacy. Syria's capital Damascus was also the seat of the first Islamic dynasty, the Umayyads, and during that period (661–750), many of the Islamic jinn traditions began to coalesce, entering the hadiths and other theological writings in the early years of the next dynasty, the Abbasids (750–1258).

Syria is a quintessentially Arab country, and its jinn lore – be it Palmyran, Palestinian or Damascene – represents an Arab interpretation of the phenomenon, at least to the extent that such cultural clarity is possible.

Egypt: Ifrits and Ghouls

Some of the richest traditions about the jinn continue to thrive in Egypt, perhaps because of that country's rich literary and cultural heritage and its millennia-long fascination with the supernatural.[34] The jinn are known to play an extraordinary role in the life of the Egyptian farmer. The bad jinn in Egypt are usually called ifrits, after the Arabic term *ifrit*, occurring once in the Qur'an and 'referring to a large and powerful jinn known for its wickedness and craftiness (the exact phrase is 'an '*ifrit* of the Jinn', 27:39). In Egyptian parlance, the word 'jinn' itself normally refers to good jinn. Like most Arabs, Egyptians believe that the jinn can transform themselves into all possible shapes and appear as men, dogs, donkeys and cats, as well as many other forms. They can also make themselves invisible at will. Yet they eat, they drink and procreate and conceive like humans; yes, they are even mortal, though the Egyptians believe they live to be some centuries old.

People in Egypt believe that because the jinn are fiery beings, they naturally like to live *in* fire. If someone throws something into a camp fire or household fire, he must say the protective formula '*Bismillahi – rahmani – rahimi*' ('in the name of God, the Compassionate and Merciful'). One supposes that any ifrit present in the fire would have time during the invocation to depart. Yet the predominant view is that it is not fire but much more often the earth that serves as the chief domicile of the jinn. The jinn normally live underground. Thus one frequently calls them 'our brothers and sisters under the earth' or simply *tahtaniyin* (those below).

If you inadvertently kick the ground, they come forth. British folklorist Winifred S. Blackman cites as an example the case of a boy – a Coptic Christian – who once stamped his foot on the floor. That evening, when he was about to go to sleep, an ifrit appeared and tried to scratch out his eyes. The boy begged, 'Oh, let me be, forgive me!' But the ifrit replied: 'You hurt one of my children in the head when you stamped on the ground.' Fortunately it occurred to the boy to quickly make the sign of the cross, so that the ifrit vanished.[35] (This account demonstrates that jinn belief in Egypt is not simply a Muslim phenomenon. Christian Copts, who consider themselves the descendants of the ancient Egyptians, also take the ifrits very seriously.)

If you spill a fluid so that it flows on the ground, one must immediately say '*dastur*' (permission) or '*dastur, ya mubarakin*' (permission, O blessed ones), for the ifrits would take revenge if offended. Although the earth is the main home of the jinn, Egyptians believe that wells, caves and ruins also qualify as places particularly afflicted by them, since these are viewed as entrances to the underworld. As is the belief throughout the Islamic world, Egyptians say jinn also haunt all seldom-visited places: such as country lanes, the desert, old houses, rivers and watering places. In houses, they choose the oven and the toilet as their preferred domiciles. If you enter the latter, you should always say a preventive '*dastur*' or '*dastur, ya mubarakin*.' Indeed sometimes you may direct a prayer to Allah, in which the divine name is nervously avoided, so as not to bring the name of the Most High into connection with filth and refuse. According to Edward Lane, the most common prayer is the following: 'By you I seek refuge from the male and female devils!'[36]

Ancient Egyptian tombs and dark corners of old temples are considered common haunting places. Lane could not persuade his servants to accompany him into the Great Pyramid: they were terrified of the *'afarit*. Interestingly, many Egyptians attribute the building of the pyramids and the other colossal remains of Egyptian antiquity to Jann ibn Jann (whom we discussed earlier as the last ruler of the pre-Adamite jinn) and his servants, because they assume that human hands could not have built such structures. This is not so very different from the claims of Erich von Däniken and other speculative writers that the pyramids were beyond the abilities of the people of their day and must have been built by advanced beings from another planet.

An Egyptian from the Upper Nile region told German anthropologist Hans A. Winkler that the ancient Egyptians made pictures of the *'afarit* they encountered, and he showed him a Bes-figure. Bes was an ancient Egyptian god who may have originated somewhere outside the country – perhaps Mesopotamia or sub-Saharan Africa – but who became one of Egypt's popular deities. His characteristics changed over time. In the Old Kingdom, he was primarily a fertility god, associated with the harvest and with circumcision. By the Middle Kingdom, he was a guardian deity (a function sometimes associated with jinn) who protected the home, infants, new mothers and pregnant women. In this period, he was portrayed in sculptures as a dwarf, clothed in animal skins, with a tail and a feathered head dress. By the Graeco-Roman period, Bes became more militaristic in character and served to protect Egyptians from their enemy, whoever that might be.

In rural and remote Egypt few dare to stay outside cultivated land at night. The *fellah* (peasant) will remain in his village in the evening, for he believes that in the desert, which often lies directly beyond cultivated areas, reside the demons. Sandstorms, which often rise up to great heights, are said to be caused by jinn flying on high, an image that harkens back to the belief that the jinn ride in the wind. Shooting stars, another natural phenomenon, are considered according to Qur'anic teaching to be projectiles which God throws at troublesome jinn, and Egyptians are comfortable with this explanation.

In Upper Egypt (i.e., the upper part of the Nile, or southern Egypt), Hungarian Orientalist Ignaz Goldziher (1850–1921), one of the legends of Western scholarship on Islam, accumulated material on a serpent cult practised at the grave of the Muslim holy man al-Haridi,[37] who, as we have seen, was said to have been transformed into a snake upon his death and was perhaps a jinn. Despite the numerous connections between the jinn of Egypt and nature, Egyptian ifrits are not primarily nature spirits. Although some accounts portray them as such, most Egyptian lore associates ifrits with spirits of the dead, in a manner that reflects the belief-system of pharaonic Egypt. Every man is said to possess, besides his soul (*ruh*), an ifrit, just as the ancient Egyptian had his *ka*. When a person dies, this ifrit separates from the body, just as the *ka* did in ancient Egypt. This is also said to be the case among animals. The stories linking ifrits to the dead are numerous and very characteristically Egyptian. The ifrits of people who unfortunately lose their lives are said to haunt the neighbourhood where they die. Many have seen them and have described their appearance as an ever-expanding nebulous white figure or, in some cases, as the shape of a dog or cat. It is also believed that jinn living in rivers or canals are the ifrits of people who have drowned. One should never go to the aid of a drowning man. What good would it do? An ifrit is pulling the person from under, and invariably it is more powerful.

Zbinden speaks of a case in which the workers of an unnamed rural village every night heard the voice of an unlucky companion who was killed when a steam boiler exploded. He cites another accident in which twelve workers were killed and says that their ghosts – their ifrits – frequently appeared afterwards at the scene of the disaster, taking the form of donkeys (a common disguise for jinn). In yet another case, Zbinden notes that in the ruins of Koptos, the ancient site in modern Qift, a city just north of Luxor, seven ifrits were seen in the shape of huge grotesque donkeys. These spirit beings may have been quite old indeed. Koptos rebelled during the rule of the Roman emperor

Diocletian in 297 AD, and in punishment the city was destroyed and many inhabitants slain.

It is believed that an ifrit will also stick to the blood of a person who has been killed or mortally wounded. Naturally this ifrit is the death-spirit of the victim and is drawn to the life-force of his blood.

For these reasons it is also critically important that burial rites be carried out properly, so that the spirits of the dead find repose. A mosque ceremony normally precedes burial, with appropriate prayers recited. There follows a procession to the cemetery, with the bier carried high by male mourners, followed by the women of the family. The deceased is laid to rest in his tomb facing in the direction of the holy city of Mecca.

* * *

Egyptian magic, closely associated with jinn lore, has a long and storied tradition and is still practised to this day. There are rituals for summoning jinn for various different purposes and binding them to do one's bidding through the use of ancient spells. A description of such a ritual from the late nineteenth century – not very different from ceremonies conducted today – appears in the *Tibb al-Rukka* (Old Wives Medicine) of Egyptian physician 'Abd al-Rahman Isma'il.[38] Isma'il, sceptic and rationalist that he was, believed that the jinn manifestations he described were illusions caused by hashish. Some of the rituals were carried out to help women keep their husbands from straying.

As Isma'il describes it:

> The strongest 'cure' and most successful drug tried among women to restrain their husbands from flirting with other women and keeping them to themselves, is the *Shabshaba*, and the '*milking of the stars*' (*halb al-nugum*) comes near it. They are almost alike so that in the course of time their two charms have become confused. (Sometimes they are employed for the 'cure' of some of the nervous diseases which the common people assert to be due to the Jinn.) The *Shabshaba* is very rare in Egypt. Only certain well-known old wives know its real nature. The most famous of these

> is the Sheikha Khadra al-Aswaniya al-Sufiya. She was until 1309 [an Islamic year, equivalent to 1891] living in a cell at the foot of the Mukattam hills (Cairo) near the tomb of Sidi 'Umar ibn al-Farid. [The famous mystical poet (1181–1235). Tr.] I believe her name is not absent from the memory of those ladies who knew her and verified the success of her 'method' and who used to throng to her.

Isma'il apparently never witnessed the ritual himself but interviewed female informants who were present. It appears to be an extreme form of the Zar ritual described earlier. According to Isma'il's account, the Sheikha would take the unfortunate woman with the unfaithful husband to a hidden location, where the woman would dress in black, have her face and hands dyed black, let down her hair and hold three fruits in her hand. Then a type of incense was burnt that included hashish and a medicinal gum called *anzarut* (sarcocol). At that point, the Sheikha recites:

Ya 'afarit ya 'afarit	*Oh, Spirits! Oh, Spirits!*
Ya ginn al-gibal	*Oh, Jinn of the Mountains!*
Ya sukkan al-buhur	*Oh, dwellers of the seas!*
Ya 'ummar al-burur	*Oh, inhabitants of lands!*
Ya bu'ad fi'l-barriya	*Oh, far off folk in the desert!*
Ya qatilin al-darriya	*Oh, slayers of offspring!*
Ya mukhalifin Suliman	*Oh, opponents of Solomon!*[39]
Ya mubarti'in fi'l-widyan	*Oh, gallopers in valleys!*

I cry to you. Come to me, and help me with the stars of the sky.

The atmosphere darkens and day turns to night – perhaps with some help from the drug-laden incense. The Sheikha then intones:

> Good evening to you, oh, stars of evening! Oh, yellow ones like apricots! I have smitten him with three fruits [*thamarat*], smite ye him with three live coals [*jamarat*]. [Thereupon she names the person in the case, and casts the fruits upon an image of the person made of clay which is in front of her.] One ember will come upon his eyes so that he will see none but her [i.e. his forsaken wife]; and an ember upon his tongue so that he will speak with none but her; and an ember upon his ears so that he will listen to none but her. Good evening to you, oh, our new moon! You

> whose father is Friday [the Moslem holy day], and whose mother is the Festival! Oh, Glorious Venus with the wakeful eyes! Take for me from the hair of so and so, the son of so and so, three hairs. Pull them off and mix them and bring them and leave them at the door of so and so the daughter of so and so. Good evening to you, oh, Sindas! [Sindas is said to be the name of the god of lust and debauchery.] Oh, Sindas! Oh, Knower of secrets and of ... [here she names a certain organ of the fair sex, which it is not allowable to mention]. [At the same time the Sheikha uncovers her genital organs and brings one of her shoes and beats that organ seven times until its 'servant', who is named Sindas, as mentioned above, appears.] Oh, Sindas! You have helpers! Oh, Sindas! Where are your brethren! Bring him and bind him and at her door release him!

At this point, the Sheikha orders the 'patient' to recite the special incantation prepared for the purpose, as follows:

> Gaga! Oh, Gaga![40] Decide this matter [*haga]*. Bring him with dust on his head and his shoe in my ... [and she mentions an expression for one of her members which it is not fitting to mention] and his turban in my girdle (*dikka*), hearing no speech but mine.

Then the Sheikha goes back to completing her original spell, and points with her hand to the sky, saying:

> Oh, whirlwind! Oh, clever one! You have satans with you!Drag him and beat him, and carry him away to the home of this poor woman, and leave him there. Oh, Sabi! Oh, Sabi![41] Oh, Hearer and Answerer! Bring so and so, the son of so and so, improved and not enraged. If he enters, well and good, and if he goes off, well and good. Let my star and his star be with you in agreement!

At this point, according to Isma'il's informants, a number of 'Helpers' – that is, jinn – arrive, in various shapes and sizes. They listen to the commands of the Sheikha and then respectfully hurry off to implement them. This is the way the Shabshaba normally goes. There are minor variations for other kinds of jinn-summoning rituals, such as the one for persons afflicted with nervous diseases.

On reflection, Isma'il decided that the appearance of jinn and other mystical aspects in the ceremony he described must have been 'imaginings' caused by the hashish and other intoxicants. The result, he said, was to 'stupefy the "remnant" of reason in the woman whom the devils of slander and defamation have deceived. Thus it appears to her eyes, what eye hath not seen, nor ear heard, nor the reason of any rational being verified.'

Despite the good doctor's scepticism and the stern warnings of religious conservatives, jinn-summoning and jinn-propitiating rituals have retained their popularity in Egypt, Sudan and other nearby countries. This speaks to their serving a real social need, regardless of what one thinks of the methods involved.

* * *

Another compelling example of jinn lore in Egypt is the persistent and pervasive interest in ghouls. Many of the stories about these frightening creatures are set in the Sinai Peninsula, a remote and harsh environment through which travellers pass quickly and sometimes fearfully. This is the landscape in which Moses and his people, the Hebrew refugees from Egypt, wandered for many years. It is the home of ascetic monks who eke out austere lives of isolation and meditation. Amidst the mountains, the narrow passes and the lonely desert stretches of Sinai, the slavering, hulking ghouls make their home, lurking and lying in wait for the innocent traveller. In this context, accounts like the following are not so unusual:[42]

Sometime in the late nineteenth century, there was a severe drought in the Sinai. The people of the village of Nuweiba were starving, so they decided to leave their village and travel on foot across the desert to Suez, where the British were and where they could find food. To get there they had to pass by Mount Barka, where the Cave of the Ghouls was located. On the mountain, in the cave, a family of ghouls were said to live, who were in the habit of kidnapping and eating passers-by.

One night, five men from Nuweiba were travelling past the mountain, and one of them fell behind and was separated from his companions. As the man – whom we will call Ahmed – wandered in the darkness, wondering where his friends had gone, a beautiful woman suddenly appeared out of the night and blocked his path. She gave him a choice: 'Sex, or be eaten!' It was not a difficult decision. As the Bedouins put it, 'the man did what a man has to do.'

A year later, the woman appeared to Ahmed again and informed him that he had a daughter. With her permission, he took the baby into his home. All went well for many years. The daughter, whom he named Amira (Princess), grew up and married one of the villagers. She and her husband had several fine children. Ahmed was proud of his daughter.

Then one day, while Ahmed was walking outside the village, he passed the local cemetery and was shocked to see that one of the graves had been desecrated. Ahmed was worried. He went to his daughter's husband, Mahmoud, and told him the story of how Amira had been born. Ahmed feared that his daughter had reverted to the habits of her mother's people.

One night, Amira left her bed and went out of the house. Mahmoud, who heard her leave, got up and followed her. Amira picked up a shovel and walked to the cemetery, where she began to dig at the site of a fresh grave. Mahmoud watched in horror as she exhumed the body of a villager and began to eat it. He ran back to the house, shocked and horrified at the reality that now faced him: he had married a ghoul.

When he returned to their bedroom, he decided what to do. The wall beside their bed was stacked to the ceiling with sacks of grain, a thousand pounds in weight, which he had stored there for the winter. When his wife returned to bed and had fallen asleep, he toppled the sacks over onto her, and she was killed. The villagers were told it was an accident.

Amira's children grew up, married, and themselves had children. It is said that they are good people and are no longer ghouls. But they are still known as El Ghouwela, the ghoul people.

The Cave of the Ghouls was real. For many years it could be reached via a hard climb up Mount Barka. But rains have since washed the path away, and although one can see the cave high up on the mountain, the only way to reach it would be by rappelling down from the mountain top.

Parts of the story can be confirmed. The cave does exist. There was indeed a severe drought and famine in that area in the late nineteenth century – so severe, in fact, that the locals were often forced to eat the undigested leavings in camel dung. And, of course, as the villagers of Nuweiba will show you, there are people called El Ghouwela who live among them.

* * *

One last Egyptian jinn manifestation: Stories have circulated in Egypt for decades about a mysterious, dog-like animal called the *sal'awa* (or *sal-awa*), which was linked in the popular imagination with jinn, and which reportedly attacked and even killed humans. We have seen creatures like this, with similar names, in our discussion of the jinn of the Arabian Peninsula. The Egyptian version was described as 'an odd creature, which allegedly looks like an anteater/jackal cross, with square ears, a droopy nose, [and] a poofy forked tail'.[43] Some eyewitnesses quoted in Egyptian newspapers described the sal'awa as about the size of a dog, with hind legs somewhat longer than front legs, a large hyena-like muzzle and big canine teeth. A creature resembling the sal'awa was, in fact, pictured by the ancient Egyptians; it represented the god Set (or Seth), again showing the link between modern Egyptian jinn belief and the traditions of their ancient ancestors. Set was considered a powerful and evil deity. He was originally the god of the desert and was associated with sandstorms and desert caravans – a very jinn-like connection.[44] The sal'awa of today is considered no less malicious than Set.

The AUC Fox Information web site on the Internet, hosted by a biology major at the American University of Cairo, sought to explain some of the reports and assure students that the wild creatures sometimes seen on or near the campus were actually foxes and not sal'awas.[45] Most likely the sal'awa was a feral dog or a canine crossbreed (e.g., dog-wolf or dog-jackal), the biologist said.

The primary evidence for the sal'awa appeared to be newspaper articles. The beast was first spotted on the eastern edges of Cairo in the 1960s and 1970s, and then it disappeared for several decades, reappearing in 1996 in the village of Armant in Upper Egypt as well as in the Cairo area. The sal'awa was also held responsible for short spates of attacks in 2005 and in October 2008. Some of these resulted in 'the death and hospitalization of some adults and a few children', according to the AUC Fox Site.

Scholars of the University of Chicago's Ancient Near East (ANE) Internet list held a short online discussion in 1997 about the reported appearance of the sal'awa in Upper Egypt the previous year. At least one of the scholars raised the question of whether the animal might be connected with the jinn.[46] One academic wrote,

> Salawa!
>
> Stories have appeared ... about a strange animal in the Sohag/Luxor area. I can add this: The animal is called a Salawa. There is a Salawa Information Centre in Armant, which was visited by [archaeologists] from Chicago House, and they acquired some photos, which I saw.
>
> Apparently several have been killed, but at least one was caught, although how long it would survive is debatable. It is like a dog with a heavier than usual muzzle and longer ears. It isn't a hyena, but comparisons have been made with the Seth animal. Rumours are circulating that it has eaten people etc., although these are almost certainly exaggerated ... .
>
> One idea was that it is an animal which usually is found further out in the desert, but human actions in the desert, like making probes for the suggested Aswan-Oases canal, may have caused it to come closer to the [Nile] Valley.

A list member replied:

> I have been interested in the discussion on the Salawa ... . Does anyone know the origin of this word? Or whether there is ever any variation in the initial sibilant – Shalawa?
>
> The Nubian shift from a wild animal to a werewolf – half human/half animal evil spirit – is also interesting, since it was the Nubian Shabaka stone version of the Seth Osiris drama which carried the demonization of the former to new heights. Also the West African version of the trickster god as 'the pale fox', and the idea that the Salawa may be at home in the outer desert, suggest that the Seth traditions ... may go back to pre-Egyptian Saharan civilization, which then spread to West Africa as well as the Nile ... .

Another member commented:

> I was here in Egypt when this mysterious animal made such a stink in the press. The photo which did appear looked rather like one of

> the stuffed animals one can see around the city in trophy shops. I must look up the word as it appeared in the press .... but I do have a guess. The possible colloquialization of Fusha [formal] Arabic *si'laah*, the mythical desert ogress, often mentioned in texts parallel to ghuwl?!

One of the most persistent themes we see in Egyptian jinn lore is its connection to ancient pharaonic traditions. The Egyptians have never forgotten their past, and it permeates their beliefs and folk traditions. This adds a unique flavour to their jinn legends as well as to their ongoing interactions with the fire spirits.

Morocco: The 'Masters'

Morocco is another important locus of jinn belief and legend. The jinn, or *jnun* as they are more commonly called in Morocco, not only interact extensively with humans on a day-to-day basis but also play a major role in Moroccan magic, which is noted throughout the Muslim world for its power.

Emile Laoust, a French scholar who specialised in the languages and culture of Morocco's indigenous Berbers, taught in Rabat in the early part of the twentieth century during the French Protectorate. Laoust focused some of his attention on the jnun, whose character derived in part from autochthonous Berber tradition and in part from an overlay of imported Arab belief.[47] The Berbers of Morocco called the countryside, mountains and desert regions their own; the Arabs, who colonised Morocco in the seventh century, dominated the cities.

As Laouste reported, the Moroccans of the countryside viewed the jnun as malevolent spirits, without well-defined personality, so mistrusted and feared that one never called their names lest they manifest themselves. Thus the jnun were designated by comfortable euphemisms: the Angels, the Muslims or the Believers, those People from Under the Earth, the Breaths, the Children of the Others, and other such terms. Edward Westermarck, an anthropologist and sociologist who recorded his observations on Moroccan jnun belief a few years before Laouste, said that calling them 'jnun' was equivalent to summoning them. They did not like being called 'jnun', which they viewed as a curse, and they were known to come and punish an offender.

Laoust discovered that the jnun lived in an organised, hierarchical society both below the surface of the earth and in the shadows above it. As with many jinn elsewhere in the Islamic world, they were said to haunt squalid places such as latrines, sewers, dung heaps, slaughterhouses, or gloomy places such as grottoes, public baths, water tanks, or watery places such as rivers or ponds, and even high places such as mountains or treetops. When it came to humans, they preferred to associate with Negroes, sorcerers, assassins and butchers – the latter because of the blood that they shed that so attracted them. They moved during the day in tornadoes and whirlwinds of dust, from which one could protect oneself by saying the *bismillah*, much as the sign of the cross would drive away a vampire. The jnun were the masters of the waters and the winds, as well as of hidden treasures. All-powerful for evil (and in rare cases also for good), they were intimately involved in the life of man, whose very homes were in their possession. Every house in Morocco was said to possesses its 'masters' – its spirits or guardians which were necessarily associated with the essential acts of domestic activity. They took asylum at the threshold of the house; a Moroccan would never sit in this location because it belonged to the jnun. We can compare this with the old Greek and Roman custom, revived in modern times, of the bridegroom carrying his bride across the threshold of their new home – that is, carrying her over this spirit domain.

The jnun were generally invisible, Laoust noted; but to torment mankind, they could assume the most grotesque – as well as the most beautiful – human forms. Moroccans claimed that there were men who had married female jnun of striking beauty, invisible to all except the husband. Jnun could also just as easily assume the appearance of an animal. These shapes included the dog, the cat, the goat, the camel, even the frog or tortoise, and above all the serpent, as we have seen in most other countries holding belief in the jinn. In another familiar type of behaviour, the jnun of Morocco were accused of afflicting men with sudden maladies, such as epileptic seizures or convulsions. Violent madmen *(majnun) we*re possessed by wicked demons, and the most inoffensive madmen by good jinn.

The latter were regarded a bit like holy men – linking demonic possession with saintliness has been a common phenomenon in many lands, including among various North American Indian peoples and in the traditions of medieval Europe. A violent horse or ox that suddenly attacked his harness mate was also called *majnun*, that is, in the grip of the jinn. Exorcisms were usually employed in such cases to heal the afflicted or to cleanse a house haunted by jnun. According to Laoust, the most widespread exorcism ritual was called the *diyafa* (a euphemism meaning 'hospitality' and normally applied to a feast prepared for visiting travellers); it took place at night and involved Negroes, butchers or initiates of the Sufi brotherhoods who recited incantations before the possessed person, or within the haunted house, and gave themselves up to violent dances that resulted in spiritual ecstasy, much like the 'trance dance' of some types of traditional Sufi *dhikr* (or *zikr*) ceremony.[48] Animal sacrifices were common at Moroccan exorcisms. Sometimes chickens or goats were strangled and later boiled without salt. To effect the exorcism, the water in which the animal was cooked was spread on the walls as well as the floor and the meat from the sacrificial victims was eaten by the attendees, including the 'possessed' person.[49]

In the hour before sunset, the jnun – having been dormant and resting during the hours of daylight – resumed their normal activity. In the hours of darkness, evil forces were most effective. They then circulated freely, invisible until the darkness once again vanished the next morning.

It was accepted by most Moroccans that humans should not oppose the jinn in any way, Laoust discovered. However, one could be protected from the jinn, of course. Islam offered in this regard the rescue through the bismallah, the sacred phrase that all jinn particularly feared. Other formulas such as 'Cursed be Satan!' or 'May God curse Satan!' or still other quotations from the Qur'an possessed the same power. Moroccans carried with them these same formulas written and enclosed in amulets that might also contain various substances with magical powers, such as alum, gum ammoniac, iron or a crystal of rock salt.

There were other, contrary practices in Morocco that permitted a person to be reconciled with the jnun and even draw off a part of their power: These were offerings, gifts and, particularly, bloody animal sacrifices, as mentioned earlier. Moroccans knew that the jnun were repelled by salt: therefore, one prepared foods for them that were unsalted. The acridity of blood was dear to the jnun. Thus one would cut the throat of a sacrificial animal on the threshold of a house one was going to buy. A well-digger would kill a black hen or a goat before striking the first blow of his pickaxe. A mason would sprinkle blood on the foundations he was about to dig.

In the same way, the Berbers of Morocco sought to appease the spirits by making sacrifices in high places where the jinn, as masters of the wind and air, moved about within whirlwinds and sandstorms, and where echoes repeated ad infinitum the sound of their games. The Aït Moghrad tribe of eastern Morocco offered sacrifices at the Tiskit of Jebel Bou Hamid, the summit of a mountain in the High Atlas range that bars access to the valley region of Oued Ziz to the south. When camps were set up on the plateau of the Idichel area, every tent leader (normally the senior male member of the extended-family tent community, or *aït uham*[50]) went to offer a sacrifice on the mountain summit in order to protect his herds from 'the jackal's tooth': the jnun, they said, most commonly assumed the shape of jackals to do harm to the shepherds of this area.

And then, of course, there was magic. Certain individuals, particularly the *tolba* (students of a *marabout,* a saintly Sufi or other religious leader, male or female) of Sous Valley in Southern Morocco, were said to have the power to invoke jnun and place them at their service. Through incantations and secret passwords, the tolba knew how to locate hidden treasures in the enchanted grottoes that the jnun were compelled to guard. Moroccan folklore has long been enriched by the exploits of these magicians, and their renown extends into the rest of the Muslim world.

Laoust discovered that side by side with regular jinn lived the ogres, devourers of humans, a kind of bogeymen whose name was used to frighten children into staying in line. They belonged without doubt to the ancient Berber stock, whereas the ghouls and ifrits – endowed with striking magical powers permitting them to assume all forms – came from the Middle East.

Certain jnun distinguished themselves from the innumerable, anonymous mass with individual names. A demon named Qao haunted a grotto among the Aït Isaffen – Chleuh Berbers of the Anti-Atlas range; this cave was the source of a spring that healed maladies. The most popular jnun were Haroun and Harouna – two Jewish names – described as male and female aquatic monsters that lived in the Sebou River of northern Morocco. Laoust realised that these jnun were identical to Hammou Qayyo and 'Aisha Qandisha, names used in Fez and in the estuary of the Bou-Regreg River. People refrained from pronouncing their names – whether Haroun and Harouna or Hammou Qayyo and 'Aisha Qandisha – when they travelled the length of the Sebou River and were careful not to kill any serpents they saw at the water's edge. Harouna sometimes came out of the river looking like a woman combing her hair. Her other name, 'Qandisha', was, according to Edward Westermarck, of Oriental origin, derived from 'Kedecha', a name for the temple prostitutes of the Canaanite cults in ancient Palestine: 'One has excellent reasons for presuming that the frivolous 'Aisha Qandisha is the ancient goddess of love, the great Astarte, fallen to the rank of a Moorish jinniya.'

Some Moroccans believed that many anonymous holy men (marabouts) were actually successors of the jnun of the waters and the mountains, of goddesses, nymphs and ancient divinities of the pagan world, vaguely Islamicised, consulted always according to rules of ritual which the passage of centuries had scarcely modified. When a person invoked a marabout at the foot of a tree, at the entrance to a grotto or his tomb, or near a spring, it was difficult to know whether that person was actually in touch with a holy man or one of the jnun. Laoust said there existed, in fact, a very intimate connection between the supernatural and often malicious power of the latter and the *baraka* (blessing) of the former. A serpent found in the tomb of a Moroccan marabout could be taken for the deceased holy man himself or as the embodiment of his soul, whereas in any other place a believer would consider it unquestionably a jinn. We earlier saw a similar case in Upper Egypt, the reported serpent-transformation of the holy man Sheikh al-Haridi.

Laoust found that Moroccans believed that every creative person, and above all every poet, was to some degree inspired by the breath of the jnun and the holy man. One could even acquire the skills of an art solely by virtue of the jnun and the holy man. A person could become a musician, singer or even sailor, fisherman, barber or doctor by sleeping an entire night in a consecrated grotto or in the tomb of a marabout. Animated upon awakening by a new and unknown force, one would possess from then on the secrets of a given art or occupation as well as the self-assurance that was a sure gauge of success. This was a very ancient practice. In Islam, there was a parallel concept called *istikhara,* an Arabic term for praying to God for guidance in making an important decision. But the phenomenon described here – seeking the intercession of a jinn or holy man to choose one's calling in life – was definitely pre-Islamic, incubated in classical antiquity but so tenacious in the Berber heart that it survived despite Muslim orthodoxy, which positively rejected it.

Edward Westermarck spent years studying the peoples and cultures of Morocco, and his insights on the jinn have stood the test of time. Westermarck identified three special categories of Moroccan jnun: Shayatin (devils) or evil jnun; Le-Ryah (the winds) or disease spirits; and 'Afareet (singular 'afrit) or the aristocrats of the jnun. The 'afareet were extremely strong and possessed seven heads. When someone was possessed by an 'afrit, he became a maniac (in an admirable sense), strong and brave. According to legend, 'afareet carried to Meknes great marble blocks that were much too heavy for man or beast to move. If a person possessed the wondrous ring called *khatem l-hekma* (ring of wisdom or ring of Solomon), the 'afareet would serve him or her and assist in performing miracles.

According to Westermarck's research, some Moroccan accounts described jnun as bodiless, resembling light, able to enter a room whose door is closed. Other Moroccan writers, he said, pictured them as having a head but no body or limbs.

Some Moroccans believed that the jnun propagated their species differently than humans do: 'The male only rubs his thigh against the thigh of the female, and the latter afterwards brings forth many young ones at the same time, which explains why there are so many more jnun than there are men.'

Westermarck found that Moroccan jnun have villages and towns and live in tribes and nations, each with its own sultan.

They have different religions like humans do: there are Muslim jnun (believers), Jewish jnun (Saturday jnun – because the Jewish Sabbath was on that day), Christian jnun (infidel jnun) and pagan jnun. Although jnun originated beneath the surface of the earth or in the air, between earth and sky, they were not restricted to living in any particular place, and sometimes they travelled vast distances at blinding speed.

In his travels throughout the country, Westermarck identified a number of jinn personalities whose existence was affirmed by Arabs and Berbers alike. Some of these are known in other North African countries.

* * *

Perhaps none of the jnun of Morocco has had such widespread influence as 'Aisha Qandisha (in French, often written Aicha Qandicha). Arabs of northern Morocco and Algeria particularly are strong believers. To Westermarck's informants, she appeared as a grown woman with a beautiful face, but she was also seen with the legs of a goat or ass, or with the legs of a woman and the body of a she-goat with long, pendulous breasts. She was very lusty and tried to seduce handsome young men. She was said to live in a river or spring, or in the sea. A Moroccan friend of Westermarck's in Tangier said that when he was a child, his mother would warn him against 'Aisha Qandisha when he went swimming in the sea. It was from the sea that she ascended to the cave above the beach of Rmelqala, at the mouth of the Wad l-Ihud near Tangier. There were also stories of her living in a river near Tetuan, in the sewers of Fez and, as we have seen, in the rivers Bou-Regreg and Sebou. Belief in 'Aisha Qandisha does not extend to the far south of Morocco. This may be because of her links to Astarte, the fertility goddess, worshipped by the Canaanites, Hebrews and Phoenicians, whose ancient adherents were found around the Mediterranean littoral but not farther south in the sands of the Sahara.

Lest readers believe that 'Aisha Qandisha is a figure solely from the past, it is worth noting that modern researchers have been investigating the phenomenon of apparent possession by her in recent years, particularly specialists in the fields of anthropology and ethnopsychiatry. Postmodern anthropologist Vincent Crapanzano of the City University of New York is said to have done the best work in English on the ethnopsychiatry of possession.[51]

In Morocco, where most marriages are still arranged by families, romantic love is sometimes viewed as a kind of 'possession'. Romantic, unplanned love and marriage may be viewed by some as undermining the structure of traditional Moroccan society, and thus it is a kind of 'madness' and romantic lovers are *majnun* or jinn-possessed. The jnun have, therefore, become involved with the emotions of Moroccan young people, in a way consistent with their propensity to meddle. Crapanzano's writings have presented several examples of possession by 'Aisha Qandisha.[52]

Although the jnun who possess Moroccans are usually referred to generically, 'Aisha Qandisha is a shining exception. She is often called Lalla (Lady) 'Aisha, to avoid the risk of explicitly naming her. She is able to appear in human form. Males are her usual victims. A possessed man is likely to become impotent or lose interest in human women and may suffer various physical or psychological effects 'unless and until his possession is brought under control by the intervention of one of the popular Moroccan curing groups.'[53]

There are numerous curing groups throughout Morocco that focus on helping individual possessed by jnun, but the Hamadsha specialise in curing possession by 'Aisha Qandisha. Hamadsha members live in most towns of northern Morocco. Often former possession victims themselves – either by 'Aisha Qandisha or other jnun – they have learnt to counter the effects of possession through trance-inducing musical performances and sacrificial rituals. In the farming town of Zawiya in northern Morocco, psychologists Douglas A. Davis and Susan Schaefer Davis report several instances of males overwhelmed by sexual or romantic problems that were said to be caused by 'Aisha Qandisha or other jnun, and which were successfully treated by Hamadsha performances.

The Hamadsha group's preoccupation with 'Aisha Qandisha was attributed in the 1980s to the fact that the jinn had fallen in love with one of the group's patron saints, Sidi Ahmed Dhughi, several hundred years earlier. Sidi Ahmed was inspired to play the flute and drum for the group, and local women who heard him play fell instantly in love with him. According to the Davises, the Hamadsha's attitude towards Qandisha is ambivalent.

> On the one hand she is seen as the source of the suffering they and their clients experience and which draws them to the Hamadsha music and trance. Yet many of the terms used to refer to her connote respect or deference, and this does not in every case seem to be a mere attempt to evade her wrath. And just as the jnun number among themselves Muslims and unbelievers, those influenced by 'Aisha Qandisha and other jnun may be seen as good and pious people, spoken of as struck by 'clean' 'Aisha, or as derelict, violent persons transgressing against Islam, and hence stuck by 'dirty' 'Aisha.[54]

The language of love-possession offers the victim a 'collective symbolism' for all-too-painful real-world experiences, that is, problems of sexuality, marriage or family responsibility. Males who are unable for whatever reason to carry out expected roles of suitor, husband or family provider may undergo an experience of possession by 'Aisha Qandisha. 'Aisha's emotional demands and jealous interference with relations with human women externalise apparent psychological conflicts. Many instances of possession by 'Aisha Qandisha occur after a failed love affair, an estrangement from a spouse or the death of a family member.[55]

Novelist and ethnomusicologist Paul Bowles, a resident of Morocco for many years, spoke of 'Aisha Qandisha in an interview with Michael Rogers for *Rolling Stone* magazine in 1974, conducted in Tangier, his adopted home. Bowles studied and recorded Moroccan traditional music, including Gnawa trance music, performed in Zar-like healing ceremonies by Sufi musicians who have in part descended from black African migrants and former slaves. Fifteen years after that interview, Bowles' comments about this famous female jinn became part of the liner notes of an album by a Moroccan 'world beat' band called 'Aisha Qandisha's Jarring Effects:[56]

> ... it's a mass psychosis around a character called Aicha Qandicha. You ever heard of it? Aicha Qandicha?
>
> ... She's a woman – a spirit in the form of a woman. Practically every Moroccan has had contact with her some way or another. She's

legion, she's manifold. I have a book that says about 25 years ago, there were 35,000 men in Morocco married to her. A lot of people in Ber Rechid – the psychiatric hospital – are married to her.

What exactly happens if you look at her?

... Then you're married to her and that's that. You begin behaving very strangely. There are several well known husbands of Aicha Qandicha around Tangier: they walk along brooks and river beds, hoping to hear her voice – you see them wandering ... .

A contagious psychosis ...

... Right. And when they find Aicha Qandicha again, they make love to her right there, doesn't matter who's there.

Another well-known Moroccan jinn, identified by Westermarck, was **'Allu**, an 'afrit who once lived in a spring called 'Ain 'Allu. He was killed by Moulay Idris, great-grandson of the Prophet Muhammad and founder of the Idrisid dynasty. The spring was located near Moulay Idris's sanctuary.

Bghilt l-Lil was a jinn of Fez, called 'the little female mule of the night' because she appeared at night in the shape of a female mule. She was covered with golden objects, which gave her a radiant appearance. If anyone saw her and attacked her to get the gold, she knocked him down – unless he was protected with some writing from the Qur'an or a dagger or knife. If he then put the writing on her or drew the knife, she became frightened and let him have the treasures she was carrying.

Two female jnun were famous in Cape Juby (Ras Buibisha), on the coast of Morocco, opposite the Canary Islands. Known as **Fatima and Ndahawa**, they would rob cows of their milk and deprive uncharitable people of half their property. They were sisters and always appeared together; but they could be seen only by people who had *baraka* (spiritual blessing).

A female jinn very widely known in Morocco was the **Ghola**, or ghoul, which appears often in other lands. She was said to be very big and have the appearance of a woman, although she had also been seen with the feet of a goat and with considerable hair all over her body and face. She spoke gently to people and was thus able to attract them into her presence, at which point she killed and ate them.

Hammu Qaiyu (or **Hammou Qayyo**) was the husband of 'Aisha Qandisha, according to the Beni Ahsen tribe of the Sebou River area.

He was a very tall individual who lived with her in the waters of the Sebou (where, as we have noted, they were also called Haroun and Harouna). Other tribes in northern Morocco also believed he existed. Westermarck cited a man in Meknes who saw Hammu Qaiyu once in a river. Westermarck also believed that Hammu Qaiyu might be associated with the Carthaginian god Haman, who was the consort of Astarte (again, probably 'Aisha Qandisha) and was also worshipped along the Mediterranean coast.

The people of Doukkala in west-central Morocco spoke of a female jinn named **Haraja** (or **l-Hraja**), who was very libidinous and capable of maddening or killing people with fear. She came from watery or haunted places and assumed different forms on different occasions. A young man from the Shawia tribe of the Casablanca area told Westermarck that Haraja was black and that her head, including the face, was covered with long hair. She had also been seen as a he-goat, and as a red dog with a big human head. Due to her watery abode and her intense sexuality, Haraja appeared to be a central Moroccan variant of 'Aisha Qandisha.

The Hiaina tribe near Fez spoke of a female jinn named **La-Hkima 'Oqla**, who, along with her son 'Airud and her sister 'Aqesa, ruled over 366 tribes of evil-minded jnun. They lived in the Bou Zemlan River between the Hiaina and the Aït Warain tribes of the northeastern end of the Middle Atlas range and were very dangerous, always ready to attack people.

Westermarck noted that the **Seven Kings of the Jnun** were of great interest to Moroccan magicians, who read about them in the old Arabic magic texts. The names of these kings varied depending on the source. According to one version, five of them were: Mudhhib (gilder), Merra, al-Ahmar (the red), Borqan (the gleaming), Semhuresh, al-Abyad (the white) and Mimun (lucky). **Mimun** was popularly known as a jnun saint by the name of Sidi Mimun or Maimun. **Semhuresh** was much spoken of, often under the name Semharush. He had a son called Sultan al-Khal (the black sultan). When Semhuresh died, he also left behind a daughter, who was still alive and was said to assist human women in practising witchcraft.

Tab'a was a very dangerous female jinn who attacked both men and women, rendering them sterile, causing their children to die in infancy, making them wasteful or addicted to some vice, or killing their animals. Unlike 'Aisha Qandisha and the Ghola, the Tab'a could not be seen by humans. She was a secret cause of evil, and thus much more dangerous than the other two. Westermarck was told that the Tab'a can be killed by a charm written by a *fqi* (Islamic theologian), but that if the charm was not sufficiently powerful the Tab'a's children would avenge her death by killing the *fqi*. The Tab'a was sometimes called Umm s-Subyan (Mother of the Youngsters), especially in her capacity to cause the death of infants. Another name for the Tab'a was Qarinah, which as we have seen was also known in the Arab East and was, in fact, the notorious Lilith demon.

The Berber tribe Aït Temsaman gave the name **Tajnnisht** to a certain female jinn with an appealing face who spoke to men, calling them by name and proposing to marry them. If the man answered, 'I take refuge with God from Satan the stoned one, I am protected against you by God and the religious law,' then she vanished. If he said 'Yes,' he was done for – he might go with her or she might accompany him to his house, either then or later, and she would kill him. This jinn was apparently equivalent to 'Aisha Qandisha.

Moroccans maintained, according to Westermarck, that the most famous of all jnun was **Shaitan** (**Shitan**) or **Iblis**, that is, Satan or the devil. Shaitan was regarded as the chief of the evil jnun (*shayatin*). Shaitan could be found everywhere, except in mosques. He could assume all sorts of shapes and was sometimes called 'Abribash' (varicoloured). He had only a few definite bodily characteristics: He had seven hairs on his chin and was blind in his right eye. His eye was put out by the prophet Idris (or Enoch), who was a tailor. Shaitan once came to him with an egg in his hand and told him that God had shaped the world like an egg. Idris was enraged by this blasphemous talk and answered, 'No, God made the world like the eye of this needle, look here.' When Shaitan looked at the needle the prophet thrust it into his eye.

An old scribe told Westermarck that Shaitan had a penis on the inner side of his right thigh and a vulva on the inner side of his left, and that to produce offspring he needed only to close his thighs, and this he did all day long, which explained why there were so many *shayatin* in the world. Other scribes told Westermarck that Shaitan has a wife named Shaitana.

* * *

In Morocco, jinn have traditionally played a major role in the activities of magicians and Sufi holy men, particularly when those activities take on a supernatural quality. British traveller/writer Rosita Forbes asserted she was a witness to such bizarre happenings. Forbes attracted considerable public attention in the 1920s with her journeys to remote, untamed climes. She travelled often to the Islamic world, and her writings are filled with references to jinn legends and magic. In Morocco, she witnessed a strange occurrence that could be variously described as jinn-inspired teleportation, an out-of-body experience or a case of hypnotism.[57]

> The Sufis of the Islamic world, and the yogis of the Hindu, believe that they can, at will, project their minds to any portion of the world they wish to visit, while their bodies remain, sometimes in a trance, sometimes following their normal avocations at home. This is the explanation of the spiritual pilgrimage to Mecca, made yearly by those sages whose bodies apparently have never left their homes. I can find no theory to account for the fact that certain great teachers in the African zawias can tell in complete detail every incident of a pilgrimage, before anyone has yet returned from Mecca, and before they could have communicated with anyone on it.

This 'spiritual travel' was accomplished with the help of jnun.

Forbes said this power was the result of an asceticism unknown in the West, even among Trappist monks. Over the previous eight years she had seen variations of the same phenomenon so often in Africa and Arabia that she was convinced it was a genuine separation of mind and body.

A learned man (*alim*) of Telehdi in Morocco once explained it to Forbes:

> You see what you expect, no more, no less. Sometimes we see nothing at all, because the shell which clothes the wisdom we have summoned is unimportant to us. To you it is essential, so, when you are in touch with a mind from far away, you clothe it in the fashion to which you are accustomed. So do our own disciples, and often each one of them sees the visitant in different garb, but, to us who have achieved

> some small knowledge, the contact is of the mind only, and our senses, which are the servants of the mind, do not operate at all.

This practice is called ''*Ilm al-Ism*' (the Study of the Name) and is based on the principles, or magic virtues, contained in the names of God and in certain other names recorded in history, such as those of Solomon and the Seven Sleepers, who were Christian martyrs and yet form part of the hierarchy of Arab magianism. It is a science that has been studied through the ages, and, with the Muslim conquest of Spain, it became a major branch of learning at the celebrated universities of Cordoba and Seville. When Granada, the last Moorish kingdom in Spain, fell to the Christians in 1492, it was presumed that many books from the great Arab libraries were taken by the fugitives to Morocco and, according to accounts related by Forbes, were preserved at the *zawiya* (Islamic school) of Telehdi in the Ahmas Mountains.

Forbes found that the study of ''*Ilm al-Ism*' was widespread among Moroccan *ulema* (learned men). Mulai Sadeq er Raisuli, who was one these Islamic scholars, 'showed me many interesting works on the subject when I was in Tazrut as a guest in the camp of his famous cousin, the brigand and patriot Raisuli'.

According to tradition, the Prophet said, 'God has 99 names – 100 minus 1: those who know them will enter into paradise.' It is believed that by using 'the great name', the hundredth, all prayers will be granted. Mulai Sadeq told Forbes that, by using these names, he could 'raise jinns'. It had taken him seventeen years to develop this skill, which he called just the first step to that 'annihilation of distance' which allows master sages to intercommunicate without personal contact. The old man related his own story of an unsuccessful attempt in this regard.

'I had been warned,' he said,

> that the jinn should appear in human form, with jellaba and turban, and, seating himself beside me, should talk to me in an ordinary voice and answer such questions as I put to him. But if he came in any other form, it was bad, and I must have no dealings with him. I made all the necessary exhortations and, at the end, I saw a shape in front of me. It had two legs like a dog, with human feet, and its body was also a dog's, but its neck was so long that it reached to the ceiling. I was in my house at Tetuan, and it seemed that the roof had become a funnel, so that the head of the beast was in the sky.

Mulai Sadeq spoke as if relating a totally normal experience. When Forbes pressed him on what he had done to deal with the unexpected appearance of the jinn, he replied impatiently, 'Well, of course, I knew I had made a mistake, so I began praying as hard as I could and, at each repetition of the name of Allah, the beast grew smaller and smaller, till finally it vanished altogether.'

Forbes eventually saw this rite performed by an expert:

> We were sitting one afternoon in a mud-walled court in front of a qubba – the tomb of a holy man. The sun was just beginning to slant down towards the ranges, which looked like crumpled cloak below us ... .
>
> I had been in Yemen, in Western Arabia, and it happened that Telehdi was in contact with an Idrissi college there – the founder of this sect was educated at the Kairouin University in Fez – so my friendly *alim*, generically named Sherif Mohammed, agreed to summon one of his Western Arabian compeers.

There was no shadow round Forbes and the *alim*. They were in a bare, empty yard in August sunshine. The *alim* drew a pentagram in the dust, marked some hieroglyphics in it and appeared to withdraw into meditation. Forbes related:

> He took no notice of me as I huddled so close that I could touch his robes. All at once there was a man sitting within the diagram. To say he 'appeared suddenly' would not express the effect, for it seemed as if he had always been there though I had only just noticed him. There was nothing startling or frightening. He was rather pale and rather hot. I could see the sweat on his forehead, under the veil worn by Yemen sherifs.

The visitor took off his sandals, which had large woven and dyed grass straps familiar to Arabians, but unknown to Moroccans. His costume consisted of Yemeni striped cloth, and his face was the hairless, hollow-cheeked type of the original Arab stock.

> For some time, Sherif Mohammed and his visitor talked in normal voices, but, while I could understand the former, the new-comer's words were incomprehensible to me. In fact, I cannot really be certain that I heard him talk. I received a normal impression of conversation, of the visitor's fidgeting in the sunshine, of his emitting

> those long-drawn grunts, which are the Yemenese version of a sigh, and then I saw him wriggling his big toes back into his sandals. I noticed they were splayed and marked by the broad bands. After that he was gone, but again I had no impression of disappearance. It was just as if a visitor had left. Sherif Mohammed said the 'Fatha' ... and that was the end of the matter.

Forbes said she had seen variations of the same performance in a Senussi college in Cyrenaica, in an Idrissi college in Asir, in a house in Fez, and in Cairo, when three sheikhs of Azhar University were discussing the powers of an Egyptian sufi, Sidi Abd er Rahman es Siuti.

Forbes conceded she could have been hypnotised. 'It would have been child's play for any of these occultists to make me see anything they chose,' she said, 'but it would be an unprecedented insult to the name of Allah they invoked, and as illogical as if the Archbishop of Canterbury should try to mystify a confirmation candidate with the three-card trick, or a crusading Pope, the keys of heaven in his hands, attempt to delude the mediaeval faithful by producing rabbits out of his triple crown.'

* * *

Morocco is a colourful land of great contrasts. It is a crossroads of cultures, with its own ancient, indigenous people – the Berbers – and an important history linking Europe, North Africa and the Arab East. We should not forget the connections it has with the forbidding Sahara and the African lands that lie beyond. It is fitting that Morocco's jinn heritage should prove to be rich, complex and filled with a panoply of marvels.

Tunisia: Air, Sea and Land

Tunisia too enjoys a rich jinn tradition but differs from that of most other Muslim countries in its inclusion of the 'jinn of the sea'. Since Tunisia was the home of the seafaring Carthaginians and some of the Barbary pirates and has an important fishing industry, this is not at all surprising. The Muslim traditions of the Arabian Peninsula know nothing of marine jinn. The Tunisian lore in this area is clearly unique to the area's history and is of great antiquity.

French folklorist Marie-Louise Dubouloz-Laffin gathered considerable information about Tunisia's jinn (called *jnoun*) while teaching as a professor at the College of Sfax from 1929 to 1934.[58] Her research was focused on the Sfax area but included informants from many parts of the country. She learned that in Tunisia the fire spirits were called by various periphrases and euphemisms to avoid pronouncing their true name, which was *jenn* (also pronounced *jinn* or *djinn*) in the singular, *jnoun* or *djnoun* in the plural. The feminine form of the name was *jennia*, plural *jenniate*. The variants of their name were not as numerous as in Morocco and were notably different.

There were three main categories: jnoun of the air, jnoun of the sea and jnoun of the land.

The jnoun of the air: These beings were called *leriah* (of *riha*, wind, air). A man possessed was described as *meriouha*. The *djenniates* of the air were called *merihaha* or, better, *rihania*. In addition to these general names, each tribe of jnoun had a specific name, for example, the *Chiaten* (sing. *Chitane*). Chitane is the same as the English word 'Satan'. These jnoun were extremely wicked. They took pleasure in harassing humans, particularly on the Chiaten's weekly day of rest – each tribe of jnoun had its own day of rest, kept secret from mankind.

Another variety of genies of the air was called *afarta*, plural form of the word *afrit*. Dubouloz-Laffin pointed out that the word 'afrit' in Tunisia occasionally meant a bird of the raptor variety that resembled an eagle. But more commonly it meant 'a fantastic being which has the form of a winged serpent, some say long-haired, which moves through the air like a blast of wind and which like a bird of prey devours chickens, lambs and little children'.[59] Such a description is often found in Tunisian nursery tales. One such story, recorded by Dubouloz-Laffin, told of a captured 'girl of the air' – a jinn – who managed to escape by donning a snakeskin which her husband had stolen and hidden for her. Dubouloz-Laffin also reported seeing winged serpents portrayed in various places in Tunisia, including old paintings and murals on café walls.

The afarta were described as messengers of the sultan of the jnoun of the land. In this capacity they travelled rapidly and over great distances. Dubouloz-Laffin noted that when a man was considered brave, resourceful and enterprising, he was called an afrit (just as in Morocco). These spirits were known to be extremely powerful. They assisted people who possessed the seal of Solomon, called *el-Khatem.* The afarta were ruled by Eblis, their chief (Tunisian Jews called him Blish), and were deemed responsible for a great number of cases of demonic possession and illness. They were the most powerful not only among the jnoun of the air but also among those of the sea.

The jnoun of the sea: These were called *jnoun-el-bahar* or *baharia* and were said to inhabit all the world's oceans; the most powerful ones were found in the deepest waters, in a region known as 'the seventh depth'. Strongly hierarchical, the inhabitants of each level of the sea did not encroach on the prerogatives of the others. They lived in marvellous palaces, built of priceless materials, diamonds and other precious stones, in the midst of gardens where submarine plants and flowers proliferated; they frolicked amidst the seaweed and marine life.

These jnoun were allies of the *solthane-el-haout,* the mighty lord of the fishes and marine animals, who headed a rigid feudal organisation. The most powerful jnoun inhabited the city of their own sultan, Sidi Moussa, who ruled all jnoun of the sea but was subject to the *solthane-el haout*. The latter was both sovereign and protector of the *jnoun-el bahar*, and the relationship was said to be a harmonious one.

The jnoun of the sea resembled mermaids and mermen; they had the head and chest of a human but the body of a fish. Said Dubouloz-Laffin:

> The djinniate are very beautiful; they have white skin and long black hair; when they grow bored of palace life, they swim up to the surface. They love men very much and stretch their arms towards them with a plaintive appeal. The mariners who observe them think they see women in distress, so they jump into the water, the djinniate embrace them to take them away to their homes and fulfil their needs. The men refuse, and the djinniate are infinitely sad. This is the theme that attracted [Hans Christian] Andersen. In transcribing this text under the gaze of the story-teller, we made the mistake, once or twice, of writing 'siren'. She corrected us briskly. 'No, they don't know that name here; they only know jnoun of the sea.' She was referring to a particular group: the Ouata, the fishermen.[60]

The similarities between these jnoun and the mer-people of European folklore are strong, thanks to cross-cultural influence. Tunisia was home to the ancient maritime traders of Carthage, ethnic

Phoenicians originally from the Levant who colonised sites far afield in West Africa, the Iberian Peninsula and perhaps beyond. Ancient Phoenicians fostered a belief in mermaids and mermen, whose earliest known traces appear in the lore of neighbouring Assyria, in about 1000 BC. The Phoenicians, during their expansion westward from today's Lebanon, probably spread the legends of the mer-people to the ancient Greeks, another Mediterranean Sea power, and from them the tales travelled to the rest of Europe. Thus the Little Mermaid of Copenhagen probably owes her origin to a tradition of maritime lore carried to European coastlines by traders from eastern Mediterranean. But whatever their origin, Tunisia's jnoun of the sea are now part of a broader folkloric framework that includes beings of both land and air.

The furies of the *jnoun-el-bahar* were responsible for tempests, strong tidal currents and shipwrecks. During the grand annual Jewish pilgrimage, the Ghriba festival, to a celebrated synagogue on the Tunisian island of Djerba,[61] pilgrims took along 'Passover biscuits' on their sea voyages; these were not unleavened bread but rather a kind of cake. If the waves were rough, they tossed a piece into the sea. They believed there could be some of the Jewish faith among the jnoun of the sea and that, recognising the cake, they would protect their co-religionists, as they were obliged to do. This method of appeasing the waves was valid under all circumstances; Muslims or Christians could use this remedy, because the jnoun would not know who threw the biscuit.

The favourite colours of the jnoun of the sea, for reasons lost to us today, were white, red and green. White and red are national colours of Tunisia; the green could be that of the Mediterranean. Dubouloz-Laffin wrote of parents seeking to protect their little children from the jnoun's escapades by dressing them in red and green shoes that could at that time be found in a number of market stalls in Sfax.

The jnoun of the sea were a phenomenon totally alien to the Qur'anic traditions on the jinn, which were based largely on the desert environment in which the faith grew, and as such were dismissed by some orthodox Muslims in Tunisia. One reportedly told Dubouloz-Laffin that the jnoun would not live in the sea because they are beings of fire and that they only inhabit islands. Yet Dubouloz-Laffin notes: 'The fishermen sometimes see a man coming to help them moor their boat; after a moment, he vanishes; they understand then that they have had an encounter with a jinn.'

Also connected with the jnoun of the sea is a totemic belief that a certain tribe of Tunisian fishermen are descended from a great fish and form a secret brotherhood called the Ouled-el-Haout, the sons of the fish. Dobouloz-Laffin tried to get confirmation of this fact from a teacher in the Zarzis region, but his response was: 'People no longer believe in such things. The Qur'an forbids it.' His response was defensive and did not really address her question, since the Qur'an does not explicitly mention animal totemic beliefs or secret brotherhoods. However, the Qur'an does indeed forbid worship of false gods; so the question would be whether worship was involved in the case of this Tunisian brotherhood. Whatever the case, Dubouloz-Laffin believed she had found in this secret society a case of totemism on the brink of extinction which was nevertheless preserved because of the secrecy surrounding it.

The jnoun of the land: Said Dubouloz-Laffin:

> The Terrestrial Jnoun (*jnoun-el-outa*) are called *siadna* (our lords), *melkine-el-ardh* (the masters of the ground) and *Ouled-tahat-el-qaa* (the people beneath the earth). A Jew told me that he called them *raiet rabbi* (the subjects of God) and also *rjal Allah* (the men of God). There are Muslims, Jews and Christians among them. This is why several of our Jewish (female) informants called the first group *Meselmine* and *Mimoun* (the Muslims) and the second group *Chiddim* [or *sheddim*], which means precisely jnoun in Hebrew. Those that are black are called the *Damda Tombakha*.

The jnoun of the land were known the best, since they lived with people.

As the Tunisians saw it, each human had two jnoun familiars, a good one and a bad one. A person's bad jnoun familiar was always of a religion 'opposite' to that of the man or woman in question; if he or she was Muslim, the jinn was Jewish, and vice-versa; but the good jnoun familiar was always of the same race and same faith as the individual.

For most of these personal jnoun who inhabited not the bodies of humans but their residences, there were tribes of jnoun of the home. Their habitat was underground and was said to reproduce exactly a traditional Tunisian home, but upside-down and much more beautiful. Jnoun homes were illuminated by a kind of supernatural light and had gardens and trees of coloured stone bearing fruits of diamond, sapphire, emerald and ruby. Other than that, they lived in a manner quite similar to that of human beings. When people moved into a new home, they traditionally placed dried fruits, fava beans, sweets or henna in the corners of the rooms as gifts for the jnoun. These items were set out at night and were recovered in the morning. The jnoun were nourished by the duplicate essence or subtle essence of these foods.

The colour of the terrestrial jnoun varied, and from their colour they received a particular name. Those who were red or who preferred red were called the Ouled-el-Ahmar, 'the sons of the red'. Those who were green or who preferred green were called the Ouled-el-Akhdar; those who favoured black were called the Ousfane (pl. of *oucif*, meaning black man). In the opinion of the sorcerers, the black jnoun were the most dangerous.

The jnoun generally looked like human beings, but with monstrous features. 'They can change shape and appear in the form of a dog, a donkey, a horse, a camel, a serpent, a white or black chicken, a large black fish, but above all a cat,' said Dobouloz-Laffin. 'A cat spotted at night is suspect, particularly if it is black: this is very probably a jinn or perhaps conceals a jinn. Even if it is a cat that people recognise, it may very well, at that moment, embody a malevolent being.'[62]

For this reason people should avoid mistreating cats. If you were compelled to chase one into the darkness, you said, '*Hashakum*' (May He [Allah] save you), an expression that protected you. If someone killed a cat, he suffered seven years of bad luck, a superstition that many in the West also hold.

According to Dubouloz-Laffin,

> a man very recently saw a jinn that took the form of a white horse; he realised that it was a spirit because the beast was alone, at night, near the cemetery. When a jinn takes the form of an animal, it generally chooses something frightening or monstrous; thus, a horse can have the head of a man or of a hideous beast. They do not obey the law of gravity; a horse can float in the air or even emit an extraordinary light.[63]

When they come up to the earth's surface, the jnoun make themselves invisible by putting on *chechias* (Tunisian red caps). But they are not invisible to everyone and become invisible only when they want to be. When they have not put on their chechias, they can be seen, particularly before the *asr* (afternoon prayer), in the shadows of houses, for this is the time when they wake up and come to do their business on the surface.

The belief is widespread in Tunisia that when you open your eyes at midnight, in a dark room, you will see jnoun or at least hear them. They are said to speak, predict events, reveal secrets that torment you and tantalise you with clues about hidden treasures. You hear them when you are awake, but also when you are dreaming. Possessed persons, called *mamloukine* in Tunisia, see them most clearly, then children, women and, lastly, men.

* * *

In nineteenth-century Tunisia, one branch of Islamic medicine – the prophetic (more spiritually based than the other major branch, the more naturally based Galenic-Islamic) – attributed disease in part to the actions of evil jnoun. If one stepped on a jinn and failed to mitigate his action, a mild illness or injury could result. A serious offence to the jnoun could result in mental illness, epilepsy, depression or madness for the human involved. Epidemic diseases could be caused by armies of swarming jnoun taking revenge for some grave offence by whole cities or societies.[64]

To counter these actions, one could employ certain substances, amulets and the intervention of holy persons (such as marabouts) possessing *baraka*. Substances capable of countering the effects of evil jnoun included sunlight, salt, silver, gunpowder, henna, kohl and strong fumes from tar or aromatic herbs. One individual method of protecting against an epidemic was the use of an amulet (*hajib*) prepared by a marabout and purchased for a small donation or gift. This amulet, as in other Islamic countries, could contain a piece of paper with sacred words or numbers written on it. It was attached to the clothing or hung around the neck. Sometimes a piece of paper with sacred text written on it was soaked in water and the dissolved ink was drunk. Tunisians also dealt with major cases of jnoun possession in the same manner as Moroccans, with exorcism and group rituals.[65]

Thus we see many familiar jinn traditions in Tunisian society, but also some unusual ones, such as the jnoun of the sea. Tunisia is closer geographically than Morocco to the Arabian heartland, but it was also the site of a powerful ancient civilisation, Carthage, whose sea-faring colonists brought from the Levant a wealth of their own traditions. The Tunisians selected the best of both worlds.

Turkey: Out of the Forest

Many think of the jinn as a 'Semitic' phenomenon, experienced and believed by peoples such as the Arabs and Hebrews. But the non-Semitic Turks too have their jinn legends.[66] Admittedly a significant portion of this lore derives from Islamic tradition, but some beliefs are much more ancient.

The Turks began migrating into Asia Minor from Central Asia in the ninth century. They embraced Islam and its civilisation and founded the Seljuk state in the mid-eleventh century, followed by the Ottoman empire at the end of the thirteenth. Before the Turks, the land was a patchwork quilt of ethnicities, with Greek cities (and ancient Troy) along the coasts and a dazzling array of peoples throughout and around Anatolia, such as the Hittite empire and its successor Phrygia, as well as Cappadocia, Paphlagonia, Galatia, Lydia and other kingdoms. Aesop the storyteller, incidentally, came from Phrygia, whose capital Gordium stood near modern Ankara, today the capital of Turkey. The people of Anatolia (Turkey's heartland) have long been famous for their narrative arts, a favoured medium for the propagation of jinn lore.[67]

The phenomenon of the jinn of Turkey is perhaps best described as a cake of many layers, assembled and baked over a long and fascinating history. The lowest level of the cake is Hittite and Babylonian, with their distinct and powerful demons; the next layer is Graeco-Roman, with *daimons*, nature spirits and guardians; next comes the Islamic layer, with its rich Arabian flavours and a taste of Sufi mysticism; then comes the Turkish top layer, adding the rich nomadic folklore of the Central Asian steppes. And yet, even with all these layers, there is still more to this particular confection.

Talat Sait Halman, the Turkish poet, translator and cultural historian, in assessing the rich, imaginative culture of Anatolia, says:

> Several millennia ... have bequeathed to Asia Minor a dazzling treasury – creation myths, Babylonian stories, the Epic of Gilgamesh, Hittite tales, Biblical lore, Greek and Roman myths, Armenian and Byzantine anecdotes. The peninsula's mythical and historical ages nurtured dramatic accounts of deities, kings, heroes, and lovers. Pagan cults, ancient faiths, the Greek pantheon, Judaism, Roman religion, Christianity, Islam, mystical sects, and diverse spiritual movements left behind an inexhaustible body of legends and moralistic stories.[68]

When the Turks arrived, they brought their own oral folkloric tradition, as well as legends and tales from India and China.

In pre-Islamic society in the land we now call Turkey – during the Graeco-Roman and Byzantine periods – the jinn were the satyrs and nymphs of the forests and mountains, just as they were the spirits of the desert for the Arabs. Some anthropologists and folklore specialists say that in both cases the jinn symbolise those remote parts of nature still uninhabited and potentially hostile to man.

The migration of the Turks into Asia Minor brought nomadic and semi-nomadic families, clans and tribes out of that very wilderness and into settled society. The Turks brought with them great defences against jinn that must have given some comfort to the indigenous Anatolians and other peoples of Asia Minor. For one thing, the traditional national and cultural symbol of the Turks was the wolf, the mortal enemy of jinn. Other important Turkish cultural symbols were the colour blue, iron and fire. The blue mineral turquoise (which means 'Turkish' in French) was used in Turkish jewellery and was a protection against the jinn-inspired evil eye. Iron was, of course, anathema to jinn. Fire (at least of the smokeless variety) was part of the very nature of jinn, but blazing camp fires and torches kept all manner of evil night creatures at bay, including jinn.

Turkey's jinn, like Arab jinn, have for many centuries appeared to humans in the shape of serpents, dogs, cats, or other human beings. Jinn in the shape of humans can be of a normal size or of giant proportions. As with most jinn beliefs across the world, good jinn appear strikingly handsome or beautiful; evil jinn are hideously ugly.

Jinn are found everywhere in present-day Turkey, especially in rural areas, where locals warn visitors about jinn-related threats against those who venture into the countryside. For example, when a person pours water on the ground or draws it from a well, especially at night, the recommended practice is to recite a *bismallah* before performing the function, as is done in most Islamic countries. This applies even when urinating in an outdoor latrine. Near small cave openings or dry wells, people are strongly advised not to use any offensive language. Anyone who ignores the existence of the jinn risks offending them and could end up being 'struck' (*carpilmak)* with a dislocated limb or joint. If one is 'struck' in this way, then an elder with knowledge of the appropriate Qur'anic prayers must be brought in to correct the dislocation.[69]

Individual jinn often choose as their abodes such places as public baths (this is why women using Turkish baths traditionally wear high wooden clogs to prevent molestation by jinn), wells, latrines (hence the warnings), ovens, ruined houses, marketplaces, the intersection of roads (demons at road junctions are a very common belief, extending as far as Europe and the Far East), the sea and rivers.

According to Turkish belief, the jinn formerly were free to enter any of the seven heavens until the birth of Jesus, when they were excluded from three of them, setting the stage for a later total exclusion. The reasons for the ban were Allah's alone; but the result was to limit the jinn's 'inside information' from heaven and thus put them on a more equal footing with mankind. On the birth of the Prophet Muhammad, the jinn were barred from the remaining four heavens. But some Turks believe they continue to ascend to the outer limits of the lowest heaven, and there they listen to the angels speak about God's decrees, as well as about the future, which they sometimes reveal to selected humans – magicians, diviners and soothsayers – who through séances, talismans and secret invocations summon the jinn to learn their secret knowledge. This story is also common in other lands, including the Arabian heartland and Morocco.

The only time humans can see the jinn is when they take on forms known to man. A jinn takes a great risk when assuming physical form (animal, human or other) because it then becomes governed by the natural laws that apply to that form; for example, a jinn shaped like a man or animal can be shot and killed, and a jinn in the form of a fish would suffocate if removed from water. Thus when a jinn assumes a new form he does so only for a very short time, for he knows that if he is recognised as one of the jinn he can be killed like any other creature of the earth. When a jinn is fatally wounded, the smokeless fire that circulates in its body in the place of blood issues from his veins and consumes him totally, leaving nothing but ashes.

As we have noted, the jinn of Turkey, like their Arabian counterparts, fear iron and steel, so some Turks wear steel rings or place steel daggers or knives wherever protection from the jinn is required. For the religiously inclined, protection from the jinn can be provided by Qur'anic or other sacred verses, the 99 names of Allah, magic squares (*muska*) or a set of magical symbols called 'the seven seals'.

* * *

Belief in jinn is not exclusively an Islamic phenomenon in Turkey. In ancient times, many of the western coastal cities of Asia Minor were Greek. Those areas are now Turkish, but the Greek connections remain, and ancient jinn tradition lives on.

An example of Greeks and Turks cooperating in response to jinn activity was reported in the Turkish press in early 2009. Visitors from the Greek mainland came to the Turkish Aegean coastal village of Yagcilar and gathered together with locals at the former home of a deceased Greek Orthodox priest, in a joint effort to recover a great treasure said to lie buried on the property. The treasure, some 400 kilograms of gold and money, was reportedly buried in the garden. It had been entrusted to the priest for safekeeping in 1923 by members of the local Greek Orthodox community, who were being relocated to Greece as part of a population exchange.[70] The priest had mentioned the treasure in his diary, which was found by his descendants.

The priest's great-grandchildren came from Greece and launched a treasure hunt in the garden, aided by Turkish authorities and local villagers. Three days of digging turned up nothing, and it was suspected that the priest had placed a protective spell on the treasure. A well-known local Muslim *hoca* (religious leader) was called in to assist. Eyyub Hoca directed another round of digging, but the treasure was still not found. The *hoca* then announced that jinn had changed the hiding place of the treasure every 41 years since the date of its burial. This was accepted by both Greeks and Turks as a reasonable explanation. The search reportedly continues.[71]

It is sometimes difficult to assign a single origin to a jinn tradition when the cultural setting is so intricate. We see this often in Anatolia. But the people of Turkey have no problem with such complexity, given their long experience with multiculturalism.

Iran: 'The Holy Jinn'

Iran, as a non-Arab but Muslim country, has a rich jinn tradition. Some aspects of Iranian jinn lore derive from Islam, but other elements are older and originate in early Persian belief.[72]

There are some differing thoughts surrounding jinn belief in Iran, whose fire spirits are variously referred to as *divs* (or *devs*), *ifrits*, *ghouls* and *pari's* (or *peris*). Some Iranians contend that each of these classes constitutes a separate race of jinn, but others say they are different tribes but a single race. Still others say that the jinn are all of one tribe, but that they are able to assume diverse forms and shapes and to live in any place under any conditions.

Mulla Muhammad Rida al-Imami, an encyclopedist from nineteenth-century Qajar Persia, asserts (like the earlier Persian authority Zakariya al-Qazwini) that the tribes of jinn are descendants of the children of Jann ibn Jann, last ruler of the pre-Adamite jinn.[73] They are creatures made of fire, able to take on the features of any living being they desire, except for those of a prophet or imam. The Sufi poet Jalal al-Din Rumi said that they were 'of fire yet not fire, of vapour yet not vapour'.[74] The tribes that cause no trouble are the pari's, and the evil ones are the divs. Some are isolated behind the mountains of Qaf and do not associate with mankind. But one group of them lives in front of the Qaf Mountains, among humans on the banks of rivers, in gardens or deserts, and particularly in ruins and dark places such as caves or old public baths. All the divs are believed to be subject to the rule of Satan, who lives on a green island near the Qaf Mountains.

The more friendly pari's are ruled by a king named Malik Afshan, whose throne is in the Qaf Mountains. To the east of Afshan's kingdom is the pari colony of the ruler Masitash, who has 300,000 slaves, each of whom is the king of other jinn. To the west side of Qaf are the possessions of pari king Abdu'r-Rahman, the son-in-law of another such monarch, Abdu'l-Kadir. The Prophet is said to have given these two pari's particular names when they became Muslims; 3,000 pari kings are subject to Abdu'r-Rahman, each of whom has an army that cannot be numbered. Yet another tribe of pari's – ruled by King Talu Khush, who is called *salim al-nafs* (of good spirit) – is said to love mankind. There are Christian jinn as well, ruled by Masidus, which means worshipper of the spirit. The Jewish jinn are under a king named Tututash, or sorcerer. There are kings of jinn who look like men; there are women as well, and their daughters are the mothers of jinn, and they live in a mysterious place called Zulmatat, near the legendary water of life.[75]

In ancient, pre-Islamic Persia, jinn beliefs crystallised from the primordial opposition of light and darkness, which formed the basis of the earliest Persian religions. 'Light was happiness,' as Thomas Keightley described it,

> and the people of Iran, the land of light, were the favourites of Heaven; while those of Turan, the gloomy region beyond the mountains to the north, were its enemies. In the realms of supernal light sits enthroned Ormuzd, the first-born of beings; around him are the six Amshaspands, the twenty-eight Izeds, and the countless myriads of Ferohers [guardian angels and unembodied souls of intelligent beings]. In the opposite kingdom of darkness Aherman is supreme, and his throne is encompassed by the six Arch-Deevs, and the numerous hosts of inferior Deevs. Between these rival powers ceaseless warfare prevails.[76]

From this conflict, the pari's emerged as the jinn of light and the divs as the jinn of darkness.

The Persians had the same conception of the pre-Adamite jinn as the Arabs did. For 36,000 years these jinn obeyed God, while air was the ascendant element in the world, but when fire prevailed they disobeyed. When the jinn eventually heard the Qur'an, some of them became believers. 'Amongst us are some that submit their wills (to Allah), and some that swerve from justice' (Quran 72:14). Some Iranian Islamic scholars claim that the only real difference among jinn is the religious difference.

Since Iran is largely Shi'ite, the Shi'ite jinn are called the 'holy jinn'. Every human being is believed to have a twin among the jinn, a *hamzad*, born at the same time. This belief is reflected in al-Ghazali's[77] commentary on the Qur'anic sura 'Yusuf' ('Joseph', the biblical prophet, son of the patriarch Jacob or Ya'qub) in which merchants encountered a gazelle that was Joseph's *hamzad*. The gazelle was, therefore, required to travel where he did, fall ill if he were sick, say what he would say, sleep whenever he would sleep, and ultimately die when he would die.

The *hamzad* may be either a Muslim or an unbeliever. If it is a Muslim, the individual will be fortunate in life, but if it is an infidel he will almost certainly suffer illness or some other misfortune brought about by this inseparable companion. Any person with a frail physique or feeble constitution is believed to have an infidel *hamzad*. There is no way to escape from this unhappy situation. The only hope for relief is to try to bring about a harmonious 'working relationship'. The usual procedure for dealing with an infidel *hamzad* is to consult a prayer-writer, who will listen to the patient's concerns and prescribe a treatment. For a price he writes three prayers: one of the prayers is sewn up in green cloth and wrapped around the right arm, the second is buried (preferably in a graveyard) and the third is burnt on a Saturday night. After this ritual, the *hamzad* will usually behave.

Beside the very great number of *hamzads*, there are multitudes of other, non-*hamzad* jinn in Iran and they are found everywhere. An Iranian sheikh who was a guide and informant to folklorist Bess Donaldson in the 1930s remarked one day that there were probably three or four jinn in the room where they were working. Humans constantly risk stepping on them, or pouring hot water on them, or burning them with live coals from the heating brazier or from the water-pipe many Iranians smoke. So, most people are in the habit of saying *bismillah* on such occasions, to give the jinn a chance to escape.

Fear of revenge by the jinn makes many people careful. Although the *hamzad* never gets in the way, other jinn are always underfoot. When a child suddenly begins crying or acts frightened without reason, many Iranians conclude that he must have hurt a jinn baby and that its mother is retaliating. If the child's mother is present, she must express some of her breast milk on the spot where the child was sitting. This generosity will please the jinn parent and she will stop punishing the human child. If the human mother is absent, a nail is sometimes driven into the ground or the floor, and when the jinn baby plays with this the trouble will end.

Jinn children enjoy playing with human children, and this naturally increases the possibility of harm to humans. They also like to play with animals; the Prophet recommended that people keep pigeons or roosters in the house, so that jinn children could play with them. If anyone has a fit or seizure, it is often said to be due to the malice of an infidel jinn. The fit may be revenge for the severe injury or scalding of a jinn child.

In addition to abodes mentioned earlier, Iranian jinn dwell also near waterfalls and springs, in fields, in trees and underground. They love tombs, wells and kitchens. The good jinn (pari's) may even inhabit religious shrines, but evil jinn steer clear of all holy places, holy persons, the Qur'an, and the name of God. There are no evil jinn in the holy city of Mashhad, people say, because it is the home of the tomb of Ali ibn Musa al-Rida (765–817), the eighth imam of Shi'ite Islam; God has commanded all divs, all satans and all evil jinn to approach no closer than four farsakhs (about 15 miles) from the city. But just outside this limit evil jinn are said to flock in great numbers.

Although most of the evil that jinn do is attributed to revenge, some believe that jinn sometimes perform weird antics merely to frighten people, especially the sick. They harass frail people particularly, both in their dreams and their waking hours. A woman with puerperal (childbed fever) should never be left alone, for 'it would be the special delight of the jinn to terrify her with their jokes'.[78] Some claim the jinn even enter dead bodies, where they caper about, making the corpse move and twitch, to frighten anyone who might see it. The great medieval Persian physician Ibn Sina is said to have put medicine into corpses in order to keep the jinn at bay.

The voices of the jinn can be heard by children, religious devotees, the sick and women in confinement. Although the jinn know many human languages, Iranians believe they also have their own language. Some people claim they can talk to the spirit creatures, and one little girl who was nearly always singing told Donaldson that she sang to the jinn. In the case of a half-witted girl who talked to herself in a language no one could understand, her friends were convinced she knew jinn language and was conversing with them. This was another example of the linkage in some Islamic countries of mental incapacity with the jinn.

For all their mischief and troublemaking, jinn can sometimes show amazing compassion towards humans. According to an Islamic tradition not limited to Iran, the jinn wept when Amina, mother of the Prophet, died, and men, jinn and angels wept when the Prophet himself was about to die. After the death of the Prophet, people in Iran were able to hear the pari's weeping. On the field of battle at Karbala, where the Prophet's grandson Hussein died, a family of the Beni al-Ridain tribe heard wailing, but when they looked around they saw no one – it was the female jinn, weeping and sympathising with the women of the house of Bibi Hashim, the Prophet's kin. The jinn and the houris also assisted the Prophet's daughter Fatima and wept with her when her son Hussein was killed.

Some Iranian women claim that the jinn have certain times they like best. Tuesday and Saturday nights are spoken of as 'jinn nights' – it is believed that on these nights the jinn are most active and can be most easily summoned. The jinn are believed to migrate like birds to warmer places in the wintertime, and upon their return in the spring they are said to be lively and eager for activity.

As in the Arab countries, crazy or insane persons in Iran are frequently spoken of as *majnuni* (jinn-possessed), an expression used also to describe uncontrollable animals. Shi'ites say that Ali's twenty-fifth miracle was the quietening of a camel that had gone mad. He employed the following well-known prayer:

> God protect me for the sake of that Prophet who is kind, and for the sake of his household, those whom thou hast chosen from the whole world. O God, quieten this unmanageable thing, and remove far from me the results of his evil. Thou hast everything in thine own hand.

It is believed that some in Iran have the ability to see jinn. In fact, if the dried and powdered brain of a fly is mixed with the egg of an ant and rubbed upon the eyelids it will enable anyone to see the jinn. Donaldson reported that Iranian prayer-writers who were also 'jinn summoners' (*jinn gir*) were said to possess this power, and through crystal-gazing they claimed to make others see the jinn. The *jinn gir* were masters of deception, in Donaldson's view – just as Bayard Dodge believed that the oracles of Harran and ancient Greece were expert deceivers.

To gain control over the jinn, a person must perform certain rituals and undergo a long period of preparation, which involves travelling to a remote cave, an old ruin or a lonely tomb, where he draws a circle and sits within it. For 40 days he sits there, reading certain verses from the Qur'an assigned by the *jinn gir.* Day by day, he reduces his food intake until his meal consists of just one almond. If he is able to endure to the end, on the fortieth day all the great jinn will come with their king to eat bread and salt with him. Afterwards they will make a covenant that whenever he needs their help he can summon an army of jinn to his aid. It is related in the Hadith that Cain's wife was one of the jinn and Abel's wife was a houri, and occasionally, as in the Arab countries, one hears stories of marriages taking place between jinn and human beings in Iran. Donaldson claimed that she heard a story of a man in Nishapur in the 1930s who was reputed to have a jinn for a wife.

The most powerful charms or talismans against the evil jinn are naturally taken from the Qur'an, since such jinn cannot come near the holy book. The verses called the 'four declarations'[79] are most powerful against the jinn; but other verses are also effective, as, for example,

> There are indeed people among men who have sought for refuge unto people among jinn: but they only increased their folly.
>
> There is no God but He, the Living, the Merciful! In truth He hath sent down to thee the Book, which confirmeth those which precede it. For He had sent down the Law, and the Evangel aforetime, as man's Guidance; and now hath He sent down the Illumination [*furqan*].

The above verses are particularly powerful, for not only are they from the Qur'an but also contain a definite reference to the holy book itself.

Iranians say that anyone who reads the following verse can render the jinn powerless to harm him or her:

> Other religion than that of God have they? To Him doth everything that is in heaven and on earth submit, in willing or forced obedience, and to Him do they return.

Traditional Iranians sometimes wear a tiny edition of the entire Qur'an on their persons. Written prayers are inserted into small, oddly shaped silver boxes and these too are worn to keep away the jinn. An iron disc with odd markings scratched upon it is likely to be worn by a person subject to fits. A prayer written with the blood of a black or yellow hen (depending on which the divination indicates) is worn on a part of the body that is in pain, in order to drive away the jinn causing the malady.

Donaldson saw a six-day-old baby who had deep scratches on its abdomen which she said were made to release the jinn that were causing a fever. According to another Iranian tradition, a needle that has never touched an onion will keep all jinn away; some people carry such a needle with them. Any steel amulet is equally effective, for the jinn flee from steel.

* * *

The jinn of Iran not only posses unique names, such as pari and div, but also enjoy distinctive influences, from the ancient Persian religions and the Shi'ite interpretation of Islam. The jinn lore of Iran spread in all directions, consistent with the geopolitical fortunes of its dynasties and regimes, influencing many other civilisations, including those of Mesopotamia, Central Asia and the Indian subcontinent.

A final observation on Iran: No clear links have been established between Iran's ancient 'fire-worshipping' tradition and the existence of the fire spirits we call jinn. Fire worship was eventually replaced by Zoroastrianism, a monotheistic faith that uses fire (and water) for ritual purposes but does not worship it. We have seen how the unending opposition of the good pari's to the evil divs was a reflection of the fundamental conflict between light and darkness in pre-Zoroastrian Iranian religion, but there is no evidence that the nature of the jinn, as endorsed by Islam, has any connection with the fire-worshippers of ancient Iran.

Kurds: Children of the Jinn

Some 25 million Kurds live in the mountainous regions of northern Iraq, southeastern Turkey, western Iran and northeastern Syria. They constitute the world's largest stateless ethnic group. Most Kurds today call themselves Muslim, but their ancestral religion is called the Cult of Angels (or Yazdanism[80]), a variant of Persian Zoroastrianism. This faith and its cultural echoes are still strong, if less publicly acknowledged than in past centuries.

Many Kurds view themselves as descendants of the biblical Noah. Others believe their ancestors were the Medes, who helped the Babylonians overthrow the Assyrian empire in the seventh century BC. But another popular legend, told by Kurdish Jews and others in the region, is that the Kurds are 'children of the jinn'.[81] Although some in non-Kurdish communities use the legend to disparage the Kurds and perhaps to heighten their isolation, some modern Kurdish authors have themselves publicised it, as a way of showing pride in their uniqueness. According to this legend, King Solomon, who, as we have seen, controlled the jinn with a magic ring, ordered 500 of his subject jinn to travel abroad to seek out and bring to him 500 of the most beautiful virgins to be found anywhere for his personal harem. (Another version of the tale has 100 jinn seeking out 100 maidens.) The jinn could not return until they had all 500 virgins in their custody.

The jinn left Jerusalem and headed to Europe in search of the virgins. They were about to return home with the 500 maidens when they learnt that King Solomon had died. At that point, the jinn were unsure what to do. They considered returning the maidens to their homes in Europe, but in the end they decided to keep them for themselves and settle down with them in the rugged mountains of what is today's Kurdistan. As the story tells it, because the young women had 'found favor in the eyes of the jinn, the jinn took them unto themselves as their wives. And they begot many beautiful children, and those children bore more children ... And that is the way the nation of the Kurds came into being.'[82]

The offspring of these marriages resulted in the foundation of the Kurdish race, 'who in their elusiveness resemble their genie forefathers and in their handsomeness their foremothers'.[83]

The Kurds share many of the jinn beliefs of neighbouring peoples in their region – the Iranians, Iraqis, Syrians and Turks, among others. The concept of jinn offspring, so closely linked with Kurdish origins, surfaces even today in reported cases of possession by a jinn-like demon of Central Asia called the *āl*, found among not only the Kurds but also numerous other peoples, Muslim and Christian. This creature is remarkably similar to the Lilith/*lilitu* demon of ancient Middle Eastern lore and certainly predates Islam and Christianity. The *āl* is found in Iran, Armenia, Central Asia, Afghanistan, the Caucasus, southern Russia and Siberia.[84] In the Kurdish language, besides the word *āl*, there is the form *alk'*, borrowed from the Armenian.

This demon is usually female, although male counterparts are acknowledged in some Central Asian cultures. The *āl* targets pregnant women, new mothers and newborn infants. She seeks to block the normal birth process, by stealing the foetus from the mother's womb, destroying new embryos (causing miscarriage) or stealing the heart, liver or lung of a woman who has just given birth. The demon may also kill or steal a newborn child, make off with his or her internal organs or even replace a child, leaving a changeling in its stead. The replaced infant is normally quite weak. Its poor health is said to be the result of a mixed liaison – intercourse between the demon and a human (for the *āl* is a succubus as well).

After carrying out her misdeeds, the *āl* attempts a quick escape, heading for the nearest body of water. If she reaches it, the woman or child she has victimised cannot be saved. But according to tradition, if the demon is still washing the stolen organs and has not yet eaten them, the nearby river or some other body of water should be stirred with a stick or sword, to prevent the creature from crossing.

The *āl* is known to possess human women and drive them insane. This can happen when a lonely woman visits a public bath-house and strikes up a conversation with another lonely woman, who happens to be a demon in disguise. The *āl* then offers to wash the woman's back. Suddenly, the demon shows its true nature and the unfortunate woman falls unconscious. When she awakens, she has lost her mind. In some areas where Farsi, the Iranian language, is spoken, such women are called *jinn-zada* (offspring of the jinn). It is said that they can eventually recover, but much time and effort must be devoted to their treatment.

The Kurds are a people apart, struggling to maintain a measure of autonomy in remote mountain regions of a handful of countries, but they have absorbed much from the various cultures around them, and this legacy is reflected in their jinn lore.

South Asia: Coat of Many Colours

Belief in the jinn permeates the vast South Asian subcontinent. Underlying the phenomenon is a layer of Hindu tradition that is rich in lore of spirit beings. But Islam has brought to India, Pakistan and Bangladesh its own explanations, tales and legends of the jinn, flavoured with the beliefs and stories of Persia.

A wonderful example of this cross-cultural melange is the classic Indo-Persian epic *Dastan-e Amir Hamza* (The Adventures of Amir Hamza), or *Hamzanama*, created in illustrated manuscript form under the Mughal emperor Akbar in the sixteenth century. The *Dastan-e Amir Hamza* is a huge collection of storytellers' tales about the Prophet's uncle Hamza, originating in Persia about a thousand years ago and comparable in scope and artistry to *The Arabian Nights* or the Persian epic *Shahnameh*. The definitive Urdu version of this work, completed in the late nineteenth century by Ghalib Lakhnavi and Abdullah Bilgrami, follows Amir Hamza on an amazing series of escapades in Arabia, Persia and the Indian subcontinent, involving battles, royal court intrigues and encounters with courtesans, tricksters, jinn and other magical creatures.

Early in the epic, the infant prince Hamza is whisked away for a brief stay at Mount Qaf, as an honoured guest of the emperor of the jinn, Shahpal bin Shahrukh. The clairvoyant vizier Buzurjmehr describes to Hamza's father, Abdul Muttalib, what awaits the fortunate baby:[85]

> With his unbounded might, the Maker of the World has created a host of wonderful creatures, and has prescribed to each species a separate abode and a diverse way of life. The inhabited part of the earth is bounded on all sides by a great sea whose vast expanse is interspersed with populous islands and ports. Beside

> it lies Mount Qaf, the domain of the dormant folk and the children of Jan, surrounded by numerous colonies of the jinn, *peris, devs, ghols, Shutar-pas, Gao-sars. Gosh-fils, Nim-tans, tasma-pas,Ghur-munhas,* and others. The Emperor of those dominions is Shahpal bin Shahrukh, a most dignified and handsome monarch, beautiful as the sun and the moon.

With the spread of Islam into India – first by Arab traders in the seventh century, and later by Muslim armies in the thirteenth – the traditions and beliefs of Arabia and Persia interacted and intermingled with the indigenous concepts of the Hindus and others. Sufis were particularly successful in spreading Islam in South Asia, because their philosophical underpinnings and their day-to-day practices resonated with Hinduism and harmonised to a degree with existing beliefs and habits. Sufis thrive nowadays in India and Pakistan, where they often practise traditional spiritual medicine, dispensing charms, amulets and herbal remedies to those seeking relief. Others serve as *pirzadas* (attendants) at the tombs of local Sufi saints, usually the attendants' own honoured ancestors.

In these contexts and others, the Sufis frequently come into contact with jinn. British travel writer William Dalrymple, who lived for a year in Delhi, spent some time with the pirzadas at the tomb of a local saint, Nizam-ud-Din, and learned much about their relationships with the jinn.[86] A Bengali dervish, for example, explained to him that jinn, like the wind, are generally invisible to humans. Another dervish, a Gujarati from Ahmedabad, observed that jinn can be seen only by the great saints and high Brahmins. The Sufis believe that jinn can live anywhere, in a person's house or up in the air. The female jinn can assume the form of any living creature. The great jinn are believed to fly around the world on the wings of eagles.

One of the pirzadas said, 'The Caliph Haroun al-Rashid used to learn songs and airs from the poets among the djinns. They took an oath of fidelity to him and helped him to build his great palace on the banks of the Euphrates.'[87]

Dalrymple sat quietly as the Sufis discussed with each other whether jinn can be Muslims. An Afghani contended that this was impossible because the jinn are devils. But the others disagreed, and the Bengali dervish pointed out that jinn are capable of salvation. 'The Prophet was sent to them as well as to us,' he said. 'The Quran says that some of them will enter the great garden of Paradise.'[88] The Gujarati dervish noted that some jinn are Muslims and others are Hindus. Muslim jinn live in mosques, another said.

The Hindu jinn live in jungles, said a third. They enjoy ruins: ancient temples, cemeteries, cremation grounds. Here the lines of separation began to blur, since cremation grounds are the favourite haunt of Shiva's ganas. Some Hindu jinn hide among the roots of large trees, a Sufi said. The Gujarati dervish insisted that a great Sufi saint would be able to capture and convert even a raja (king) of the Hindu jinn. Dalrymple asked who could do such a thing today.

A hermit in Sindh, named Sayyid Raiz, was mentioned. He lived in the desert near Hyderabad and had reputedly captured many jinn and forced them to help build his monastery. The Bengali dervish said one of the greatest of all dervishes lived in Delhi, and that he performed wonders using the powers of his jinn. His name was Pir Sadr-ud-Din Mahboob Ali Shah Chisti.

Dalrymple managed to track down this celebrated Sufi dervish at a shrine near the Turkoman Gate of the Old City of Delhi. This holy man, Pir Sadr-ud-Din, had recently cleared a house of a family of 208 malignant jinn. The creatures were invisible to most humans, but to Sadr-ud-Din they looked black in colour and had very ugly complexions. They were male and female. The dervish had tracked down 52 of them hiding under the stairs, 52 of them in the attic, and the rest in the kitchen. Sadr-ud-Din had cooked a kilogram of curds in a frying pan, performed some appropriate rituals and driven the jinn out of the house, according to the owner.

Sadr-ud-Din was a large man, with big feet, a firm handshake, a saturnine face and 'a rotting-red betel-nut grin'. He wore a high-necked Peshwari waistcoat with a loose red and white *keffiyeh* on his head. Dalrymple interviewed the dervish in the candle-lit shadows of the shrine, beside a saint's tomb.

Sadr-ud-Din said he possessed the power to compel the jinn, and that he had acquired this power by becoming a great dervish. To achieve this, a person must first learn how to leave his body, to have an out-of-body experience. This technique can take many years to perfect. 'Only then can you ascend directly to God.'

Sadr-ud-Din first left his body when he was 16 years old. His own pir had required him to fast for 41 days, submerged up to his neck in the

Jumna River.[89] He was taken out of the river twice a day, for an hour at a time, and was given a glass of orange juice. After 41 days, he was taken to a graveyard and compelled to fast there for another 41 days. Finally he was taken to a mountaintop and made to fast for 21 days more.

'On the last day of the fast I left my body and ascended towards a light in the sky,' he said. 'The light was God. It was a huge light, like many suns, but I could not see its centre for it was covered with a cloak ... . Now every time when I fast and leave my body I see a little more of this light. When people come to me with their problems I talk to the light, and I ask for the success of their petition.' Sadr-ud-Din told Dalrymple he could now solve any problem. He could capture jinn, cast out demons, cure headaches, heal broken limbs and even 'restore milk to the breasts of a dry woman'.

'Nothing,' he declared, 'nothing is beyond me.'

* * *

In parts of India and Pakistan where Muslims and Hindus live in close proximity, the spirit creatures of each culture show distinctive characteristics, allowing the locals to know which is which.

Before Pakistani independence in 1947, when Muslims and Hindus lived side by side in the crowded neighbourhoods of old Lahore, jinn of both religions were believed to reside among the city's human inhabitants, haunting the back rooms of old buildings and homes. 'It was said that a Hindu jinn could be distinguished by his bodi or ponytail that orthodox Hindus and their priests wear,' recalled Pakistani novelist A. Hameed.[90]

In a recently published reminiscence, Hameed said that the Hindu population was convinced that the jinn would possess humans whose faith was weak or who suffered from chronic diseases. Young Hindu widows, who could not remarry and were forced to remain celibate, were also easy prey for the jinn. Young Muslim widows on the other hand were immune, since they could remarry.

Hameed described how both Muslim and Hindu exorcists coped with jinn possession in old Lahore:

> If some Muslim became possessed, an amil or spirit-master was sent for to exorcise the foreign spirit. He would arrive, say his prayers, blow into the face of the possessed man or woman several times

and then order the jinn in a loud voice to depart the body he had occupied otherwise he would be burnt to a cinder. If the amil had the powers he claimed, the jinn would say in the voice of the man he had possessed, 'Have mercy, I am exiting.' The amil would ask, 'Leave a sign when you depart.' The jinn would answer, 'This brass mug resting on that table will topple to the ground when I leave.' The next moment, the mug would come tumbling down and the possessed man would return to his normal self.

Hindus too had their own 'ghost masters', who would arrive together in a group. First they would tie up the possessed man and light an incense stick. They would then beat drums and clash cymbals. All of these actions would be accompanied by the recitation of sacred mantras.[91]

* * *

A young Muslim woman from Bangladesh told a story on the Internet about a decade ago describing her friendship with an unusual roommate at the University of Dhaka, a girl named Lucy who she firmly believed was a jinn.[92]

The young woman moved into Rokeya Hall on the university campus in August 1995. She soon learned she had a roommate.

'To my youthful and curious eyes, everything seemed to be beautiful; everything seemed novel and colourful,' she said. 'My room number was 247 and in my room I met another girl named Lucy, who was extraordinarily beautiful.'

Lucy's bright eyes and dazzling smile confused her somewhat. The roommate had a dimple and a mole on her left cheek, long dark hair and a tall, slim figure. 'With her unparalleled beauty, she appeared before me as though she were a fairy who had just arrived on land from the sky.' Within a few days, she came to know Lucy's 'exceptional goodness of mind and amiable character'. She said, 'I could not but love her and I am sure that she loved me the same.'

In time they became very close friends, confiding in each other and sharing good times and bad over the months ahead. 'Sometimes, however, some of her activities or behaviour seemed unusual to me,' the young woman said. 'For instance, Lucy was amiable to me but not to everybody. She would not try to please every girl, which led others to deem her to be vain. Moreover, she would sometimes perform a task so quickly it seemed impossible to me, and I could not but wonder at her and praise her. The more I saw her, the more I loved her.'

As a token of her love for Lucy, she decided to give her a pearl necklace – which she bought at Cox's Bazaar, the world's longest sea beach, situated south of Chittagong – on her birthday, December 13.

On December 11, at 11 p.m., Lucy went to meet a friend in the same dormitory, promising to return soon. 'She was late, however, and a cold wind entering through the open door was making me shiver. So I decided to lock the door, thinking that I would open it when Lucy would knock.' She began reading a novel, and soon grew drowsy and fell asleep. When she awoke in the morning, to her great surprise she found Lucy lying on her bed. 'When I asked about the door, she informed me that it had not been locked. It seemed unbelievable to me, as I could clearly remember that I had locked the door.'

Lucy was critical: 'Certainly, you are not thinking that a spirit has opened the door for me, are you?'

'Certainly not,' she replied, and added in a joking way, 'A brave person like me would never think in such a foolish manner.'

She tried to remain logical, in an effort to find an explanation. She decided that perhaps she had imagined locking the door and had never truly done so.

The next day was Lucy's birthday. The plan was to wish her a happy birthday at 12:01 a.m. on December 13. 'At night, I tried to keep her awake until 12:01 a.m. by telling her funny stories.' When it was midnight, Lucy felt tired and wanted to go to sleep. Before going to bed, she sat down at the dressing table to untie her ribbon and brush her hair.

'At 12:01 according to my plan, I placed the pearl necklace around her neck while standing behind her and wishing her a happy birthday. I looked at the mirror to see how she looked. To my horror, I saw in the mirror that there was no reflection of Lucy, but the necklace was just hanging before me.' Terrified, she screamed and fainted.

When she regained consciousness, she found herself surrounded by a crowd of girls. As she opened her eyes, she was subjected to a flood of questions about what had happened. She kept silent and looked around for Lucy but did not see her anywhere.

Lucy was never seen again. 'I told them what had happened. Though at first they thought that I was nuts, they believed it later, as Lucy was found no more. Everybody became afraid of coming to my room, number 247.'

The girl fell ill soon afterwards and went to her parents' home for a while, leaving the dormitory temporarily. Her nervousness gradually eased and when exam time drew near, she returned to her dormitory. 'In my room I felt very lonely and began to recall the memories of the happy days I had passed with Lucy. She had been an excellent girl with whom I spent most of my time. I could not forget my kind friend Lucy.'

The other girls told her that sometimes one of the jinn decides to study at the university in the shape of a human being and perhaps Lucy was a jinn. 'But I wondered if Lucy had been a jinniya, why she would use mirror? That a jinni does not need mirror was common knowledge. I understood that Lucy would try to pretend to be a human being only to carry on her study. I felt pity for her that she could read no more. I realised that only my silly behaviour compelled her to stop her study. I felt guilty.'

At that moment, the dorm supervisor arrived at her room with a new roommate for her, named Mini, who was also a peerless beauty. Her face was different from Lucy's but just as lovely. 'When I stood up to welcome her, she glanced at me with a smiling face and I noticed she had a dimple and a mole on the left of her cheek. The glance she glanced and the smile she gave me were very familiar to me, though I had never met her before.'

* * *

About five years ago, a Bangladeshi graduate student in the United Kingdom described an incident he had witnessed several decades earlier: the summoning of a jinn.[93] The jinn was invoked by a friend of the student's grandfather.

The incident had occurred one afternoon in 1975 at his grandfather's home in Dhaka. As he described it, a small group of people sat in a modest, thoroughly clean room from which the furniture had been removed. The windows were sealed shut and the curtains were drawn, casting the room in darkness. The room had been sprayed with rose water and scented with pungent incense. 'We all sat on the marble floor,' the student said. 'A chair with a prayer mat was placed at one corner. The door was shut but not locked.'

The summoner set forth some rules for the ritual. Those present were not allowed to open their eyes and see the jinn directly, because the light that radiated from his body would be so intense that it could cause blindness in humans. They were also told not to move around the room, but to remain seated on the floor.

When everyone was ready, the summoner began reciting words unintelligibly in a low voice. With a piece of chalk he drew a protective circle around himself. He burnt a few matches and with the blackened remnants drew mysterious symbols on the floor. 'This lasted about 20 minutes,' the student said. 'I was extremely dubious, however [I] remained silent and sat among everyone else. What happened next changed my life completely.'

With a sudden bang, the door flew open and then shut just as quickly. They felt a strong rush of warm wind. The jinn sat down on the chair above the prayer mat. The people greeted him, saying, 'Salamu alaikum.' The room grew very hot, and the student said he began sweating.

> The Jinn spoke with a very deep voice and I could sense that his personality was very strong and dominant. He was a Muslim Jinn. Now I wanted to see what was going on. I asked if I could open my eyes. The Jinn said that I could open my eyes but not look at him for too long as it would cause me pain. However he said he would try and turn down his emitting glow from his body and then I was to look at him. He gave me the go ahead and I opened my eyes. What I saw was incredible.
>
> There sat before me – three feet away on the chair – the shape of a human being but much more tall, I would say about at least eight feet in size. From head to toe there was a bright light emitting, like the light emitted when fire burns at its max.

He moved closer, in spite of warnings from the others, and sat down right in front of the jinn, who began laughing and asked why he was so curious. The student was at a loss of words, in fact, in shock. The light was so bright that he was unable to distinguish the jinn's facial features.

'He asked if I had enough and I said no. I wanted to touch him. He said go ahead. I was expecting to be burnt, but the opposite happened. I reached out with my right hand and touched his hand, which rested on his thigh. It was very hairy and extremely soft. He stroked my palm and I sensed harmony and friendship.'

They spoke, he said, for hours. The jinn talked of his home, which he said was in the Qaf Mountains. He was very old, and a very senior jinn, the student said.

The summoner was sitting far away, in his chalk circle. He kept telling the student to hurry, because it was growing late, and the longer the jinn was delayed, the more pain he experienced. For his part, the jinn said he didn't mind and told the student to continue. 'I learnt a lot that day. I learnt about how life is being a Jinn. The Jinn like to eat a lot of "halwas" [Arabic sweets] and drink sweet sherbets.'

They finally said farewell. The jinn stood up and exited through the door like a flash of light, 'with a massive sound, like a bomb.'

The student said he met the jinn several more times. The jinn would say, 'I am very old, I will die soon, please pray for me. When you humans call Allah once, He replies back to you 50 times. But when we Jinns call Him 50 times, He only replies back once.'

The summoner passed away not long afterwards, and the student had no way of contacting the jinn. He never saw him again.

* * *

This incident, and the previous one at the University of Dhaka, portray good jinn, who are not seen as threats and are, in fact, helpful to humans. They show the seriousness and sincerity with which the jinn phenomenon is treated in Bangladesh – just as in India and Pakistan. In the case of the summoning at the grandfather's house, we are not sure of its purpose, but it clearly served a social function, as did the other encounter at the university. In the Indian subcontinent, the jinn often become a part of day-to-day life, and interacting with them, although sometimes shocking at first, eventually becomes familiar and even comforting.

Zanzibar and Beyond: Spreading the Wealth

Jinn are found in the scattered islands and coastal areas of the Indian Ocean, where Arab, Persian and other Muslim merchants visited over the course of many centuries, beginning as early as the seventh century. Islam spread initially by trade rather than conquest into the lands around this great body of water: eastern Africa and southern and eastern Asia in particular. And the Islamic lore of the jinn travelled with the merchants.

There is a charming legend, of apparent Arab origin, that links the jinn to the creation of the Comoros Islands.[94] The Comoros is an idyllic archipelago of volcanic islands east of Mozambique and the home of the fragrant plant ylang ylang, whose essential oil was once in great demand around the world as a floral perfume base. Islam has had a strong impact on these islands, and 98 per cent of the people are Muslim. The ruling families of the Comoros have traditionally learned Arabic, performed the Hajj and maintained links with other Muslim communities in the region, including those of Zanzibar and Oman.

Early Arab traders carried many myths and legends about these beautiful and exotic islands with them on their journeys between Africa and Arabia. In one such tale, King Solomon gave his ring to a jinn to carry to his beloved Queen of Sheba in Yemen. The jinn apparently became lost, and flying out over the Indian Ocean he accidentally dropped the ring into the sea. The ring was transformed into the summit of the mighty Comorian volcano Karthala – today the largest active volcano in the world.

Farther to the east, the picturesque Maldive Islands off the coast of India are a hotbed of jinn activity. A local press report in May 2008 spoke of a 'bizarre sickness' terrorising the community of a northern Maldive atoll. At least 20 schoolchildren of the island of Makunudhoo in the Haa Dhaal Atoll were afflicted, each reportedly 'falling down, suffering seizures, and losing consciousness'. The illness was described by islanders as jinn possession, and 'white magicians' were called in to conduct exorcisms.[95]

The incident began when a 20-year-old female teacher was reportedly possessed during a trip to an uninhabited island. Six schoolchildren were said to be possessed by the end of the week. Eventually more than 26 people had fallen victim to the 'jinn catastrophe', with more reported every day. In a bid to curb the mysterious illness, villagers cut down a large tree in the centre of the school grounds, which they believed was the source of the jinn activity – but to no avail.

As we have seen in the case of the teachers at a girls' school in Saudi Arabia, Maldivian political leaders, medical workers and the American Red Cross attributed the seizures and other symptoms to 'mass hysteria' – but villagers vehemently denied this, affirming their belief in supernatural jinn activity. Said one Makunudhoo resident, 73-year-old Saeed Moosa: 'There are one thousand jinni for every living human.'

Jinn involvement with the Maldives predates the introduction of Islam to the archipelago in the twelfth century. H.C.P. Bell – a former British commissioner in Ceylon (Sri Lanka) who excavated ancient sites in the Maldives in the 1920s and researched the islands' earlier Buddhist period – recorded a local tale linking pre-Islamic jinn to the islands' acceptance of Islam.[96] According to this account, a frightening jinn used to come ashore from the sea each month at the site of an ancient idol temple on the east cape of the main island of Male. The jinn demanded that a young human virgin be brought to him each time. The local people complied, and the next morning, the virgin was found dishonoured and dead at the temple site. This grisly tradition continued until a pious Muslim (some say from Berber North Africa, but more likely from Tabriz in Persia) visited the island in the twelfth century. He offered to put a stop to the monthly horror, and he went to the temple on the appointed night, taking the place of the designated virgin. He began reciting the Qur'an, continuing throughout the night. By reciting from the Holy Book, he succeeded in driving away the jinn, who never returned. According to some Maldive traditions, this is why the Maldivian people decided to accept the Islamic faith.[97]

An even more detailed version of this account appears in the writings of Arab traveller Ibn Battuta, who came to the Maldives in 1343. Adventurer Thor Heyerdahl, who explored archaeological sites in the archipelago in the 1980s, associated the story of the fiend from the sea not with the Buddhism of the twelfth century, but with the Hindu beliefs and rituals of even earlier times.[98]

* * *

Jinn are also said to be very common along the East African coast, which has, for more than a thousand years, been a favourite trading destination for Arab merchants and seamen. Tanzania, particularly the spice island Zanzibar (its very name probably comes from a spice, the Arabic word for ginger, *zanjabil*), is regarded as the home of very powerful jinn. German scholar Lisa Mackenrodt, who has studied spirit beliefs in Tanzania, particularly in the coastal town of Tanga and the island of Zanzibar, says 'daily life in Tanga and Zanzibar is absolutely imbued with the presence of spirits'.[99]

In Swahili-speaking coastal areas of Tanzania, traditional healers called *waganga* specialise in confronting and expelling spirits. There are various kinds of spirits in Zanzibar and its environs that harass and possess humans, but two are paramount and most revealing of local culture. In the hierarchy, the *ruhani* spirits are the highest and most powerful – indeed, the most honourable. They are part of the Arab/Islamic tradition, and as Muslims they demand that the people they partner with live an exemplary religious life. Despite their basic goodness, these jinn are high-maintenance; if they feel displeased or neglected, they will mercilessly inflict their hosts with illness and misfortune. Thus the *ruhani* need to be appeased with offerings and ultimately exorcised.

Offerings for the *ruhani* include 'sweet-smelling products such as *udi*, rosewood-incense sticks, whose smoke is inhaled by the possessed individual, or *marashi*, rose-water, which is either drunk or poured over the head, and sprinkled upon clothing and the ritual area', according to Mackenrodt.[100]

The other main type of jinn in Zanzibar and other Swahili areas (including Tanga on the mainland coast) is a wilder, less sophisticated indigenous being called the *kimasai*. This being is an 'up-country' spirit, which originated with the celebrated Maasai tribe that serves as gatekeeper for the interior of Tanzania. These jinn at times rival the Arab/Islamic *ruhani* in influencing the lives of coastal peoples. People possessed by *kimasai* suffer from symptoms of the flu, facial skin rashes and other unpleasant illnesses. Some are said to flee their homes and eat grass – a sure sign of possession by *kimasai*. Nearly all Swahili healers in Tanzania, including Qur'anic healers, master the rituals for exorcising both *ruhani* and *kimasai* spirits.

In neighbouring Kenya, the port of Mombasa has also long been famous for its troublemaking spirits. These jinn often take the form of long-dead people. According to Kenyan Muslims, the jinn of Mombasa are active to this day, demonstrating their supernatural powers, harassing residents, beating unfortunate passers-by and even committing crimes such as rape and sodomy.

The Standard of Nairobi published a major report in June 2008 on jinn activity in Mombasa.[101] The article was prompted by a rash of apparent jinn sightings several weeks earlier in Mombasa's Old Town. The sightings seemed connected to a number of abandoned houses in the old quarter, said to be haunted by jinn. 'Invisible families' were heard conversing in apparently vacant houses. Dozens of beautiful houses were said to have been totally abandoned by their owners because of the hauntings. Strange people were seen wandering in the area at night and innocent residents were reportedly accosted, beaten, slapped and even strangled by these strangers. 'One moment you see naked people and the next, they are dressed,' said an Old Town resident named Mohammed. 'At other times you hear invisible people talking and laughing around you.'

The newspaper reported strange goings-on beneath nearby bridges, including sodomies and rapes by invisible persons. 'You hear their voices, their groans, and you see the victim's clothes being removed,' local resident Ali Mahmud told the paper. 'You see clothes being detached from the body but you don't see the person removing them. The next moment, the victim is crying in pain.'

Sheikh Juma Ngao, secretary general of the Supreme Council of Kenyan Muslims, was quoted in this same article as saying that jinn are real and that they live like normal human beings. Some are good, and some are evil. They can turn into anything, he said – a human being, an animal or a shoe.

Asked why stories of jinn are common in Mombasa, Ngao told *The Standard*: 'They are just like human beings. Some like living in the sea, others prefer the hills, while some stay in exile in forests and deserts. Some might actually be living on top of your roof, that is just their preference.'

* * *

The jinn of Zanzibar and the East African coast as well as those in the islands of the Indian Ocean are of great antiquity, often pre-dating Islam. But the evil ones among them are strikingly contemporary in their actions, sometimes participating in what appears to be thoroughly modern criminal activity. This makes these jinn highly relevant to the everyday lives of the people they afflict.

Nigeria: 'Children of Jangare'

The Hausa people of northern Nigeria are predominantly Muslim, but there are many 'pagan' Hausa communities in the rural districts. These non-Muslims are called Maguzawa, a word that probably derives from the Arabic *majusi* (a Magian or Zoroastrian), suggesting the influence of early Persian or Indian Zoroastrian (Parsi) merchants.[102] The Maguzawa acknowledge Allah as the Supreme Being but their religion focuses almost exclusively on the *iskoki* – indigenous African spirit beings that have, however, been influenced by Islamic jinn beliefs as maintained by Hausa Muslims and have in a sense been legitimised by them.

Anthropologist Joseph Greenberg, who did field work among the inhabitants of Kano province in northern Nigeria in 1938–1939, provides us with one of the few detailed descriptions we have of the Maguzawa's *iskoki*.[103]

According to Greenberg, the *iskoki* that play such a central role in Maguzawa belief were generally held to be infinite in number, although some of them were known by name and had definite personalities and powers. It was around these named beings that the religious life of the Maguzawa revolved.

Sometimes the *iskoki* were called *y'an gabas* (children of the east), or *y'an jangare* (children of Jangare). The latter referred to Jangare, a fabled city in the east that is invisible to men and which the *iskoki* are supposed to inhabit.

A number of Maguzawa words derived from Arabic reflect the identification of the Hausa *iskoki* with the Muslim jinn, an important point in Greenberg's view. These are *aljan* (feminine, *aljana*, plural *aljanu*), *shay'dan* and *iblis* (feminine, *iblishiya*, plural, *iblisay*).

The *iskoki* were found everywhere – in the skies, forests, hills, bodies of water and cities of men. Those whose names were known and who had a definite cult generally had a favourite kind of tree or some other specific locale where they liked to stay. In these places, sacrifices of sheep, goats or fowl were offered to them, each *iskoki* having its appropriate animal.

Sometimes the *iskoki* revealed themselves to worshippers through the medium of selected human beings. They were summoned by appropriate drum rhythms to possess the summoner, who wore a costume characteristic of the *iskoki*. The spectators then conversed directly with the *iskoki,* who spoke through the mouth of the one possessed.

Most of the time, however, the *iskoki* were said to live in their invisible city of Jangare. One of Greenberg's guides placed Jangare in the vicinity of Argungu in western Hausa region, although it was also often identified with a town in the south of Kano province called Baw'da. Near the town gate of Baw'da was a famous baobab tree and a well, at the bottom of which the *iskoki* were said to dwell.

In the city of Jangare, the *iskoki* were ruled by a king called Sarkin 'Aljan (king of the jinn). He had a waziri (vizier) and various other officers of state. There was a sarkin k'ofa (king of the gate) who inspected those who went in and out, and a group of warrior jinn assigned to defend the city.

The *iskoki* were normally classified as white (good) and black (evil). For the most part, the black *iskoki* were regarded as pagan and said to live in the countryside, while the white *iskoki* were thought of as Muslim and said to live in towns and cities. Sometimes other criteria were used, such as when the massak'i (the weaver) was defined as a white spirit because he wove white cloth; or the Ba'awzini (the Touareg) was also called white because the Berber Touareg were light-skinned. The Maguzawa also said that the spirit might be white for a man who worshipped him, although he was black for everyone else. However, this kind of classification, which was Muslim in origin, was of secondary importance to the Maguzawa, and there was often doubt as to which category applied to many of the spirits. It was generally asserted that only black spirits caused illness and that white spirits were harmless, when in reality any spirit could be malevolent or good. In general, however, the most malignant diseases were said to be caused by black spirits.

Nigerian Muslim religious scholars identified the spirits worshipped by the pagan Hausa with the unbelieving, or pagan, jinn, as postulated by Muslim religious doctrine. By believing in the actual existence and power of these jinn, these scholars created a condition which permitted considerable survival of the *iskoki* cult among the Muslim Hausa people. Greenberg noted that this phenomenon showed the difficulty of investigating in other areas the mechanism by which belief in pagan deities had survived the adoption of a monotheistic religion by their worshippers.

* * *

Eight years ago in Nigeria, a friend of the Zamfara state governor – a federal state that has applied Islamic shariah law – was arrested on fraud charges. He claimed that jinn had forced him to commit the crime. Here are the state's information commissioner's comments on the case, excerpted from an interview in a Nigerian newspaper:[104]

> *Alhaji Tukur Umar Dangaladima, the Commissioner of Information, Zamfara state, spoke to* Weekly Trust *on a wide range of issues bordering on the allegations of non-performance, discriminatory application of the shariah levelled against the government of the state.*
>
> **WT:** What do you know about Abdullahi Dan Gusau said to be a close ally of the state governor and who was accused of forging the governor's document to defraud some individuals. What is the truth in the allegation that a top government official has intervened in the legal process so as to get him off the hook?
>
> **Dangaladima:** That issue has even affected the ministry of information. What happened was that when this thing was discovered, the person whose name appeared on the memo written to the governor was contacted, and he reported Abdullahi Dan Gusau to the police. Dan Gusau was arrested and charged to court where he admitted that he actually committed that offence. He claimed that

> he was compelled to act by some supernatural forces. According to him by the jinns. The case is before the court for adjudication. I don't know what happened afterwards.

In Nigeria, we find a rich indigenous spirit tradition that has voluntarily linked itself with the Islamic tradition and thereby lent credibility to its beliefs. The possibility that the local spirit tradition was separately influenced by Persian-origin beliefs is tantalising, but this suggestion requires a great deal more historical and anthropological research.

Malays: Jinn in the Jungle

The Malay people of Southeast Asia have a great deal to say about the jinn and their interactions with humans.[105] The Malay ethnic group is the majority in Malaysia and Brunei with a sizeable minority in Indonesia and Singapore. Malays are also the majority in southern Thailand, in the five provinces which historically made up the old Malay kingdom of Patani. They believe that the jinn sprang from three mangrove-leaves: the green jinn from a leaf that soared into the sky, the black jinn from a leaf that fell at the gate of the forest, and the white jinn from a leaf that fell into the sea.

According to another tradition suggested by the wording of certain ancient magical incantations, the jinn were created from the soil of the mountain Mahameru, the Malay equivalent of Mount Olympus or, perhaps more appropriate in this context, Mount Qaf.

According to other incantation traditions, the jinn of the earth were born of afterbirth, or of the morning star. One magician's account says that jinn sprang from the coconut monkey. Another asserts they were created from Sakti-muna, a great serpent: the king of the jinn from his breath; the white jinn from the whites of his eyes; the black, blue, green and yellow jinn from his irises and the jinn that lives in the lightning from his voice.

Sir Richard O. Winstedt, a specialist in Malay history and British colonial administrator in Malaya and Singapore, recorded some of these beliefs in the 1920s. He noted that Malays accepted the Muslim tradition that Jann ibn Jann was the father of all the jinn, and that 'jann' in the Qur'an also signified a serpent. There was another legend of Muslim origin that when Cain and Abel were still in the womb they bit their thumbs until they bled, and when they were born, jinn were born along with them: black jinn from the blood that spurted as high as the clouds, and white jinn from the blood that dripped on the ground. Such accounts were passed along by Malay magicians, who also held to the Qur'anic version that jinn were created from smokeless fire.

As the Malays told it, jinn were present in the Garden of Kings (or Garden of Eden): Jann was originally an angel and was first called Aristotle but later Azazil. ('Aristotle' here is probably not the Greek philosopher, but rather a bit of folk etymology to puzzle out the unfamiliar word 'Azazil'.) When Azazil refused to bow down before Adam, his name was changed to Iblis or Jann and his form became that of a jinn.

Begetting a child every two days, Jann became the ancestor of all the jinn, 'countless shadowy beings, numerous as the sands of the earth and filling hill and cave, forest and plain'.[106] At first they inhabited the lowest level of heaven. From there, they won Allah's permission to descend to the earth, 7,000 of them in all. In time they fought among themselves and disobeyed Allah. So he sent prophets and angels to subdue them and confine them in a corner of the world.

One Malay tradition spoke of three classes of jinn, one winged, another in the form of dogs and insects, and yet another in human form. A few were good Muslims and would go to heaven; most were infidels doomed to hell. Their great age was illustrated in the story of the jinn that Muhammad detected disguised as a very old man. Having been recognised as a jinn, he admitted that he had met Noah and all the prophets after him.

Malay Muslims had read about jinn in their version of the adventures of Alexander the Great[107] in which the world-conqueror met a descendant of Sakhr, the jinn who stole Solomon's ring and assumed the king's bodily form, thus reigning in his place for forty days. In punishment for this deed, Sakhr and his descendants were tasked with guarding until Judgement Day a 'mosque' (or more properly for a pre-Islamic structure, a temple) built for Solomon by Sakhr. An unnamed descendant of Sakhr appeared to Alexander near the mosque in the form of a handsome youth but when asked, he assumed his own true shape: a creature as huge as that mosque, having seven two-faced heads, each with four flaming eyes, a vast mouth, teeth ablaze like fiery tongues and a bull's nose; the creature had two snakelike locks descending from each brow, not to mention duck's feet and a bull's tail.

Near the edge of the world where the sun goes down – somewhere in the far west, probably Morocco – Alexander found jinn guarding King Solomon's treasure-house of jewels. These jinn were the descendants of human men and ten daughters of Iblis. When Alexander marvelled at this, his companion, the Prophet al-Khidr, cited the case of Bilqis, Queen of Sheba, who had a human father and a jinn mother, and whose origin was revealed when Solomon exposed her hairy calves. Such tales, as read and enjoyed by the Malays, show the widespread dissemination of the medieval Alexander romances, particularly once they were absorbed into Islamic folklore.

To Malay Muslims, the jinn were subjects not of the Prophet Muhammad but of Solomon, to whom Allah gave authority over jinn, all animals and the winds. One Malay charm speaks of 'Jinn the son of Jann of the line of the Pharaohs', a pedigree based on the Arab legend that the last king of the pre-Adamite jinn was Jann the son of Jann, and that he built the Great Pyramids of Egypt.

Syncretistic tendencies regarding matters of faith in Southeast Asia have resulted in incorporation of Indonesian soul-substance and nature-spirits and Hindu divinities into the different classes of Malay jinn. Malay medical lore, having borrowed from the Arabs Plato's theory of the origin of disease, differentiated yet another class, the jinn of fire and fiery sunsets.

The colour of a Malay jinn varied depending on where he lived. Jinn of earth and the dark forests and mists were black. Those that inhabited the skies were blue or to the Malay eye green. The jinn of fire and sunset were yellow. The ones that made their homes in puffy clouds and in the shimmering sea were white.

Just as the ancient Greeks sometimes attributed disease to an imbalance in the four basic elements that make up the human body – earth, air, fire and water – so the Malay shaman blamed all diseases on the four classes of jinn presiding over those elements. The jinn of the air caused wind-borne complaints, dropsy, blindness, hemiplegia and insanity. Those of the black earth were responsible for vertigo and sudden loss of vision. The jinn of fire produced hot fevers and jaundice. White jinn of the sea caused chills, colds and common fevers.

Winstedt said that these four types of spirit beings were 'external' jinn. They were visible to lonely wayfarers, to the magician in a trance or, according to Kelantan belief, to a person who gazed at the fingernails of innocent little boys. These jinn could speak on their own or through a shaman's mouth. Jinn of the earth might appear in human form, 'floating in the air and not always remaining the same size', or in the form of animals, ants or scorpions or any shape they please.[108]

Muslim jinn were said to haunt two mosques in the Malaysian state of Negri Sembilan, flitting to and fro in long white robes and sometimes chanting the Qur'an. If a person stood under a ladder and bathed in water in which a corpse had been washed, he could then stoop and look between his legs where he would see crowds of jinn and demons sipping the water. In Patani, Thailand, infidel jinn of the earth were thought to assume the form of dogs and guard hidden treasure. If they took a liking to some among the humans, they changed into little old men and left sacks of gold for their favourites. Peculiar bubbles on the surface of water bodies indicated the presence of jars of treasure placed by jinn. There was said to be a jinn that was 'supposed to resemble the human form but to dart about like a will-o'-the-wisp' and daze the man that crossed it.

If someone seized a jinn and held onto him, no matter how frightening he looked, one could wrest from him the secret of invisibility, according to Winstedt. 'If a man had a tame genie, he could cause the meat from another man's cooking-pot to come to him.'[109] Winstedt cited the story of the founder of a house of great chiefs in the state of Perak, Malaysia, who was originally a poor fisherman. His traps were repeatedly thrown on the bank and his weirs opened. He watched from a hiding place on the shore and eventually saw the offender, a jinn dressed in the green robes and turban of a Muslim pilgrim. He seized the jinn and refused to let him go. The jinn said, 'Swallow this,' spat in his mouth and told him that he would become the greatest chief in the land and his family would prosper for seven generations.

But these external jinn could not inflict disease without the help of the class of jinn that inhabited the bodies of men. So said, at least, people in the Malaysian state of Kelantan. When the genie living inside a man had weakened him by loss of blood, coughing and dyspepsia, only then could jinn from the outside enter the man and cause him hurt. There was a yellow jinn controlling a man's five senses. There was a white jinn (*malaikat*), also called the Light of the Prophet, that 'takes up its abode in the heart of every [Muslim] and prevents him from being wicked'.[110]

The moral character of the white jinn in a man's bosom might be due to confusion of this spirit with the Light of the Prophet. Jinn destined for heaven were moral beings and belonged to the various schools of Muslim belief. The others were capricious and did not distinguish between good and evil.

The syncretism that characterises Malay jinn lore was clearly apparent in the Perak magician's incantation addressed to 'the procession of the thousand jinn'. In that invocation, Winstedt reported, appeals were made to a panoply of spirits: to the evil influence believed by Malay animists to invest the corpses of deer; to Indonesian soil goblins; to the Misty Beauty that floats over wells; to the Piebald Pony; to the four spirit guardians of the corners of the world; to Kala or Siva in his destructive form; to Sri, the Hindu Ceres; to a Hindu Moon Fairy; to the Herald of the World that dwells in the clouds; to Jamshid, a headlands spirit named after a Persian king; and to the spirits of the Muslim dead. These and dozens more were addressed and appealed to, so that the magician might display the wealth of his spirit lore, offend no one in the world beyond and let no jinn escape the net of his magic.

Winstedt provided an equally persuasive example of syncretism in the list of the guardian jinn of Perak, or, to give them their other name, the 'jinn of the royal trumpets', whose indwelling spirits were fed and revived each year, centuries before the coming of Islam. Included among them were the Four Children of the Iron Pestle, Old Grannie from Up-River, the Prince of the Rolling Waves and the Children of the Gaffer Who Lives in the Sky. Brahma, Vishnu and Indra were also in their company, as were King Solomon and 'Ali, the fourth caliph. There were royal familiars of the state shaman and his assistant. Also among them was the raja of all the jinn, who was enthroned on the breeze of heaven. There was the sultan of the Unsubstantial World (Maya), who came down in a crystal car followed by all the sultans of the universe. Also part of the assemblage were spirits with Persian royal titles and female fairies with Sanskrit names. The list showed wide knowledge of the Malay romances, such as the Hikayat Shamsu'l-Bahrain and the Hikayat Indraputra, which were based on Indian models and packed with heroes and jinn bearing Indian names. Familiarity with such literature was considered a highly esteemed accomplishment at Malay courts. Among the jinn favoured by Perak commoners was 'Umar Ummaiya, the 'Ulysses' of the Indo-Persian romance of Amir Hamza.

* * *

Traditional Malay jinn lore was thus a colourful melange of religious and cultural beliefs and legends, blended in an atmosphere of flexibility and collaboration. It was hard to match for excitement and emotive power.

Chapter Five

Cultural Echoes

I am one of the heretical Jinn: I rebelled against Suleyman the son of Da'ud; I and Sakhr the Jinni; and he sent to me his Wezir, Asaf the son of Barkhiya, who came upon me forcibly, and took me to him in bonds, and placed me before him: and when Suleyman saw me, he offered up a prayer for protection against me, and exhorted me to embrace the faith, and to submit to his authority; but I refused; upon which he called for this bottle, and confined me in it, and closed it upon me with the leaden stopper, which he stamped with the Most Great Name: he then gave orders to the Jinn, who carried me away, and threw me into the midst of the sea. There I remained a hundred years.

– The Thousand and One Nights (Lane Translation)

How I Met the Ghul

A handful of Arabian poems have survived from pre-Islamic times, before the seventh century AD. The poetry of this period dealt with Bedouin themes – love, war and desert adventures. In one of these works, the Arabian poet Ta'abbata Sharran, of the Banu Fahm tribe, describes an encounter with a ghoul (*ghul*) in the wilderness:[1]

O who will bear my news to the young men of Fahm
of what I met at Riha Bitan?

Of how I met the ghul swooping down
on the desert bare and flat as a sheet.
I said to her, 'We are both worn with exhaustion,
brothers of travel, so leave my place to me!'
She sprang at me; then my hand raised
against her a polished Yemeni blade.
Then undismayed I struck her: she fell flat
prostrated on her two hands and on her throatlatch.
She said, 'Strike again!' I replied to her, 'Calm down,
mind your place! For I am indeed stouthearted.'
I lay upon her through the night
that in the morning I might see what had come to me.
Behold! Two eyes set in a hideous head,
like the head of a cat, split-tongued,
Legs like a deformed foetus, the back of a dog,
clothes of haircloth or worn-out skins!

Historian Robert Irwin reprinted this poem in *Night, Horses and the Desert: An Anthology of Classical Arabic Literature* (2000), with his own comment:

> According to E.W. Lane's *Arabic-English Lexicon* [which is essentially a compilation based on medieval Arab dictionaries], a ghul is a 'kind of goblin, demon, devil or jinnee which, the Arabs assert, appears to men in the desert, assuming various forms, causing them to wander from the way and destroying them'. Lane also quotes one of the medieval dictionaries, the *Taj al-'Arus*, as adding that the ghul was 'terrible in appearance, having tusks or fangs, seen by the Arabs, and known by them; and killed by Ta'abbata Sharran'. According to Jahiz, the ghul rode on hares, dogs and ostriches ... . Riha Bitan was part of the territory of a hostile tribe. The poem is most unusual as an example of pre-Islamic fantasy literature.

William Robertson Smith, professor of Arabic at Cambridge in the nineteenth century, had his own interpretation of Sharran's fight in the desert. In his *Lectures on the Religion of the Semites*, he observed,

> Taabbata Sharran is an historical person, and the incident also is probably a fact. From the verses in which he describes his foe it would seem that the supposed *ghūl* was one of the feline carnivores. In Damīrī, ii, 212, last line, a *ghūl* appears in the form of a thieving cat.

Regardless of whether the ghoul was historical, such monstrous jinn played an important role in Arabic literature, from pre-Islamic times onwards. They provided foils for the heroes, complexities for the plots of stories and good old-fashioned chills.

The Arabian Nights

One of the best places to find jinn lore is in *The Arabian Nights* (or *The Thousand and One Nights*).[2] These tales, composed and compiled over centuries, reflect the strong storytelling tradition of the Arab and Islamic worlds, with influences from many lands and cultures. The original model for the tales was likely Persian, and certainly pre-Islamic. The stories were set in the familiar 'frame tale' of Scheherazade telling nightly stories to King Shahryar, ending each time with a 'cliffhanger' to avoid being put to death the next morning. The tales were assembled over many years from a wide variety of sources, including Arabic, Persian, Egyptian and Mesopotamian folklore and legend.

In *The Arabian Nights*, the jinn are acknowledged as being created from smokeless flame and are normally invisible. But they often materialise before humans, usually in human likeness but sometimes as the most bizarre creatures imaginable.

In 'The Tale of Zayn al-Asnam', Prince Zayn al-Asnam of Basra is ferried across a lake in Egypt by a jinn ferryman who has the head of an elephant and the body of a lion. (In fact, the ferryman hoists the prince and his companion Mubarak into the boat by using his elephant trunk wrapped around them.) On the other side awaits a large host of jinn who are terrifying to gaze upon: 'all frightful of favour and fear-inspiring of figure', each one carrying steel javelins that flash in the sun.[3] The jinn king, however, has taken the form of a handsome young man, doubtless to facilitate his meeting with the prince. Zayn al-Asnam has come to receive from the jinn king an inheritance from the prince's late father: the last of nine statues carved from precious gems and this one is incredibly valuable, worth as much as all the others combined. The jinn king tells him he will give him the statue in exchange for an innocent young human maiden who will be his bride. Zayn al-Asnam searches for and finds a bride for the jinn king, only to learn that the king of the jinn had really intended the maiden for him, Zayn, to take as his own bride. The two young people marry and live happily ever after as king and queen of Basra.

Robert Irwin notes that

> such accounts of meetings with the kings of the jinn and their legions can easily be paralleled in medieval Arab sorcerers' manuals which purported to be nonfiction. In the treatises of the thirteenth-century sorcerer Abu'l Qasim al-Iraqi, for example, there are a variety of spells for summoning jinn, for learning their secrets and for using them as treasure-hunters. (Abu'l Qasim also knew spells for flying, walking on water, mastering telepathy, giving people dogs' heads and giving women beards.)[4]

Various jinn characteristics emerge throughout the tales, such as the ability to shape-shift and travel as whirlwinds or sandstorms. Despite such fantastical elements, jinn society is, as we have seen, essentially similar to human society. In 'The Adventures of Bulukiya', Bulukiya, a young king of the Israelites on a quest that takes him to the very ends of the earth, is brought before Sakhr, king of the jinn, who is attended by lesser jinn kings and princes, as well as counsellors and officers of state. This royal court of the jinn is remarkably like its human counterparts in the ancient Middle East. Frustrated by his failure to obtain the magic ring of Solomon or to gain immortality by drinking of the Water of Life, Bulukiya seeks Sakhr's aid in returning to his home. King Sakhr grants him a fine mare to carry him to the next kingdom. The details of his return are, as they say, another story … .

As we have also seen, jinn are known to haunt dark, dank places. In 'The Tale of Nur al-Din Ali and his Son', an ifrit emerges from a water tank in a bathroom to persecute and terrify an ugly hunchback designated by the Sultan of Cairo to marry the most beautiful woman in the land. The ifrit, on a matchmaking mission to pair the beautiful maiden with a handsome youth from Basra, emerges from the water in the shape of a mouse and then transforms himself into a cat, then a dog, then an ass colt and finally a water buffalo – all in an effort to dissuade the hunchback from marrying the maiden. In another tale, Caliph Harun al-Rashid's slave-girl singer Tohfat al-Kulub is conducted by Iblis, 'the Father of the Jinn', to the land of the jinn via a magic exit hidden in one of the palace's toilets. Ruins – as illustrated in the stories 'The King's Son and the Ogress' and 'Ma'ruf the Cobbler' – and cemeteries are also favoured by the jinn, particularly by ghouls.

Many of the jinn encountered in the *Nights* have been imprisoned in flasks or columns of stone by King Solomon. The jinn are also compelled by certain objects, such as the signet ring discovered by Ma'ruf the Cobbler in a hidden underground chamber. It turned out that the chamber held the treasures of Shaddad son of 'Ad, who had built the ill-fated Iram of the Pillars. Ma'ruf was a henpecked husband who patched old shoes for a living in Cairo and yet yearned for adventure; when he found the ring and gave it a rub, a jinn appeared. Said the jinn:

> I am Sultan over two-and-seventy tribes of the Jinn, each two-and-seventy thousand in number every one of which thousand ruleth over a thousand Marids, each Marid over a thousand Ifrits, each Ifrit over a thousand Satans and each Satan over a thousand Jinn: and they are all under command of me and may not gainsay me. As for me, I am spelled to this seal-ring and may not thwart whoso holdeth it. Lo! thou hast gotten hold of it and I am become thy slave.[5]

Thus began a string of adventures that led to the lowly Ma'ruf becoming an immensely wealthy king.

* * *

'The Story of the City of Brass',[6] a wondrous tale of the jinn from *The Arabian Nights*, involves a real historical figure, Emir Musa ibn Nusair, Umayyad governor of North Africa, best known for commanding the forces that launched the Arab invasion of Spain in the eighth century AD. In 'The City of Brass', Musa goes searching in North Africa for some stoppered brass bottles said to contain jinn imprisoned by King Solomon. In the course of his quest, he comes across the fabled lost City of Brass.

Abdul Malik, Umayyad caliph in Damascus, was amazed to receive a reliable report that a fisherman on the African coast had recovered in his nets a bottle of brass, stopped with lead and sealed with the signet ring of Sulaiman ibn Da'ud (King Solomon son of David). When the fisherman broke open the bottle, witnesses said blue smoke poured forth and rose into the sky. A horrible voice cried out, 'Repentance!

Repentance! O Prophet of God!' Suddenly the smoke coalesced into a huge and frightening person, high as a mountain, who just as quickly vanished into thin air.

The explanation of this bizarre occurrence came from a local ruler, who observed that it happened rather often:

> This is one of the jinn that Sulaiman son of Da'ud, when he was incensed against them, imprisoned in these bottles; he poured lead over them, and threw them into the sea. When the fisherman casts his net, it generally brings up these bottles, and when they are broken, there comes forth from them a jinn, who imagines that Sulaiman is still alive; that is why he repents, and says, 'Repentance! O Prophet of God!'

Abdul Malik then dispatched Emir Musa, governor of the province of Ifriqiyah (North Africa), to locate and bring back some of these brass bottles. Musa's guide on this expedition was a well-travelled, elderly sheikh named Abdul Samad, who knew the deserts and wastelands and the seas of the world. They were accompanied by a force of soldiers. Their destination was the lost City of Brass, near which a number of jinn bottles were said to be located.

The expedition proceeded deep into unknown North African territory – in which direction, no one today knows. Sheikh Abdul Samad led the way, ahead of the troops. One day passed, then another and another. Finally they reached a high hill, on which was perched a horseman of brass, whose upraised spear was topped by a wide and glistening head that rendered one sightless. On the head was inscribed:

> You who approach me, if you know not the way that leads to the City of Brass, rub the hand of the horseman, and he will turn, and then will stop, and in whatever direction he stops, proceed there, without fear and without difficulty; for it will lead you to the City of Brass.

When Emir Musa rubbed the hand of the horseman, it spun like a blinding bolt of lightning and faced a different direction from that in which they were travelling. So the party turned in that direction and journeyed on, and it turned out to be the right way. By the next night, they had traversed a wide tract of country. As they continued along, eventually they came to a pillar of black stone, in which was held captive a person sunk up to his armpits, who had two huge wings and four arms. Two of his arms were like those of normal men, and two were like the forelegs of lions, with claws. The hair on his head resembled horses' tails. He had two eyes like burning coals, and a third eye in his forehead, like the eye of a lynx, emitting sparks of fire. He was black and tall, and he was crying out, 'Extolled be the perfection of my Lord, who has appointed for me this severe affliction and painful torture until the day of resurrection!'

When the party saw the trapped creature, all reason left them, and they fled in fear and confusion. Emir Musa said to Sheikh Abdul Samad, 'What is this?' 'I don't know what he is,' he answered. 'Draw near to him and investigate his situation,' the Emir said. So Sheikh Abdul Samad approached the creature and said to him, 'Person, tell me your name, and your nature, and what caused you to be put in this pillar?' 'I am an ifrit of the jinn,' he said, 'and my name is Dahish son of El-A'mash. I am restrained here by the majesty, confined by the power of Allah, tormented as long as He wills.'

The party was amazed by him, and they marvelled at the horrible nature of his form. 'There is no god but Allah! Sulaiman was endowed with a mighty dominion!' said Emir Musa. The sheikh Abdul Samad said to the ifrit, 'I would like to ask you something.' 'Ask what you wish,' the ifrit replied. The sheikh asked: 'Are there in this place any of the ifrits confined in bottles of brass from the time of Sulaiman, on whom be peace?' The ifrit answered, 'Yes, in the Sea of El-Karkar, where one can find people descended from Noah whose land was not reached by the Flood; they live apart there, separated from the rest of the sons of Adam.' 'And where,' asked the sheikh, 'is the way to the City of Brass, and the place where the bottles can be found? How far away is it?' 'It is near,' the ifrit said.

So the party left him and proceeded; there appeared in the distance before them a great black object, with what looked like two symmetrical fires as distant as the black object. Emir Musa said to the sheikh, 'What is this great black object, and what are these two fires?' The guide answered him, 'Rejoice, Emir; for this is the City of Brass, and this is how it appears in the *Book of Hidden Treasures:* its walls are of black stone, and it has two towers made of the brass of El-Andalus, which appears from a distance like two fires; and so it is called the City of Brass.'

They continued travelling until they reached the city. It was lofty, strongly fortified, rising high into the air, impenetrable: The height of its walls was eighty cubits, and it had 25 hidden gates, none of which would open except by means of some artifice. They stopped in front of the city and tried to locate one of its gates; but they could not. Emir Musa said to Abdul Samad, 'Sheikh, I don't see any gates to this city.' 'Emir,' replied the sheikh, 'this is how it is described in the *Book of Hidden Treasures:* it has twenty-five gates, and none of them may be opened except from inside the city.' 'So how,' asked the Emir, 'can we contrive to enter it and divert ourselves with its wonders?'

Emir Musa ordered one of his young soldiers to mount a camel and ride round the city, in the hope that he might discover signs of a gate or a wall lower than the one that faced them. So one of his men mounted up and proceeded around the city, riding for two days and nights, prosecuting his journey with diligence and not resting. When the third day arrived, he came back in sight of his companions, and he was astounded by what he had seen of the extent and height of the city. He said, 'Emir, the easiest place way into the city is right here where you have stopped.'

Emir Musa took Abdul Samad, and they climbed a mountain opposite the city. When they reached the top of the mountain, they looked out over the city, and never before had they beheld one any greater.

Its pavilions were lofty and its domes were shining; its mansions were in good condition, and its rivers were running; its trees were fruitful, and its gardens bore ripe produce. It was a city with impenetrable gates, empty, still, without a voice or a cheering inhabitant, only an owl hooting in its quarters, and birds skimming in circles above it, and the raven croaking in its districts and its great thoroughfares and bewailing those who had been in it. Emir Musa paused, greatly saddened that the city was apparently devoid of inhabitants and despoiled of people.

After great difficulty and the death of twelve soldiers, they managed to open a gate and enter the city. They encountered the desiccated bodies of countless dead citizens, great treasures and many wonders.

The Emir gave orders for the entry of the troops, who accordingly entered and loaded their camels with part of those riches and minerals; after which Emir Musa commanded them to close the gate as it was before.

They then proceeded along the sea-coast until a high mountain overlooking the sea came in sight. In the mountain were many caves, and in these caves lived black men clad in hides wearing hide burnouses (hoods) on their heads. Their language was unknown. When they saw the troops, they ran from them and fled to their caves. Their women and their children stood watching from the entrances of the caves. So the Emir Musa said, 'Sheikh Abdul Samad, who are these people?' 'These are the ones inquired about by the Prince of the Faithful (the Caliph Abdul Malik),' the sheikh said.

They alighted, their tents were pitched and their riches put down. They had not had time to rest before the King of the blacks came down from the mountain and approached the troops. He was familiar with the Arabic language. When he reached Emir Musa, he saluted him. The Emir returned his salutation and treated him with honour.

Then the King of the blacks said to the Emir, 'Are you of mankind or the jinn?' The Emir answered, 'As to us, we are of mankind; and as to you, there is no doubt you are of the jinn, because of your seclusion in this mountain separated from the world, and because of the greatness of your make.' But the King of the blacks replied, 'No, we are a people of the race of Adam, of the sons of Ham son of Noah, on whom be peace! And as to this sea, it is known by the name of El-Karkar.' Emir Musa then said to him, 'We are associates of the King of Islam, Abdul Malik son of Marwan; and we have come because of the bottles of brass that are here in your sea, which contain devils imprisoned from the time of Sulaiman the son of Da'ud. Abdul Malik has commanded us to bring him some of them, so that he may see them, and examine them.' The King of the blacks replied, 'Most willingly'.

Then he feasted him with fish and ordered divers to bring up from the sea some of the bottles of Sulaiman. They recovered twelve bottles. Emir Musa was delighted with these, as was Sheikh Abdul Samad and the soldiers, because they had accomplished the task set for them by the Prince of the Faithful.

Emir Musa presented many gifts, large and small, to the King of the blacks. In like manner the King of the blacks gave to Emir Musa a present consisting of wonders of the sea, in the form of human beings – mermaids, no doubt – and said to him, 'Your entertainment for these three days shall be of these fish.' The Emir replied, 'We must carry with us some of them, so that the Prince of the Faithful may see them; this would please his heart even more than the bottles of Sulaiman.'

Then they bade him farewell and journeyed back until they came to the land of Syria, where they presented themselves to the Prince of the Faithful. Emir Musa acquainted him with all that he had seen, and all that had occurred to him with respect to the verses and histories and admonitions.

The Prince of the Faithful said to him, 'Would that I had been with you, that I might have seen what you saw!' He then took the bottles and proceeded to open them one after another, and the devils came forth from them, saying, 'Repentance, O Prophet of God! We will not return to such conduct ever!'

Abdul Malik son of Marwan was amazed by this. But as to the mermaids, presented by the King of the blacks, they made for them troughs of wood, which they filled with water, and they put the mermaids into these. They died, however, due to the intensity of the heat.

After this, the Prince of the Faithful had the treasures of the City of Brass brought before him, and he divided them among the Muslims. Then Emir Musa begged the Prince of the Faithful to appoint his son in his place as governor of the province, so that he himself might travel to noble Jerusalem, to worship Allah there. So the Prince of the Faithful appointed Emir Musa's son to the government and Musa himself went to noble Jerusalem, where he died.

So ends the tale of the City of Brass. Interestingly, this storyteller's favourite has a basis in truth. Musa ibn Nusair apparently did travel into a remote part of North Africa, probably deep in the desert, and located the ruins of a lost city. Historian al-Mas'udi presents a version of this account in his *Meadows of Gold*:

> Then comes the country of Sous al-Adna, which is about two thousand three hundred miles from Kairowan, and some twenty days march from Sous al-Aksa, in an area constantly fertile and cultivated; but beyond this last point one arrives at Wadi al-Raml [river of sand], then at the black castle and at the sand deserts in which are found the city known as Madinat al-Nouhas [city of brass] and the cupolas of lead. It was in this area that Musa, son of Nusair, arrived in the time of 'Abd al-Malik ibn Marwan, and saw all the wonders he described in a book that everyone knows. Some others say that

> this city was found in the deserts located in Spain [al-Andalus] and called *the great land*.[7]

What al-Mas'udi calls the 'book that everyone knows' is apparently not *The Arabian Nights*, since the City of Brass tale had not been added to that collection by the tenth century, when *Meadows of Gold* was written. Folklore scholar Mai I. Gerhardt believes that al-Mas'udi's account was reasonably factual and probably derived from a report written by Musa ibn Nusair himself, which has since been lost.[8] Other Arab historians wrote varying versions of the City of Brass story over the centuries, including Ibn al-Fakih, al-Tabari and Abu Hamid al-Andalusi. Ibn Khaldoun, the great Tunisian historiographer of the fifteenth century, dismissed most of the lore surrounding the City of Brass as nonsense, but the core of the tale, the discovery of an archaeological site by Musa ibn Nusair, remains essentially unchallenged. Needless to say that 'lost city' remains lost to the present day.

* * *

In 1991, a Turkish-American writer, Güneli Gün, wrote a remarkable novel called *On the Road to Baghdad: A Picaresque Novel of Magical Adventures, Begged, Borrowed, and Stolen from the Thousand and One Nights.*[9] It has been described as part post-feminist fable, part magical mystery tour. The work takes the tales of *The Arabian Nights* to a new and more timely level. The heroine of the novel, set in the sixteenth-century Ottoman Turkish Empire, is a thoroughly modern minstrel named Hürü. As it happens, the jinn are having an effect on Hürü's education:

> Besides being slow with her memorizations, Hürü, who ordinarily stammered only a little, stammered hard when faced with the [Koranic] texts. Her tied tongue was a sign, her tutoress informed her, that Iblis, or a lesser jinni, had taken a keen interest in Hürü's peccability. Those repulsive beings, too, were peccable and proud of it. When God introduced Adam to the Angels and the jinn, He invited all to bow down before Man. The Angels, who were impeccable and created out of light, had complied; not Iblis and Co. They didn't want to bow down before any creature made of clots of blood and were immediately fired for their vanity. For it is written that mischief opened the hearts of men to Iblis, his sons

> and his perfidious troops who skulked and lurked in baths, latrines, wells, ovens, marketplaces, ruined houses, junctures of roads, the sea, rivers – waiting for a heedless and unaware person like Hürü to invoke them between her stutterings of the sacred texts. Girls like Hürü were the very meat of Iblis, whose food was whatever was killed without the Blessing of God being pronounced over it first, who drank whatever intoxicates, who was called to prayer by musical pipes, whose Koran was poetry, whose speech was falsehood and whose snares, women.
>
> So, to Hürü's mind, the road to virtue didn't appear open ... .

The Arabian Nights collection is a rich mine of jinn lore, some of it springing from the great storytellers' imaginations as they performed before hushed crowds in Damascus, Baghdad and Cairo, and some of it from the age-old legends and practices of Muslim peoples from Morocco to India.

Southey's Genii

In the eighteenth and nineteenth centuries, a genre of literature known as Romantic Orientalism flourished in Europe, particularly in Great Britain. Inspired by early translations of *The Arabian Nights* and fuelled by colonial adventures in the greater Middle East, British Romantic writers began generating Oriental tales, replete with exotic settings, supernatural happenings and flights of imagination.

Prominent examples of Romantic Orientalism include Samuel Johnson's *History of Rasselas, Prince of Abyssinia* (1759), William Beckford's Abbasid-era novel *Vathek* (1786), Walter Savage Landor's seven-volume blank-verse Egyptian epic *Gebir* (1798), Lord Byron's Turkish narrative poem *Giaour* (1813) and Thomas Moore's Persian poetic epic *Lalla Rookh* (1817).[10]

Another writer who made major forays into Romantic Orientalism was the English poet Robert Southey, one of the 'Lake Poets' (along with William Wordsworth and Samuel Coleridge) and himself Poet Laureate for three decades, from 1813 to 1843. Southey was a rival of Byron's, though most experts argue of lesser brilliance. He was a prodigious writer with broad cross-cultural interests who authored epic poems, novels, literary critiques, histories, biographies and reams of letters. Southey was the first writer ever to use the term 'autobiography', in an 1809 literary review, but his most enduring claim to fame is as the author of the original children's tale 'Goldilocks and the Three Bears', which appeared in one of his novels in 1834.

In 1801, Southey published a blank-verse romantic epic called *Thalaba the Destroyer: A Metrical Romance*, as part of a larger project to present to the English readers the flavour and magic of the folklore and traditions of distant cultures.[11] Other works in this project included *Madoc* (about a Welsh prince's legendary travels to the New World 300 years before Columbus) and *The Curse of Kehama* (a folkloric tale set in old India, much admired by Keats and Shelley).

Thalaba the Destroyer is a remarkable adventure steeped in the legends and lore of the Arab Bedouins. Central to the story is a society of powerful magicians who operate from their headquarters in a hidden cave beneath the ocean, known as the Domdaniel cavern. The magicians learn by supernatural means that they are destined to be killed by a certain man born in Arabia, unless they succeed in killing him first. They learn that this man is one of the sons of a Bedouin chief named Hodeirah. So the magicians select one of their number, named Okba, to set out, track down and kill Hodeirah, his wife and all eight of his children. Okba almost succeeds. Hodeirah's wife Zeinab and one son – Thalaba – escape the massacre and go into hiding. In time, Thalaba, grown to manhood, searches for and finds the undersea cavern of Domdaniel, where he engages in a final, epic confrontation with the evil magicians.

Throughout the 12 books of *Thalaba the Destroyer*, we are presented with a wealth of Arabian folklore and custom, carefully researched by Southey as part of his grand cross-cultural experiment.[12] The jinn, because of their close association with Arab magic, are constantly haunting the margins of the tale, sometimes entering the story and taking action on behalf of the magicians, at other times simply watching the actions of the characters unfold. Sometimes they are called 'demons' – or evil jinn – and sometimes 'Genii', a Latin form that can include both good and bad jinn.

Among the observer-jinn are those that Southey calls 'the Genii of the Air'. At times, he asks rhetorical questions of these jinn, who witness the events of the tale. On one occasion, describing a spell of a sorceress called Maimuna, Southey exclaims: 'Heard ye not, Genii of the Air, her spell, / That o'er her face there flits / The sudden flush of fear?'

Another important member of the jinn family in Southey's romance is Eblis (Iblis), master of the evil magicians. A 'Giant Idol' made in Eblis's image, constructed magically of human bone and tissue, is a central focus of the Domdaniel realm and plays a major role in the climax of the story.

The supernatural prophecy of the destruction of the sorcerers, which begins the romance in the gloom of the cavern hall of Domdaniel, is delivered by a grim magical object called a *teraph* – a shadowy biblical term for an idol associated with a 'household god' (another manifestation of the jinn) and used for divination. In this case, the teraph consulted by a sorceress called Khawla is the talking severed head of an infant, resting on a golden platter that bears the name of an evil jinn:[13]

A Teraph stood against the cavern-side,
A new-born infant's head,
Which Khawla at its hour of birth had seized,
And from the shoulders wrung,
It stood upon a plate of gold,
An unclean Spirit's name inscrib'd beneath.
The cheeks were deathy dark,
Dark the dead skin upon the hairless skull;
The lips were bluey pale;
Only the eyes had life,
They gleamed with demon light.[14]

The fiery-eyed teraph has the ability to scan the entire world and report its findings to the magicians. This is a talent of the jinn, who can travel great distances in an instant and observe even the most secret of happenings from behind a curtain of invisibility.

At one point in the story, the sorceress Khawla wants to know where young Thalaba is hiding. But the youth is being protected by a power greater than the jinn:

Khawla to the Teraph turn'd,
'Tell me where the Prophet's hand
Hides our destined enemy?'
The dead lips spake again,
'I view the seas, I view the land,
I search the Ocean and the Earth!
Not on Earth is the Boy,
Not on Earth his steps are seen.'

Another object in this romance with clear jinn associations is a magic ring worn by an evil sorcerer called Abdaldar, which contains a crystal stone lit with elemental fire (which happens to be the source of the jinn, who are fire spirits). The other magicians send Abdaldar on a quest to find Thalaba and kill him. Abdaldar instilled the flame in the gemstone of his ring by speaking 'the language which the Elements obey', presumably Syriac, said to be the language of the jinn. When Abdaldar happens to find and touch 'the destined Boy', the flame will be quenched from the ring and 'the freed Element / Fly to its sacred and remember'd Spring.'

Abdaldar eventually finds Thalaba and watches the ring's fire diminish, confirming that this youth is the one he seeks. But Abdaldar does not survive to complete his mission to kill Thalaba – instead he is slain by the Blast of the Desert, a sudden sandstorm apparently sent by God. Thalaba takes the ring from the dead sorcerer's finger and puts it on his own.

Another magician, Lobaba, comes to replace Abdaldar. Disguised as a harmless old traveller, he befriends Thalaba and travels with him. One night, as they sleep beneath the moon, Lobaba spots the magic ring on Thalaba's finger, gleaming in the moonlight. Lobaba calls upon his malicious jinn servants to help him recover the ring:

Vainly the Wizard vile put forth his hand,
And strove to reach the gem;
Charms, strong as hell could make them, kept it safe.
He call'd his servant-fiends,
He bade the Genii rob the sleeping youth.
By virtue of the Ring,
By Mahommed's holier power,
By the holiest name of God,
Had Thalaba disarm'd the evil race.

When faced with the power of faith – which Thalaba eventually recognises as his 'talisman' – even the powerful jinn are ineffectual.

After many adventures, Thalaba casts the magic ring into the sea and descends deep into the earth, to the cavern of Domdaniel. At the gates of the magicians' cavern, he confronts a guardian *afreet* – a huge, powerful man-eating jinn:[15]

... [A]t the threshold of the rocky door,
Hugest and fiercest of his kind accurst,
Fit warden of the sorcery-gate,

A rebel Afreet lay;
He scented the approach of human food,
And hungry hope kindled his eye of fire.

But Thalaba draws his bow and slays the jinn with an arrow. As he bounds over the dying afreet, he strikes the stone doors of Domdaniel and orders them to open in the name of God. The evil jinn are tormented by the divine name, the 'bismallah', and as Thalaba calls upon God, the 'dying Fiend beneath him, at that name / Tost in worse agony.'

The doors rumble open, and in strides Thalaba, ready for his final confrontation with the accursed magicians. Inside Domdaniel, Thalaba recovers the sacred sword of his slain father and uses it to battle the sorcerers. As he hefts the sword, in the inner cave, the 'Giant Idol' – made of living human flesh in the image of pre-fall Lucifer, 'Son of the Morning' – begins to stir. In one hand, the idol grasps a sceptre; the other arm is held high, supporting the roof of the cavern, above which lies the ocean floor. The idol slams the sceptre on a round altar, shaking the earth and in the process summoning magicians from far and wide to confront Thalaba. A great battle ensues, and Thalaba, one man against many, prevails. The surviving magicians huddle at the feet of the idol. Okba, the magician who slew Thalaba's father, reveals himself to the young man and awaits his death. But Thalaba shows mercy and declines to kill him.

The romance ends with Thalaba accepting Paradise and being reunited with his deceased wife Oneiza, as his reward for vanquishing the evil magicians. In his final act on earth, he drives the holy sword into the heart of the living idol:

The Ocean-vault fell in, and all were crush'd.
In the same moment, at the gate
Of Paradise, Oneiza's houri form
Welcomed her Husband to eternal bliss.

Thalaba's faith has served him well and shown the limits of the powers of the evil jinn and their sorcerer masters. Even Eblis, the mightiest of the evil spirits and the force behind the 'Giant Idol', is made to yield before the righteous sword of Thalaba.

Granted, Southey's portrayal of 'Genii' in *Thalaba the Destroyer* is limited by his sources and is quite one-sided, emphasising the evil in beings that have free will and can choose good as well. The nature of his story and the cultural filter of Orientalism dictated this emphasis. It is known, however, that Southey was an admirer of the lifestyle, values and simple ethics of the Arab Bedouins. Thalaba is a hero who exemplifies these qualities. Southey viewed the Bedouins as 'noble savages' who often found themselves in rebellion against the complexity and corruption of 'man-made systems' such as the evil society of magicians in Domdaniel.[16] The jinn are an integral part of the uncomplicated natural world of the Bedouins, just as they permeate the complex world of man-made systems. In Southey's *Thalaba the Destroyer*, we are given a glimpse of both of these worlds.

Hugo's 'Jinn'

French novelist Victor Hugo (1802–1885), author of *The Hunchback of Notre Dame*, penned an intriguing though now seldom-read poem about the jinn, 'Les Djinns'. The work was an experiment in Orientalist literature. It appeared in one of his early works, *Les Orientales*, a collection of creative poetry often employing exotic verse forms, which was published when Hugo was just 27 years old.

The poem captures, in its appearance, cadence and rhyme, the approach of a swarm of jinn upon a port town (probably in Algeria), their assault upon a man's home and their eventual retreat. In the words of Jorge Luis Borges: 'With each stanza, as the Jinn cluster together, the lines grow longer and longer, until the eighth, when they reach their fullness. From this point on they dwindle to the close of the poem, when the Jinn vanish.'[17]

'Les Djinns' attracted a good amount of attention and even controversy in its day for its inventiveness, and it inspired many 'disastrous imitations' by lesser artists, according to Hugo biographer Graham Robb.[18] The poem was later set to music on separate occasions by French composers Gabriel Fauré and Camille Saint-Saëns and by Belgium's César Franck.

Here is an English translation:

The Jinn

Walls, town
And port,
Refuge
From death,

Grey sea
Where breaks
The wind
All sleeps.

In the plain
Is born a sound.
It is the breathing
Of the night.
It roars
Like a soul
That a flame
Always follows.

The higher voice
Seems a shiver.
It is the gallop
of a bounding dwarf.
He flees, he springs,
Then in cadence
On one foot dances
At the end of a stream.

The murmur approaches,
The echo repeats it.
It is like the bell
Of a cursed convent,
Like a crowd sound
That thunders and rolls
And sometimes crumbles
And sometimes swells..

God! The sepulchral voice
Of the jinn! ... What a sound!
We flee beneath the spiral
Of the deep staircase!

My lamp has already died,
And the shadow of the ramp,
Which crawls along the wall,
Ascends to the ceiling.

The swarm of jinn is passing,

And it whirls, hissing.
Old conifers, stirred by their flight,
Crackle like burning pine.
Their herd, heavy and swift,
Flying in the vacant space,
Seems a livid cloud
With lightning flashing at its edge.

They are so near! – We keep closed
This room where we defy them.
What noise outside! Hideous army
Of vampires and dragons!
The beam of the loosened ceiling
Sags like soaked grass,
And the rusted old door
Trembles, unseating its hinges.

Cries from hell! voice that roars and weeps!
The horrible swarm, driven by the north wind,
Doubtless, or heaven! assails my home.
The wall bends under the black battalion.
The house cries out and staggers tilted,
And one could say that, ripped from the soil,
Just as it chases a dried-out leaf,
The wind rolls it along in a vortex!

Prophet! If your hand spares me
From these impure demons of the night,
I would go prostrate my bald forehead
Before your sacred incense burners!
Make their breath of sparks
Die on these faithful doors,
And make the talons of their wings
Scrape and cry in vain at these black windows!

They have passed! – Their cohort
Takes flight and flees, and their feet
Stop beating on my door
With their multiple blows.
The air is filled with a sound of chains,
And in the nearby forests
All the great oaks tremble

Bent beneath their fiery flight!

The beating of their wings
Fades in the distance.
So vague in the plains,
So faint, that you believe
You hear the grasshopper
Cry with a shrill voice
Or the hail crackling
On the lead of an old roof.

Strange syllables
Still approach us.
Thus, of the Arabs,
When the horn sounds,
A chant on the shore
Rises up in moments,
And the dreaming child
Has dreams of gold.

The funerary jinn,
Files of death,
In the shadows
Hurry their step;
Their swarm rumbles;
Thus, deep,
Murmurs a wave
That no one sees.

This vague sound
That falls asleep,
It is the wave
On the edge;
It is the moan,
Almost extinct,
Of a saint
For a death.

One doubts
The night ...
I listen: –
All flees,
All fades;

The space
Erases
The sound.

The Mystery of Ishmonia

The mystic theosophist and spiritualist Madame Helena Petrovna Blavatsky (1831–1891),[19] in her two-volume opus *Isis Unveiled*, mentions the following old Arab legend about a jinn-haunted ruin:

> There are widespread traditions of the existence of certain subterranean and immense galleries, in the neighbourhood of Ishmonia [or Ishmonie] – the 'Petrified City', in which are stored numberless manuscripts and rolls. For no amount of money would the Arabs go near it. At night, they say, from the crevices of the desolate ruins, sunk deep in the unwatered sands of the desert, stream the rays of lights carried to and fro in the galleries by no human hands. The afrites study the literature of the antediluvian ages, according to their belief, and the djin learns from the magic rolls the lesson of the following day.[20]

Ishmonia corresponds to present-day Ashmunein (classical Hermopolis Magna) on the 'border' between Lower and Upper Egypt, a major cult centre and pilgrimage site during Ptolemaic and Roman times. The 'Petrified City' probably refers to the nearby necropolis of Tuna el-Gebel, a Ptolemaic burial city of mausoleums, small temples and subterranean catacombs. The underground tunnels and chambers were found by modern archaeologists to be filled with mummified ibises and baboons – sacred animals of Thoth (or Hermes), the scribe deity honoured at Hermopolis Magna. Archaeologists also found scrolls in the catacombs, some of which can be viewed in Egyptian regional museums.

It appears that the underground tunnel network is very extensive and has not been completely explored. According to Egyptian antiquities official Zahi Hawass, part of the Tuna el-Gebel catacomb network suffered a devastating fire in 1969, apparently sparked by a guard's cigarette butt and fuelled by thousands of pitch-coated animal mummies. The fire burnt for a month. Who knows what treasures were reduced to ashes by the blaze?

The Ishmonia legend, the tale about lights coming from the ruins at night, is difficult to research due to a lack of source materials. Blavatsky took the account from an eighteenth-century travel book called *A View of the Levant, Particularly of Constantinople, Syria, Egypt and Greece* (1743), by British physician Charles Perry.[21]

Ishmonia and the Petrified City used to be listed in *Brewer's Dictionary of Phrase and Fable*, but they are no longer mentioned in current editions. Perhaps the dictionary's editors no longer found the accounts credible; it was more likely, though, a matter of changing tastes and the fact that the Petrified City was no longer being mentioned in literature. Here are the listings from the 1894 edition:

> **Ishmonie** – The petrified city in Upper Egypt, full of men and women turned to stone. (Perry: *View of the Levant*.) Marryat has borrowed the idea in his *Pacha of Many Tales*.
> **Petrified (3 syl.)** – *The petrified city*. Ishmonie, in Upper Egypt, is so called from the number of petrified bodies of men, women, and children to be seen there. (Latin, *petra-fio*, to become rock.)

There are no signs of 'petrified' people anywhere in the area today. However, Hermopolis would perhaps be a natural site of jinn activity, since its ruins once served as one of the world's most important religious centres.

As for Blavatsky's assertion that there were hidden archives in Egypt, the ancient Egyptians themselves believed so. French Egyptologists Dimitri Meeks and Christine Favard-Meeks describe this belief in *Daily Life of the Egyptian Gods* (1996):

> The archives of the [ancient Egyptian] libraries contained treasures – the writings of Thoth himself, copied and recopied generation after generation. Indeed, this god left a considerable quantity of texts in secret hiding places on earth; with sufficient patience, wise men could ferret them out. Certain works the Egyptians often turned to, such as the Book of the Dead or the Book of the Opening of the Mouth, were specially composed by Thoth for their use. A book placed under the side of the god Khnum came to the knowledge of mortals, no one knows how. The gods themselves did not hesitate to pass some of their secrets on to people by letting a providential manuscript fall from the heavens. Writing was, plainly, the instrument of revelation; it provided access to the world of the gods.

Hermopolis was the home of the Ogdoad, the eight gods who created the world. Known to the ancient Egyptians as Khmun, this city was the main cult centre of the Ptolemaic era, with a great temple dedicated to Djehuty or Thoth.

The Greeks equated Djehuty – a patron of wisdom, writing and healing – with their god Hermes. The existing remains of the great temple building are attributed to the pharaoh Nectanebo I of the thirtieth Dynasty, but the structure is probably of earlier origin. Other temple ruins in the area date to the Middle and New Kingdom, and a colossal statue of Thoth in baboon form dates from the time of Amenhotep III.

Not far to the west of the city of Hermopolis is a major necropolis or cemetery, known as Tuna el-Gebel, beneath which lies an extensive network of catacombs. In these tunnels, modern archaeologists found countless mummified baboons and ibises – both symbols of Thoth, apparently sold by the priests to pilgrims for ritual purposes. Also found were an unspecified number of papyrus documents of various types, which now reside in regional museums and for the most part remain untranslated. As we have seen, a fire devastated the subterranean tunnels in 1969.

The Ogdoad, the creation myth that originated in Hermopolis, consisted of eight primeval forces, conceptualised as four divine couples. It was probably from this concept that the ancient name of Khmun or 'eight-town' originated. Of these eight deities, only Amun developed into a prominent god and was transferred to Thebes with his female counterpart Amaunet.

Very few inscriptions have been unearthed at Ashmunein that tell us anything about this cosmogony. The main evidence for the Ogdoad comes from Theban monuments pieced together in 1929 by German archaeologist Kurt Sethe in his survey *Amun and the Eight Primeval Deities of Hermopolis.*[22]

The earliest reference to the Hermopolitan cosmogony is found in the Pyramid Texts:[23]

> You have your offering-bread, O Niu and Nenet, you two protectors (?) of the gods Who protect the gods with your shadow. You have your offering-bread, O Amun and Amaunet, You two protectors (?) of the gods Who protect the gods with your shadow. You have your offering-bread, O Atum and Ruti, Who yourselves created your godheads and your persons. O Shu and Tefenet who made the gods, Who begot the gods and established the gods ...

There are four pairs of complementary deities. For every 'male' deity there is a 'female' counterpart. The males have frog-heads and the females snake-heads – reminiscent of jinn shapeshifting. The Ogdoad and their concepts are as follows:

Nu ↔ Naunet	=	*primeval waters*
Heh ↔ Hauhet	=	*boundlessness*
Kek ↔ Kauket	=	*darkness*
Amun ↔ Amaunet	=	*air*

The Ogdoad were 'the fathers and the mothers who came into being at the start, who gave birth to the sun and who created Atum', according to the Pyramid Texts. From these divinities the rest of the universe developed. The eight members of the Ogdoad jointly created the Cosmic Egg from the primeval waters (Nun). This egg was invisible because it was created before the sun came into being. From this egg emerged the bird of light, an aspect of the sun-god, some sources say.

After Alexander the Great's conquest of Egypt, in 332 BC, a tomb resembling a small temple was built for Petosiris, high priest of Djehuty, in the cemetery of Hermopolis, above the vast network of catacombs. Inscriptions in Petosiris's tomb describe Djehuty as 'Lord of Khemnu'. Petosiris had directed extensive restorations of the temple complex at Hermopolis, including construction of a wall around the temple to keep out vandals. This site is now called the 'birthplace of every god' and is said to be the location where the relics of the Cosmic Egg were buried. Djehuty flew with the egg to the primeval mound which later became Hermopolis, so the sun-god could be born there.

Today, Hermopolis is a rarely visited archaeological site. Its necropolis, Tuna el-Gebel, may have been the locale cited by Blavatsky and Perry, where lights burned at night as jinn pored over ancient documents. But the lights, if they ever existed, have been extinguished for many years.

Arab Folktales

The jinn live in the oral tradition of the Arab world, in the tales parents and grandparents tell to their young ones, in the stories Bedouins tell around campfires, and in the thrilling epics related to crowds by *hakawatis* (professional storytellers). One of the best modern collections of popular stories from the Arabian heartland is *Arab Folktales* (1986), compiled and translated by Palestinian writer Inea Bushnaq.[24] The stories she translates have much to say about the jinn, ghouls, ifrits and other members of the spirit family.

Bushnaq observes that magical adventures are at the heart of Arab storytelling and that 'much of the excitement in the tales of magic lies in the removal of the boundary between the two worlds'. Whether the spirit creatures are sought as helpers or confronted as dangerous foes, they are as much a part of the landscape as the heroes. 'When a merchant watering his camels pulls a handsome youth up from the bottom of the well with his rope, or when a prince hunting in the wilderness comes upon a girl whose hair shines like threads of gold, the question "Are you Ins [human] or are you Djinn?" is asked as a matter of course,' she explains.

In the people's imagination, jinn are master craftsmen, especially in metal. No human is able to copy the work of a jinn. Knowing this, the fair maiden in a tale called 'The Bird of the Golden Feather' agrees to be married, but only to someone who can duplicate her earring. The goldsmiths' guild is forced to confess that this task is beyond their combined ability. The maiden is actually relieved to hear this, because she has given the earring's twin to a man she loves and expects only him to match it. A similar device is found in the plot of Bushnaq's 'The Ring of the King of the Djinn'.

Jinn can be terrifying in appearance and in power. In one popular tale, three sisters faint outright when they see them. Of course, the jinn's strength too is overwhelming: they can enter a house by splitting open the wall from ceiling to floor. 'To face them is like facing a storm,' Bushnaq says, 'and the earth itself trembles at their tread.' But in many a tale, the wits of a jinn rarely equal his might. In 'A Tale within a Tale', the hero escapes from a jinn who is about to behead him by begging to be allowed to say one last prayer. 'It does not occur to the spirit that the rug on which the man stands is no prayer mat but a magic carpet, and that it is not the name of Allah but a magic formula that he is reciting.' Later in the same story, two young jinn are cheated out of their treasure when the hero has them race to recover a distant stone while he makes off with their property.

Ghouls, as we know, are the wildest and most repulsive-looking of the jinn. They are hairy and filthy. Their teeth are long and sometimes made of brass. They love to eat people and are acutely sensitive to the smell of human flesh. They have a set entrance speech in the folktales, as the human hero stammered his '*Salamu alaikum*':

> *Lawla salaamak*
> *Sabaq kalaamak*
>
> *Had not your greeting*
> *Come first before your speaking,*
> *I would have torn your muscles each from each*
> *And used your bones to pick my teeth.*

Yet Bushnaq notes that in Arabian folktales the ghouls often prove surprisingly sentimental and good-natured, especially if they are treated well. They respond to politeness and in exchange for a little grooming or a piece of mastic gum, they are often ready to carry the hero wherever he wishes to go. 'Make no mistake; their diet is carrion and preferably human flesh, but the wise hero knows how to disarm them.'

In the case of the ghoulah, the female ghoul, the trick is to establish a foster relationship. The she-ghoul is most often encountered squatting at her hand mill, working hard, her pendulous breasts flung over her shoulders to keep them out of the way. If the hero manages to creep up behind her and suck from her breast, she will treat him as a child of her bosom and protect him even from her own ghoul children. 'The "milk relationship" is a real one in Islam,' Bushnaq observes. 'If they were nursed from the same breast as infants, two otherwise betrothable people are "milk brother and sister" and therefore unable to marry.'

It is easy enough to stray into the jinn's world if one happens to be a hero or a fool. Fortunately, the spirit world is so different from ours that one cannot mistake it. For example, in the spirit world, a lighted candle makes its bearer invisible. When a demon is deep in sleep, its eyes will come open. One blow of a sword will kill a demon, but two blows will bring it back to life. If a hero has a friendly jinn as a guide, he can easily travel through the spirit world unscathed. We saw an example of this in 'The Tale of the Damsel Tohfat al-Kulub' in *The Arabian*

Nights, where Iblis, father of the jinn, serves as guide to the slave-girl singer Tohfat on her journey to the land of the jinn.

Even the most horrible of monsters are vulnerable to those who know their weakness or the secret to releasing their chains. A few drops of water can break a spell. In 'The Camel Husband', a spirit banquet becomes visible after a rain shower. A mighty demon depends for his life on three little white hairs that grow between his eyes, or on a fragile flask, tied to a deer's hind leg, in which he keeps his soul. 'Once the rules are set and the obstacles identified, the listener can happily settle down and follow the hero as he picks his way to the triumphant finish.'

The supernatural world is invariably sumptuous. Banquets are always laid for forty guests. The diners sit on thrones of gold. Dishes come and go of their own accord and even speak. Birds have golden plumage, and the palaces of the jinn are constructed with bricks of silver and gold. Spirit women are always more beautiful than their earthly counterparts, and their horses fleeter.

And yet, despite all this, the jinn go about their lives with the same trials and troubles as human beings. The jinn king in 'One-Tooth and Two-Teeth' suffers from a boil at the back of his throat. In 'The Ring of the King of the Djinn' the ghoul, just like any Arab host, is unable to refuse a guest's request. The jinn suffer fits of jealousy. They fall in love, sometimes with humans, and even marry them, as in 'The Camel Husband'.

'However unearthly their nature, the Djinns' existence was disturbingly real for most people who listened to the stories about them,' Bushnaq says. Many a personal tale is told of actual meetings with jinn. People swear to the truth of the tale of a woman who agreed to go out early with her neighbour so they could fill their water jars before the crowds arrived at the well. In the middle of the night, she was awakened by what she thought was her friend. Then she saw sparks flying from hooves beneath the dress of the creature walking in front of her and realised that it was long before dawn and she was alone with a female jinn of the night.

Many a time a person has wasted away for no explicable reason – like the sister in 'The Girl Who Banished Seven Youths' – and a religious sheikh or a Sufi dervish has been summoned to save the sufferer.

A sacred inscription on a powerful amulet or possibly a flogging with twigs of pomegranate (a tree said to grow in Paradise) may drive off whatever evil jinn was 'riding' the invalid.

* * *

Folktales demonstrate perhaps better than most forms of communication that the concept of the jinn is fundamentally a very human way of explaining and thus coping with the mysterious and the unknown. Our brains are wired to seek cause and effect, to craft explanations for things that may not be explainable. The phenomena that people throughout the world attribute to jinn – both evil and friendly varieties – are for the most part actual physical happenings that beg for explanation.

In the context in which they operate, jinn are a very reasonable – and in a sense reassuring – solution to the mysteries that surround us. Our exploration of this phenomenon has not been designed to prove or disprove the existence of the fire spirits. Since we are not ourselves jinn, we may never really understand what they are. But we can understand how they affect us, and how we respond to them and how we interact with each other as we try to deal with them.

The existence of jinn in other cultures beyond the Arab and Islamic worlds has been hinted at. The Europeans have their elves and faeries, the Hindus their *ganas*, the South Africans their *tokolosh*, the Japanese their *kami*. In fact, most – if not all – peoples of the world have their legends of nature spirits, 'little people', shapeshifters and horrific demons.[25] The jinn have their home in one region, the Middle East, and are today roughly coterminous with the spread of Islam through Asia and Africa. But the existence of strikingly similar traditions across the planet shows us that we are dealing with something truly fundamental to and a significant part of what it means to be human.

Appendix A

Edward Lane's Notes on the Jinn

Edward W. Lane (1801–76) was one of the West's most celebrated Orientalist scholars. His Account of the Manners and Customs of the Modern Egyptians *(1836) is still regarded as a classic. He also translated* The Thousand and One Nights, *and included copious notes on various aspects of Arab and Islamic life, including this valuable discussion of the jinn.*

On the Jinn, or Genii

The Muslims, in general, believe in three different species of created intelligent beings; namely, Angels, who are created of light; Genii, who are created of fire; and Men, created of earth. The first species are called 'Meláïkeh' (sing. 'Melek'); the second, 'Jinn' or 'Ginn' (sing. 'Jinnee' or 'Ginnee'); the third, 'Ins' (sing. 'Insee'). Some hold that the Devils (Sheytáns) are of a species distinct from Angels and Jinn; but the more prevailing opinion, and that which rests on the highest authority, is that they are rebellious Jinn . . . .

The species of Jinn is said to have been created some thousands of years before Adam. According to a tradition from the Prophet, this species consists of five orders or classes; namely, Jánn (who are the least powerful of all), Jinn, Sheytáns (or Devils), 'Efreets, and Márids. The last, it is added, are the most powerful; and the Jánn are transformed Jinn; like as certain apes and swine were transformed men (Kur-án 5:65). It must however, be remarked here, that the terms Jinn and Jánn are generally used indiscriminately, as names of the whole species (including the other orders above mentioned) whether good or bad; and that the former term is the more common. Also, that 'Sheytán' is commonly used to signify any evil

Jinnee. An 'Efreet is a powerful evil Jinnee: a Márid, an evil Jinnee of the most powerful class. The Jinn (but generally speaking, evil ones) are called by the Persians 'Deevs'; the most powerful evil, 'Narahs' (which signifies 'males', though they are said to be males and females); the good Jinn, 'Perees'; though this term more commonly applies to females.

In a tradition from the Prophet, it is said, 'The Jánn were created of a smokeless fire.' The word which signifies 'a smokeless fire' has been misunderstood by some as meaning 'the flame of fire': El-Jóharee (in the Seháh) renders it rightly; and says that of this fire was the Sheytán (Iblees) created. 'El-Jánn' is sometimes used as a name for Iblees; as in the following verse of the Kur-án: – 'And the Jánn [the father of the Jinn, i.e. Iblees] we had created before [i.e. before the creation of Adam] of the fire of the samoom [i.e. of the fire without smoke].' 'Jánn' also signifies 'a serpent'; as in other passages of the Kur-án; and is used in the same book as synonymous with 'Jinn'. In the last sense it is generally believed to be used in the tradition quoted in the commencement of this paragraph. There are several apparently contradictory traditions from the Prophet which are reconciled by what has been above stated: in one, it is said, that Iblees was the father of all the Jánn and Sheytáns; Jánn being here synonymous with Jinn: in another, that Jánn was the father of all the Jinn; here, Jánn being used as the name of Iblees.

'It is held,' says El-Kazweenee,

> that the Jinn are aerial animals, with transparent bodies, which can assume various forms. People differ in opinion respecting these beings: some consider the Jinn and Sheytáns as unruly men; but these persons are of the Moatezileh [a sect of Muslim freethinkers]: and some hold, that God, whose name be exalted, created the Angels of the light of fire, and the Jinn of its flame [but this is at variance with the general opinion] and the Sheytáns of its smoke [which is also at variance with the common opinion]; and that [all] these kinds of beings are [usually] invisible to men, but that they assume what forms they please, and when their form becomes condensed they are visible.

– This last remark illustrates several descriptions of Jinnees in this work; where the form of the monster is at first undefined, or like an enormous pillar, and then gradually assumes a human shape and less gigantic size. The particular forms of brutes, reptiles, &c., in which the Jinn most frequently appear will be mentioned hereafter.

It is said that God created the Jánn [or Jinn] two thousand years before Adam [or, according to some writers, much earlier]; and that there are believers and infidels and every sect among them, as among men. Some say that a prophet, named Yoosuf, was sent to the Jinn: others, that they had only preachers, or admonishers: others, again, that seventy apostles were sent, before Mohammed, to Jinn and men conjointly. It is commonly believed that preadamite Jinn were governed by forty (or, according to some, seventy-two) kings, to each of which the Arab writers give the name of Suleymán (or Solomon); and that they derive their appellation from the last of these, who was called Jánn Ibn-Jánn, and who, some say, built the pyramids of Egypt. The following account of the preadamite Jinn is given by El-Kazweenee.—

> It is related in histories, that a race of Jinn, in ancient times, before the creation of Adam, inhabited the earth and covered it, the land and the sea, and the plains and the mountains; and the favours of God were multiplied upon them, and they had government, and prophecy, and religion, and law; but they transgressed and offended, and opposed their prophets, and made wickedness to abound in the earth; whereupon, God, whose name be exalted, sent against them an army of Angels, who took possession of the earth, and drove away the Jinn to the regions of the islands, and made many of them prisoners; and of those who were made prisoners was 'Azázeel [afterwards called Iblees, from his despair]; and a slaughter was made among them. At that time, 'Azázeel was young: he grew up among the Angels [and probably for that reason was called one of them], and became learned in their knowledge, and assumed the government of them; and his days were prolonged until he became their chief; and thus it continued for a long time, until the affair between him and Adam happened, as God, whose name be exalted, hath said, 'When we said unto the Angels, Worship ye Adam, and [all] worshipped except Iblees, [who] was [one] of the Jinn.'

'Iblees,' we are told by another authority, 'was sent as a governor upon the earth, and judged among the Jinn a thousand years, after which he ascended into heaven, and remained employed in worship until the creation of Adam.' The name of Iblees was originally, according to some,

'Azázeel (as before mentioned; and according to others, El-Hárith: his patronymic is Aboo-Murrah, or Abu-l-Ghimr. It is disputed whether he was of the Angels or of the Jinn. There are three opinions on this point.

1. That he was of the Angels, from a tradition from Ibn-'Abbás.
2. That he was of the Sheytáns (or evil Jinn); as it is said in the Ku-rán, 'except Iblees, [who] was [one] of the Jinn': this was the opinion of El-Hasan El-Basree, and is that commonly held.
3. That he was neither of the Angels nor of the Jinn; but created alone, of fire.

Ibn-'Abbás founds his opinion on the same text from which El-Hasan El-Basree derives his: 'When we said unto the Angels, Worship ye Adam, and [all] worshipped except Iblees, [who] was [one] of the Jinn' (before quoted: which he explains by saying, that the most noble and honourable among the Angels are called 'the Jinn', because they are veiled from the eyes of the other Angels on account of their superiority; and that Iblees was one of these Jinn. He adds, that he had the government of the lowest heaven and of the earth, and was called the Táoos (literally, Peacock) of the Angels; and that there was not a spot in the lowest heaven but he had prostrated himself upon it: but when the Jinn rebelled upon the earth, God sent a troop of Angels who drove them to the islands and mountains; and Iblees being elated with pride, and refusing to prostrate himself before Adam, God transformed him into a Sheytán. – But this reasoning is opposed by other verses, in which Iblees is represented as saying, 'Thou hast created me of fire, and hast created him [Adam] of earth.' It is therefore argued, 'If he were created originally of fire, how was he created of light? For the Angels were [all] created of light.'

The former verse may be explained by the tradition, that Iblees, having been taken captive, was exalted among the Angels; or perhaps there is an ellipsis after the word 'Angels'; for it might be inferred that the command given to the Angels was also (and à fortiori) to be obeyed by the Jinn.

According to a tradition, Iblees and all the Sheytáns are distinguished from the other Jinn by a longer existence. 'The Sheytáns,' it is added, 'are the children of Iblees, and die not but with him: whereas the [other] Jinn die before him'; though they may live many centuries. But this is not altogether accordant with the popular belief: Iblees and many other evil Jinn are to survive mankind; but they are to die before the general resurrection; as also even the Angels; the last of whom will be the Angel of Death, 'Azraeel: yet not all the evil Jinn are to live thus long: many of them are killed by shooting stars, hurled at them from heaven; wherefore, the Arabs, when they see a shooting star (shiháb), often exclaim, 'May God transfix the enemy of the faith!'

Many also are killed by other Jinn; and some, even by men. The fire of which the Jinnee is created circulates in his veins, in place of blood: therefore, when he receives a mortal wound, this fire, issuing from his veins, generally consumes him to ashes.

The Jinn, it has been already shown, are peccable. They also eat and drink, and propagate their species, sometimes in conjunction with human beings; in which latter case, the offspring partakes of the nature of both parents. In all these respects they differ from the Angels. Among the evil Jinn are distinguished the five sons of their chief, Iblees; namely, Teer, who brings about calamities, losses, and injuries; El-Aawar, who encourages debauchery; Sót, who suggests lies, Dásim, who causes hatred between man and wife; and Zelemboor, who presides over places of traffic.

The most common forms and habitations or places of resort of the Jinn must now be described.

The following traditions from the Prophet are the most to the purpose that I have seen.

- The Jinn are of various shapes; having the forms of serpents, scorpions, lions, wolves, jackals, &c.
- The Jinn are of three kinds; one on the land; one in the sea; and one in the air. The Jinn consist of forty troops; each troop consisting of six hundred thousand.
- The Jinn are of three kinds; one have wings, and fly; another are snakes, and dogs; and the third move about from place to place like men. – Domestic snakes are asserted to be Jinn on the same authority.

The Prophet ordered his followers to kill serpents and scorpions if they intruded at prayers; but on other occasions, he seems to have required first to admonish them to depart, and then, if they remained, to kill them. The Doctors, however, differ in opinion whether all kinds of snakes or serpents should be admonished first; or whether any should; for the Prophet, say they, took a covenant of the Jinn [probably after the above-mentioned command], that they should not enter the houses of the faithful: therefore, it is argued, if they enter, they break their covenant, and it becomes lawful to kill them without previous admonishment. Yet it is related that 'Áïsheh, the Prophet's wife, having killed a serpent in her chamber, was alarmed by a dream, and, fearing that it might have been a Muslim Jinnee, as it did not enter her chamber when she was undressed, gave in alms, as an expiation, twelve thousand dirhems (about £300), the price of the blood of a Muslim.

The Jinn are said to appear to mankind most commonly in the shapes of serpents, dogs, cats or human beings. In the last case, they are sometimes of the stature of men, and sometimes of a size enormously gigantic. If good, they are generally resplendently handsome: if evil, horribly hideous. They become invisible at pleasure (by a rapid extension or rarefaction of the particles which compose them), or suddenly disappear in the earth or air, or through a solid wall. Many Muslims in the present day profess to have seen and held intercourse with them.

The Zóba'ah, which is a whirlwind that raises the sand or dust in the form of a pillar of prodigious height, often seen sweeping across the deserts or fields, is believed to be caused by the flight of an evil Jinnee. To defend themselves from a Jinnee thus 'riding in the whirlwind', the Arabs often exclaim 'Iron! Iron!' (Hadeed! Hadeed!), or, 'Iron! Thou unlucky! (Hadeed! yá mashoom!), as the Jinn are supposed to have a great dread of that metal: or they exclaim, 'God is most great!' (Alláhu akbar!), A similar superstition prevails with respect to the water-spout at sea, as the reader may have discovered from the first instance of the description of a Jinnee in the present work, which occasions this note to be here inserted.

It is believed that the chief mode of the Jinn is in the mountains of Káf, which are supposed (as mentioned on a former occasion) to encompass the whole of our earth. But they are also believed to pervade the solid body of our earth, and the firmament; and to choose, as their principal places of resort, or of occasional abode, baths, wells, the latrina, ovens, ruined houses, market-places, the junctures of the roads, the sea, and rivers. The Arabs, therefore, when they pour water, &c., on the ground, or enter a bath, or let down a bucket into a well, or visit the latrina, and on various other occasions, say, 'Permission!' or 'Permission, ye blessed!' (Destoor! Or, Destoor yá mubarakeen!). – The evil spirits (or evil Jinn), it is said, had liberty to enter any of the seven heavens till the birth of Jesus, when they were excluded from three of them: on the birth of Mohammed, they were forbidden the other four. They continue, however, to ascend to the confines of the lowest heaven, and there listening to the conversation of the Angels respecting things decreed by God, obtain knowledge of futurity, which they sometimes impart to men, who, by means of talismans, or certain invocations, make them to serve the purposes of magical performances. To this particular subject it will be necessary to revert.

What the Prophet said of Iblees, in the following tradition, applies to the evil Jinn over whom he presides: – His chief abode [among men] is the bath; his chief places of resort are the markets, and the junctures of roads; his food is whatever is killed without the name of God being pronounced over it; his drink, whatever is intoxicating; his muëddin, the mizmár (a musical pipe; i.e. any musical instrument); his kur-án, poetry; his written character, the marks made in geomancy; his speech, falsehood; his snares are women.

That particular Jinnees presided over particular places, was an opinion of the early Arabs. It is said in the Kur-án, 'And there were certain men who sought refuge with certain of the Jinn.' In the commentary of the Jeláleyn, I find the following remark on these words: – 'When they halted, on their journey, in a place of fear, each man said, "I seek refuge with the lord of this place, from the mischief of his foolish ones!"' In illustration of this, I may insert the following tradition, translated from El-Kazweenee: – 'It is related by a certain narrator of traditions, that he descended into a valley, with his sheep, and a wolf carried off a ewe from among them; and he arose, and raised his voice, and cried, "O inhabitant of the valley!" whereupon he heard a voice saying, "O wolf, restore to him his sheep!" and the wolf came with the ewe, and left her, and departed.' – The same opinion is held by the modern Arabs, though probably they do not use such an invocation. – A similar superstition, a relic of ancient Egyptian credulity, still prevails among the people of Cairo. It is believed that each quarter of the city has its peculiar guardian-genius, or Agathodæmon, which has the form of a serpent.

It has already been mentioned that some of the Jinn are Muslims; and others, infidels. The good Jinn acquit themselves of imperative duties of religion; namely, prayers, alms-giving, fasting during the month of Ramadán, and pilgrimage to Mekkeh and Mount 'Arafát: but in the performance of these duties they are generally invisible to human beings. Some examples of the mode in which good Jinn pay the alms required of them by the law, I have given in a former work.

Of the services and injuries done by Jinn to men, some account must be given.

It has been stated, that, by means of talismans, or certain invocations, men are said to obtain the services of Jinn; and the manner in which the latter are enabled to assist magicians, by imparting to them the knowledge of future events, has been explained. No man ever attained such absolute power over the Jinn as Suleymán Ibn-Dáood (Solomon, the Son of David). This he did by virtue of a most wonderful talisman, which is said to have come down to him from heaven. It was a seal-ring, upon which was engraved 'the most great name' of God; and was partly composed of brass, and partly of iron. With the brass he stamped his written commands to the good Jinn; with the iron (for a reason before mentioned), those to the evil Jinn, or Devils. Over both orders, he had unlimited power; as well as over the birds and the winds, and, as is generally said, the wild beasts. His Wezeer, Ásaf the son of Barkhiya, is also said to have been acquainted with 'the most great name', by uttering which, the greatest miracles may be performed; even that of raising the dead. By virtue of this name, engraved in his ring, Suleymán compelled the Jinn to assist in building the Temple of Jerusalem, and in various other works. Many of the evil Jinn he converted to the true faith; and many others of this class, who remained obstinate in infidelity, he confined in prisons. He is said to have been monarch of the whole earth. Hence, perhaps, the name of Suleymán is given to the universal monarch of the preadamite Jinn; unless the story of his own universal dominion originated from confounding him with those kings of the Jinn.

The injuries related to have been inflicted upon human beings by evil Jinn are of various kinds. Jinnees are said to have often carried off beautiful women, whom they have forcibly kept as their wives or concubines. I have mentioned in a former work, that malicious or disturbed Jinnees are asserted often to station themselves on the roofs, or at the windows, of houses, and to throw down bricks and stones on persons passing by. When they take possession of an uninhabited house, they seldom fail to persecute terribly any person who goes to reside in it. They are also very apt to pilfer provisions, &c. Many learned and devout persons, to secure their property from such depredations, repeat the words 'In the name of God, the Compassionate, the Merciful!' on locking the doors of their houses, rooms, or closets, and on covering the bread-basket, or anything containing food. During the month of Ramadán, the evil Jinn are believed to be confined in prison; and therefore, on the last night of that month, with the same view, women sometimes repeat the words above mentioned, and sprinkle salt upon the floors of the apartments of their houses.

To complete this sketch of Arabian mythology, an account must be added of several creatures believed to be of inferior orders of the Jinn.

One of these is the **Ghool**, which is commonly regarded as a kind of Sheytán, or evil Jinnee, that eats men; and is described by some as a Jinnee or an enchanter who assumes various forms. The ghools are said to appear in the forms of various animals, and of human beings, and in many monstrous shapes; to haunt burial-grounds and other sequestered spots; to feed upon dead human bodies; and to kill and devour any human creature who has the misfortune to fall in their way: whence the term 'Ghool' is applied to any cannibal. An opinion quoted by a celebrated author, respecting the Ghool, is, that it is a demoniacal animal, which passes a solitary existence in the deserts, resembling both man and brute; that it appears to a person travelling alone in the night and in solitary places, and, being supposed by him to be itself a traveller, lures him out of his way. Another opinions stated by him is this: that, when the Sheytáns attempt to hear words by stealth [from the confines of the lowest heaven], they are struck by shooting stars; and some are burnt; some, falling into the sea, or rather a large river (bahr), become converted into crocodiles; and some, falling upon the land, become Ghools.

The same author adds the following tradition: – 'The Ghool is any Jinnee that is opposed to travels, assuming various forms and appearances'; and affirms that several of the Companions of the Prophet saw Ghools in their travels; and that 'Omar, among them, saw a Ghool while on a journey to Syria, before El-Islám, and struck it with his sword. – It appears that 'Ghool' is, properly speaking, a name only given to a female demon of the kind above described: the male is called 'Kutrub'. It is said that these beings, and the Gheddár, or Gharrár, and other similar creatures which will presently be mentioned, are the offspring of Iblees and of a wife whom God created for him of the fire of the Samoon (which here signifies, as an instance before mentioned, 'a smokeless fire'); and that they sprang from an egg. The female Ghool, it is added, appears to men in the deserts, in various forms, converses with them, and sometimes prostitutes herself to them.

The **Sealáh**, or Saaláh, is another demoniacal creature, described by some [or rather, by most authors] as of the Jinn. It is said that it is mostly found in forests; and that when it captures a man, it makes him dance, and plays with him as the cat plays with the mouse. A man of Isfahán asserted that many beings of this kind abounded in his country; that sometimes the wolf would hunt one of them by night, and devour it, and that, when it had seized it, the Sealáh would cry out, 'Who will liberate me? I have a hundred deenárs, and he shall receive them!' but the people knowing that it was the cry of the Sealáh, no one would liberate it; and so the wolf would eat it. – An island in the sea of Es-Seen (or China) is called 'the Island of the Sealáh', by Arab geographers, from its being said to be inhabited by the demons so named: they are described as creatures of hideous forms, supposed to be Sheytáns, the offspring of human beings and Jinn, who eat men.

The **Ghaddár**, or Gharrár (for its name is written differently in two different MSS. In my possession), is another creature of a similar nature, described as being found in the borders of El-Yemen, and sometimes in Tihámeh, and in the upper parts of Egypt. It is said that it entices a man to it, and either tortures him in a manner not to be described, or merely terrifies him, and leaves him.

The **Delhán** is also a demoniacal being, inhabiting the islands of the seas, having the form of a man, and riding on an ostrich. It eats the flesh of men whom the sea casts on the shore from wrecks. Some say that a Dalhán once attacked a ship in the sea, and desired to take the crew; but they contended with it; whereupon it uttered a cry which caused them to fall upon their faces, and it took them. – In my MS. Of Ibn-El-Wardee, I find the name 'Dahlán'. He mentions an island called by this name, in the Sea of 'Omán; and describes its inhabitants as cannibal Sheytáns, like men in form, and riding on birds resembling ostriches.

The **Shikk** is another demoniacal creature, having the form of half a human being (like a man divided longitudinally); and it is believed that the Nesnás is the offspring of a Shikk and of a human being. The Shikk appears to travellers; and it was a demon of this kind who killed, and was killed by, 'Alkameh, the son of Safwán, the son of Umeiyeh; of whom it is well known that he was killed by a Jinnee. So says El-Kazweenee.

The **Nesnás** (above mentioned) is described as resembling half a human being; having half a head, half a body, one arm, and one leg, with which it hops with much agility; as being found in the woods of El-Yemen; and that one was brought alive to El-Mutawekkil: it resembled a man in form, excepting that it had but half a face, which was in its breast, and a tail like that of a sheep. The people of Hadramót, it is added, eat it; and its flesh is sweet. It is only generated in their country. A man who went there asserted that he saw a captured Nesnás, which cried out for mercy, conjuring him by God and by himself. A race of people whose head is in the breast is described as inhabiting an island called Jábeh (supposed to be Java), in the Sea of El-Hind, or India. A kind of Nesnás is also described as inhabiting the Island of Ráïj, in the Sea of Es-Seen, or China, and having wings like those of the bat.

The **Hátif** is a being that is heard, but not seen; and is often mentioned by Arab writers. It is generally the communicator of some intelligence in the way of advice, or direction, or warning.

Appendix B

Muhammad Asad on the Jinn

Muhammad Asad (1900–1992), born Leopold Weiss, was a European Jewish convert to Islam. He studied in the holy cities of Mecca and Medina and served as a government official and diplomat for the new state of Pakistan from 1947 to 1952. Asad wrote extensively about his life experiences and religious beliefs. In the 1980s he published his own English translation of the Qur'an. In an appendix[1] *to that work, he discussed the reality of the jinn ...*

On the Term and Concept of Jinn

In order to grasp the purport of the term *jinn* as used in the Qur'an, we must dissociate our minds from the meaning given to it in Arabian folklore, where it early came to denote all manner of 'demons' in the most popular sense of this word. This folkloristic image has somewhat obscured the original connotation of the term and its highly significant – almost self-explanatory – verbal derivation. The root-verb is *janna*, 'he [or 'it'] concealed' or 'covered with darkness': cf. 6:76, which speaks of Abraham 'when the night overshadowed him with its darkness (*janna 'alayhi*)'. Since this verb is also used in the intransitive sense ('he [or 'it'] was [or 'became'] concealed', resp. 'covered with darkness'), all classical philologists point out that *al-jinn* signifies 'intense [or 'confusing'] darkness' and, in a more general sense, 'that which is concealed from [man's] senses', i.e., things, beings, or forces which cannot normally be perceived by man but have, nevertheless, an objective reality, whether concrete or abstract, of their own.

In the usage of the Qur'an, which is certainly different from the usage of primitive folklore, the term *jinn* has several distinct meanings. The most commonly encountered is that of *spiritual* forces or beings which, precisely because they have no corporeal existence, are beyond the perception of our corporeal senses: a connotation which includes 'satans' and 'satanic forces' (*shayatin*) as well as 'angels' and 'angelic forces', since all of them are 'concealed from our senses' (Jawhari, Raghib). In order to make it quite evident that these invisible manifestations are not of a corporeal nature, the Qur'an states parabolically that the jinn were created out of 'the fire of scorching winds' (*nar as-samum*, in 15:27), or out of 'a confusing flame of fire' (*marij min nar*, in 55:15), or simply 'out of fire' (7:12 and 38:76, in these last two instances referring to the Fallen Angel, Iblis). Parallel with this, we have authentic *ahadith* [recorded traditions] to the effect that the Prophet spoke of the angels as having been 'created out of light' (*khuliqat min nur*: Muslim, on the authority of 'A'ishah) – light and fire being akin, and likely to manifest themselves within and through one another.

The term *jinn* is also applied to a wide range of phenomena which, according to most of the classical commentators, indicate certain *sentient organisms* of so fine a nature and of a physiological composition so different from our own that they are not normally accessible to our sense-perception. We know, of course, very little as to what can and what cannot play the role of a living organism; moreover, our inability to discern and observe such phenomena is by no means a sufficient justification for a denial of their existence. The Qur'an refers often to 'the realm which is beyond the reach of human perception' (*al-ghayb*), while God is frequently spoken of as 'the Sustainer of all the worlds' (*rabb al-'alamin*): and the use of the plural clearly indicates that side by side with the 'world' open to our observation there are other 'worlds' as well – and, therefore, other forms of life, different from ours and presumably from one another, and yet subtly interacting and perhaps even permeating one another in a manner beyond our ken. And if we assume, as we must, that there are living organisms whose biological premises are entirely different from our own, it is only logical to assume that our physical senses can establish contact with them only under very exceptional circumstances: hence the description of them as 'invisible beings'. Now that occasional, very rare crossing of paths between their life-mode and ours may well give rise to strange – because unexplainable – manifestations, which man's primitive fantasy has subsequently interpreted as ghosts, demons and other such 'supernatural' apparitions.

Occasionally, the term *jinn* is used in the Qur'an to denote those elemental forces of nature – including human nature – which are 'concealed from our senses' inasmuch as they manifest themselves to us only in their effects but not in their intrinsic reality. Instances of this connotation are found, e.g., in 37:158 ff. (and possibly also in 6:100), as well as in the earliest occurrence of this concept, namely, in 114:6.

Apart from this, it is quite probable that in many instances where the Qur'an refers to *jinn* in terms usually applied to organisms endowed with reason, this expression either implies a symbolic 'personification' of man's *relationship* with 'satanic forces' (*shayatin*) – an implication evident, e.g., in 6:112, 7:38, 11:119, 32:13 – or, alternatively, is a metonym for a person's preoccupation with what is loosely described as 'occult powers', whether real or illusory, as well as for the resulting practices as such, like sorcery, necromancy, astrology, soothsaying, etc.: endeavours to which the Qur'an invariably refers in condemnatory terms (cf. 2:102; also 6:128 and 130, or 72:5–6).

In a few instances (e.g., in 46:29–32 and 72:1–15) the term *jinn* may conceivably denote beings not invisible in and by themselves but, rather, '*hitherto unseen* beings'.

Finally, references to *jinn* are sometimes meant to recall certain legends deeply embedded in the consciousness of the people to whom the Qur'an was addressed in the first instance (e.g., in 34:12–14) – the purpose being, in every instance, not the legend as such but the illustration of a moral or spiritual truth.

Appendix C

Jinn Physics

Can the jinn be explained in terms of our current knowledge of basic physics? Twenty years ago, in an article called 'Jinn from a Scientific (?) Viewpoint'[1], UFO writer Chris Line made a (for some, surprisingly level-headed) case that they can.

His theory is that the jinn are 'beings which dwell on a parallel level to man, but *due to their existing at a different vibratory rate, they are not normally visible to us or detectable by us.*' Despite the fact that jinn are usually invisible, when they materialise, an energy change results – one that scientists can theoretically measure in the electromagnetic spectrum.

Line's starting point is Islamic tradition, in particular the Qur'an, which contains information of a metaphysical nature, some of which deals with the jinn.[2] As we have seen, the jinn are described as having 'bodies of essential flame', 'smokeless flame', or 'smokeless fire'. Line proposes that jinn's bodies radiate energy from the infrared part of the spectrum. Angels, meanwhile, are described in the Qur'an as having 'bodies of light'. Since angels are generally presumed to be invisible to humans, Line suggests that angels' bodies are made of an invisible energy from the opposite end of the spectrum – that is, the ultraviolet.

Microwave radiation is found just below infrared in the electromagnetic spectrum. Line's theory suggests that man's release of microwaves into the Earth's atmosphere may well disrupt or disturb the bodies of the jinn and/or the medium in which they live.

Islamic tradition maintains that jinn can materialise or vanish at will. According to Line, this suggests one of three things:

1 The jinn are able to control the matter that we call 'everyday reality',
2. They possess control over certain aspects of the human psyche and can create in people's minds the subjective experience of matter; or
3. They can create external and very realistic illusions in the same manner that our technology creates *holograms*. (This last suggestion may include the first.)

Various researchers on the cutting edge of quantum physics, such as the Australian physicist Paul Davies, and in borderline medicine, such as biologist and human aura scanner Harry Oldfield, have speculated about the possible existence of some kind of blueprint for physical beings and objects – perhaps an electromagnetic lattice or hologram that in effect instructs each atom or molecule what to do and where to go.

Such speculation arises quite naturally because man's present scientific knowledge is inadequate to explain the high degree of specialisation exhibited by many atoms, molecules and biological cells.

Chris Line hypothesises that the jinn are able to construct and destroy these electromagnetic blueprints. He also proposes that these lattices attract, from the surrounding environment, the minerals, gases and other substances required to make up physical forms. When the blueprint is removed or destroyed, the physical form disintegrates.

In ascribing intelligent behaviour to the jinn, Line believes that these beings function on at least two levels: (1) in a system of electromagnetic energy, and (2) as a finer, psychic energy. The first level might be the equivalent of the concept of the 'etheric' in the Western mystery tradition – the lowest level of the human energy field or 'aura'. The second might be the same as what this same tradition calls 'astral' or higher-level energy, he says.

Line says he conducted an investigation of the Earth's atmosphere and its practical structure, based on the hypothesis that there are various different planes in the unseen world surrounding the Earth and that these planes might be connected with electromagnetic energy.

High-energy radiation from the Sun and beyond, such as cosmic rays, penetrate the Earth's atmosphere and get absorbed by the planet, to be re-emitted as infrared radiation, thus producing most of the warmth we experience. Reflected downward by clouds and by the ionosphere and ozone layer, the infrared radiation is restricted to the lower part of the atmosphere.

Lower-frequency infrared penetrates deep into the Earth. 'Consequently,' Line proposes, 'if a being had a body of low-frequency infrared, it could live deep down inside the Earth, interpenetrating what we consider to be solid materiality.'

Considering that angels are believed to possess bodies of light – corresponding to the lighter or finer end of the spectrum, the ultraviolet – one may be able to explain the age-old tradition that angels live 'in the clouds', that is, up above the ozone layer where ultraviolet prevails.

Line concludes,

> The tradition that unseen beings originate from different areas within the etheric (i.e., dense etheric) may be explained by variations in frequency of infrared: i.e., dense etheric around 10^{12} Hz and finer etheric nearer 10^{14} Hz, which would seem to imply that there should be a corresponding frequency gradient through the lower part of the atmosphere, the frequency rising with the height above the Earth's surface.

He concedes that this hypothesis remains unproven.

* * *

Another scientific perspective on the nature of jinn is provided by Professor Ibrahim B. Syed, an American Muslim born in India who teaches nuclear medicine at the University of Louisville in Kentucky. Syed, who also heads the Islamic Research Foundation of Louisville, earned his doctorate in radiological sciences from Johns Hopkins University.

Syed points to the incredibly hot temperatures inside stars such as our Sun, where we find the state of matter called *plasma* – free-moving electrons and ions, or atoms separated from their electrons. Here, Syed suggests, may be where jinn are born. 'Plasma could be interpreted as the smokeless Fire described in the Quran,' he says.

Scientists have long speculated about the existence of life forms in stellar plasma.[3] Some have called such life forms 'plasmabeasts'. Syed contends,

> Plasmabeasts can be construed as nothing but the Jinns. Life on Earth is called Chemical life, whereas the life in the Plasma of the Sun is based on Physical life. In the Plasma, the positively charged ions and the freely floating electrons (negative ions) are both acted on by intense magnetic forces present in the sun (star). The Jinns are interpreted to be composed of patterns of magnetic force, together with groups of moving charges in a kind of symbiosis.[4]

Syed postulates a complex existence for the inhabitants of 'plasmaland', or the jinn, involving both charges and magnetic forces. 'The positive and negative ions interact and respond to the presence of magnetic forces,' he says.

> The stable structure and movement of the Jinns is influenced by the magnetic forces. In physics we know that the moving charges influence the motion of these electrical charges or ions. This situation is similar to the influence of proteins and nucleic acids in Earth life. Finally these processes result in a favored form. For this to take place supply of free energy is required which is obtained from the flow of radiation within the sun. Therefore the Jinn can be construed to use radiant energy in their vital processes.

The notion that jinn may be plasma life forms has also been advanced by writer-researcher Jay Alfred, author of *Our Invisible Bodies: Scientific Evidence for Subtle Bodies*[5] and other books. Echoing Chris Line's theory, Alfred says that as plasma creatures, jinn 'exist at a different "vibratory rate" or "energy level" and, therefore, are not normally visible or detectable by us,' he says. 'In other words, they can be said to be living in a parallel world which interpenetrates our own.'[6]

Alfred believes that most jinn have difficulty seeing humans clearly – that people appear to them as 'blurred images'. Some jinn can see humans more clearly than others and are the equivalent of psychics in their parallel world. Most jinn would probably regard humans as 'ghosts' living as we do in a parallel Earth.

As seen previously, Alfred says that it is clear from descriptions in the Qur'an that jinn, like humans, must be organised into different religions – Muslims, Christians, Jews and others – and have their own mosques, churches and temples. 'In other words,' he adds, 'jinns operate in societies, communities and within political systems and are startlingly similar to humans. Their plasma-based civilization has probably a longer history than ours.'

Plasma life forms would be electromagnetic, employing magnetic fields to form structures and electric fields as 'agents of transport' much as water serves as an agent of transport for carbon-based life forms. Alfred asserts that, similar to biological cells in the human body, complex plasma can exist in a liquid-crystal state. 'Particles in a liquid-crystal phase are free to move about in much the same way as in a liquid,' he explains, 'but as they do so they remain oriented in a certain direction. This feature may make it superior to water in its ability to support life in a higher energy location or universe.'

While the human carbon-based body has a brain composed of billions of neurons and neural networks that can encode vast quantities of information, the jinn's bioplasma body may possess sophisticated holographic memory systems that employ plasma liquid crystal.[7]

'If we strip away the folklore and superstitions that have mired the study of the jinns through more than a millennium we will see that there is probably a kernel of truth that can be extracted from the literature to establish jinns as one category of plasma life forms,' Alfred concludes.

The physics of the jinn phenomenon is a topic not just for fringe science publications. In 2006, *The Economist* sent a correspondent to Somalia and Afghanistan in search of information on the jinn phenomenon, including its possible scientific basis. Among other things, the reporter found the following:

> **A Parallel Universe**
>
> Islam teaches that jinn resemble men in many ways: they have free will, are mortal, face judgement and fill hell together. Jinn and men marry, have children, eat, play, sleep and husband their own animals. Islamic scholars are in disagreement over whether jinn are physical or insubstantial in their bodies. Some clerics have described jinn as bestial, giant, hideous, hairy, ursine. Supposed yeti sightings in Pakistan's Chitral are believed by locals to be of jinn. These kinds of jinn can be killed with date or plum stones fired from a sling.

But to more scholarly clerics jinn are little more than an energy, a pulse form of quantum physics perhaps, alive at the margins of sleep or madness, and more often in the whispering of a single unwelcome thought. An extension of this electric description of jinn is that they are not beings at all but thoughts that were in the world before the existence of man. Jinn reflect the sensibilities of those imagining them, just as in Assyrian times they were taken to be the spirits responsible for manias, who melted into the light at dawn.[8]

Notes

Introduction

1. Jinni is masculine, jinniya (or jinniyah) is feminine. Another popular spelling is djinn – singular: djinni (m.), djinniya (f.). While jinn or djinn is usually plural, sometimes it is also used in English as a singular noun. We follow that approach in this book.
2. The Arabic name for God, used by Arabic-speaking Muslims, Christians and Jews alike.
3. A recent public opinion survey in Pakistan found that 89 per cent of respondents believe in the existence of jinn. About 96 per cent of the country's population is Muslim. The poll was conducted by Gallup for the Gilani Research Foundation. See *The News*, Karachi, 1 Sept. 2009.
4. *The Encyclopaedia Britannica* describes jinn as 'beings of flame or air who are capable of assuming human or animal form and are said to dwell in all conceivable inanimate objects – stones, trees, ruins – underneath the earth, in the air, and in fire'. They are said to possess human bodily needs and can even be killed but are free of all physical restraints.
5. *Ajā'ib al-makhlūqāt wa-gharā'ib al-mawjūdāt (Marvels of Things Created and Miraculous Aspects of Things Existing)* by Zakarīyā' ibn Muḥammad al-Qazwīnī. Translated in Edward Lane's 'Notes on the Jinn, or Genii' (see Appendix A).
6. Asad, who was born in Lwow (now Lviv) in the Ukraine, then part of the Austro-Hungarian Empire, assisted in the building of the new state of Pakistan in 1947, served in its Foreign Ministry and was named Pakistan's Minister Plenipotentiary to the United Nations. For details on his life, see Ismail I. Nawwab, 'Berlin to Makkah: Muhammad Asad's Journey into Islam', *Saudi Aramco World*, Jan./Feb. 2002.

Chapter One

1. The word has many spellings: *efreet*, *afreet*, *afrit*, *'afrit* or *afrite*. Conventional Arabic spellings are *'ifrit* (male), *'ifritah* (female) and *'afarit* (plural). The ifrits in Islamic mythology are a class of infernal jinn noted for their strength and cunning. An ifrit is sometimes described as an enormous winged creature of smoke, either male or female, that lives underground and often haunts ruins. Ifrits live in a society structured along ancient Arab tribal lines, complete with kings, tribes and clans. They generally marry one another, but they can also marry humans. While ordinary weapons and forces have no power over them, they are susceptible to magic, which humans can use to kill them or to capture and enslave them. As with the jinn, an ifrit may be either a believer or an unbeliever, good or evil, but he is most often depicted as a wicked and ruthless being. The rare appearance of the term ifrit in the Qur'an and in hadith (eyewitness narratives recounting Muhammad's words and actions) is always in the phrase 'the ifrit of the jinn' and probably means 'rebellious'. The word subsequently came to refer to an entire class of formidable, rebellious beings.
2. Mas'oudi, *Prairies d'or*, ed. and trans. Barbier de Meynard and Pavet de Courteille, Vol. III, 1861–1877. Reprinted in: Basset, Rene. *Mille et un contes, recits et legendes arabes.* Vol. I. Paris: Maisonneuve Freres, 1924. English translation by Robert W. Lebling.
3. Joseph Henninger, 'Pre-Islamic Bedouin Religion', in *Studies on Islam* (1981), translated and edited by Merlin L. Swartz.
4. Nabih Amin Faris, trans., *The Book of Idols: Being a Translation from the Arabic of the Kitab Al-Asnam by Hisham Ibn-Al-Kalbi.* Princeton, NJ: Princeton University Press, 1952.
5. Dushara comes from the Arabic *dhu shara*, 'lord of the mountain', i.e. the Shara mountain range (Mount Seir of Edom) southeast of the Nabataean capital Petra in present-day Jordan. Dushara was a well-known deity of the Middle East worshipped by the Nabataeans and identified with Zeus and/or Dionysus in the Graeco-Roman period. Ibn al-Kalbi said in his *Book of Idols* that Dushara was worshipped by a branch of the 'Azd tribe. Merchants spread Dushara's cult far beyond Petra to Phoenicia, Asia Minor and even Italy.
6. Nils P. Heeßel, 'Pazuzu', *Iconography of Deities and Demons in the Ancient Near East*. University of Zurich, 10 Dec. 2007.
7. Ibid.
8. William Wood, *A History of the Devil.* London: W.H. Allen, 1973.

9. Lewis Spence, *Myths and Legends of Babylonia and Assyria.* London: George G. Harrap & Co., 1916. Republished: Detroit: Gale Research Co., 1975.
10. In nineteenth-century Britain, the plural term *genii* was applied not only to Roman tutelary deities but also to Arabian jinn, without much concern or discussion over whether there existed any link between the two types of spirit being.
11. Fritjof Capra, *The Science of Leonardo: Inside the Mind of the Great Genius of the Renaissance*, New York: Doubleday, 2007.
12. The New Jerusalem Bible.
13. They were also known as the *shideem* or *shehireem*.
14. Richard F. Burton, *The Book of the Thousand Nights and a Night.* London: 1885.
15. Carl Sagan, *The Demon-Haunted World: Science as a Candle in the Dark*, London: Headline, 1997.
16. Tertullian of Carthage (ca. 160–220 AD) was the first Christian theologian to advance the concept of the Trinity.
17. Al-Tabari, 2/207: 'After mentioning the coming of the Revelation, the Messenger of Allâh said: "I have never abhorred anyone more than a poet or a mad man. I can not stand looking at either of them. I will never tell anyone of Quraish [the Prophet's tribe] of my Revelation." '
18. Duncan Black Macdonald, 'The Attitude of the Semites toward the Unseen World; Prophecy as a Semitic Phenomenon and Especially among the Arabs', Lecture I, *Haskell Lectures in Comparative Religion*, University of Chicago, 1906.
19. Sir Richard F. Burton, *Personal Narrative of a Pilgrimage to El-Medinah and Meccah ...* 3 Vols. London: Longman, 1855–1856. Reprinted New York: Dover Publications, 1964.
20. Al-Bukhari, Vol. 1, Book 8, No. 450.
21. Ibid., Book 12, No. 740.
22. Ibid., Vol. 5, Book 58, No. 199.
23. Ibid., No. 206.
24. Ibid., Vol. 4, Book 54, No. 533.
25. Ibid., Vol. 9, Book 93, No. 650.
26. Sunan al-Tirmidhi, Hadith No. 618.
27. Joseph Henninger, 'Belief in Spirits among the Pre-Islamic Tribes', trans. Gwendolyn Goldbloom, in Emilie Savage-Smith, *Magic and Divination in Early Islam*, Aldershot, UK: Ashgate, 2004.
28. There are four main Sunni schools of Islamic law. All are regarded as legitimate by most Sunnis but are particularly popular in specific

regions: Maliki (North Africa and parts of the Gulf region), Hanbali (Saudi Arabia, UAE), Hanafi (Asia Minor, Central Asia, South Asia) and Shafi'i (Yemen, Sudan, East Africa, Southeast Asia). Shi'ite Islam has its own school, the Ja'fari.

29. The defining characteristic of the 'anqa, or simurgh, seems to have been that people could not track it down. For Sufis, the bird was sometimes a symbol for Allah.
30. Muhammad al-Kisa'i, *The Tales of the Prophets of al-Kisa'i,* Translated with Notes by W. M. Thackston, Jr. Boston: G.K. Hall & Co., 1978.
31. The elusive Qaf is beautifully described by Khairat Al-Saleh in *Fabled Cities, Princes and Jinn from Arab Myths and Legends.* New York: Schocken Books, 1985.
32. J.F.P. Hopkins, trans., *Corpus of Early Arabic Sources for West African History*, Cambridge: Cambridge University Press, 1981.
33. This view of the universe was actually much older. In the ninth century, al-Kisa'i describes a version of this cosmology:

    > And He [Allah] commanded the rock to settle beneath the angel's feet. The rock, however, had no support, so God created a great bull ... and commanded it to bear the rock on its back and on its horns. The name of the bull is al-Rayyan. As the bull had no place to rest its feet, God created a huge fish.... This fish God commanded to be a foothold for the bull, and it was done. The name of this fish is Behemoth. Then He made its resting place the waters, beneath which is the air, and beneath the air is the Darkness, which is for all the earths. There, beneath the Darkness, the knowledge of created things ends.

    See Muhammad al-Kisa'i, *The Tales of the Prophets of al-Kisa'i.*
34. Duncan Forbes, trans., *The Adventures of Hatim Tai, A Romance*, London: Murray, Parbury and Co., 1830. This is a translation of a Persian collection of much older tales about an Arabian folk hero.
35. Thomas Keightley, *The Fairy Mythology: Illustrative of the Romance and Superstition of Various Countries.* New and Revised Edition. London: Henry G. Bohn, 1850.
36. Mohammed ibn Jarir al-Tabari (Hermann Zotemberg, trans.), *Chronique de Tabari: Histoire des Prophètes et des rois: De la création à la dernière Révélation.* Paris: Editions La Ruche, 2006. Al-Tabari's account appears in English translation in Mohamad Yasin Owadally, *Qaf: The Mysterious, EmeraldMountain Decoded.* Kuala Lumpur: A.S. Noordeen, 2002.

37. The term 'Jabulqa' is believed by some Islamic scholars to be a compressed form of *jabal qaf*, Arabic for Mountain of Qaf. The term 'Jabulsa' is thought to be either *jabal sina'* (Mount Sinai) or *jabal sin* (Mountain of China). Jabulqa and Jabulsa are the original 'emerald cities', so called because of the emerald origin of Mount Qaf.
38. In this miraculous journey, Muhammad is said to have travelled by night on a flying beast called al-Buraq from Mecca to Jerusalem, where he met the prophets Abraham, Moses and Jesus and then flew to heaven. He also witnessed the suffering of those in hell. Muhammad was returned to Mecca just before dawn.
39. The 'two horns' were sometimes explained as two prominent curls on Alexander's temples, often shown in portraits of the Macedonian leader.
40. Khairat Al-Saleh, *Fabled Cities, Princes and Jinn*.
41. The reference appears in a work called 'The Case of the Animals versus Man before the King of the Jinn', translated in Robert Irwin's literary compilation, *Night, Horses and the Desert: An Anthology of Classical Arabic Literature*. New York: Overlook Press, 2000
42. Jan Knappert, *Islamic Legends: Histories of the Heroes, Saints and Prophets of Islam*, Leiden: Brill, 1985.
43. This name is found in the Old Testament (Leviticus 16): Azazel, a spirit creature linked to goat sacrifice that the Jewish Encyclopedia calls 'the most mysterious extrahuman character in sacred literature'. The same source says most modern biblical scholars believe that Azazel belongs to the class of 'se'irim', goat-like demons or jinn haunting the desert, to which the ancient Israelites were accustomed to offering sacrifice. See Morris Jastrow Jr. et al., 'Azazel', Jewish Encyclopedia, 1901–1906.
44. '(Allah) said: "What prevented thee from bowing down when I commanded thee?" He [Iblis] said: "I am better than he: Thou didst create me from fire, and him from clay"' (Qur'an 7:12).
45. Gordon Darnell Newby, *The Making of the Last Prophet: A Reconstruction of the Earliest Biography of Muhammad*. Columbia, SC: University of South Carolina Press, 1989.
46. Qur'an 38:79–81. Judgement Day is a concept Islam shares with the Judaeo-Christian tradition.
47. Adam's first wife, according to Jewish legend, was Lilith. As we shall soon see, Lilith is actually Sumerian in origin and is regarded as the mother of the jinn. Lilith left Adam due to a marital dispute. It was at this point that God created Eve for him.

48. Newby, *The Making of the Last Prophet.*
49. Thomas Patrick Hughes, *A Dictionary of Islam: Being a Cyclopaedia of the Doctrines, Rites, Ceremonies, and Customs, Together with the Technical and Theological Terms, of the Muhammadan Religion.* London: W.H. Allen, 1885.
50. Samael is actually the Angel of Death, according to Jewish lore. He is the figure that we know today as 'the Grim Reaper'.
51. Raphael Patai, *The Hebrew Goddess.* New York: Avon Books, 1978.
52. A succubus (plural succubi) is a demon that takes the form of a woman to seduce men in their sleep and have intercourse with them. An incubus (plural incubi) is a demon in male form that has intercourse with a sleeping woman.
53. The so-called Burney Relief, owned by the British Museum, dated to about 1950 BC. The plaque is now named 'Queen of the Night' signifying Lilith. Some experts dispute Sumerian scholar Samuel Kramer's identification of the nude figure with Lilith and say it may represent the goddess Inanna or her underworld sister Ereshkigal.
54. Jesus Ben Sira was a scribe from Jerusalem who wrote the deutero-canonical book Sirach or Ecclesiasticus about 190–180 BC, possibly in Alexandria, Egypt. Catholics and Orthodox accept this as part of the biblical canon but most Protestants do not.
55. Translated in David Stern and Mark Jay Mirsky, *Rabbinic Fantasies: Imaginative Narratives from Classical Hebrew Literature.* Philadelphia: Jewish Publication Society, 1990.
56. Ernst Zbinden, *Die Jinn des Islam und der Altorientalische Geisterglaube* (The Jinn of Islam and Ancient Eastern Spirit Belief). Bern and Stuttgart: Verlag Paul Haupt, 1953.
57. Hanauer taught Arabic to his fellow countryman Marmaduke Pickthall, who eventually converted from Anglican Christianity to Islam and authored a well-known translation of the Qur'an.
58. J.E. Hanauer, *Folk-Lore of the Holy Land: Moslem, Christian and Jewish.* London: Sheldon Press, 1907 and 1935 [revised].
59. Edward Westermarck, *Ritual and Belief in Morocco.* London: Macmillan and Co., 1926.
60. The rabbinical commentaries discuss an elaborate throne made of new ivory overlaid with pure gold, with many steps and figures of humans, lions, eagles and other creatures, and they say it resembled God's throne in heaven. For Muslims too the throne of Solomon was a symbol of dominion and of power over the supernatural. In 1902, rumours swept Asia that Lord Curzon, British viceroy of India, had found the lost throne of Solomon and would sit on the throne at the great Durbar in Delhi,

ushering in an era of marvels and peace in India. See Sir Edwin Arnold, 'The Throne of Solomon: Rhapsody Apropos of the Report That Lord Curzon Will Use It at the Coming Durbar', *The New York Times*, 21 Dec. 1902.

61. Bayard Dodge, ed. and trans., *The Fihrist of al-Nadim: A Tenth-Century Survey of Muslim Culture*. New York: Columbia University Press, 1970.
62. F.C. Conybeare, 'The Testament of Solomon', *The Jewish Quarterly Review*, Vol. 11, No. 1 (October 1898).
63. The Haggadah of Pesach is a Jewish religious text from about the third to sixth centuries of our era, compiled as a guide to Passover seders.
64. According to the Jewish Encyclopedia (1901–1906), 'Ashmedai remained with Solomon until the Temple was completed. One day the king told him that he did not understand wherein the greatness of the demons lay, if their king could be kept in bonds by a mortal. Ashmedai replied that if Solomon would remove his chains and lend him the magic ring, he (Ashmedai) would prove his own greatness. Solomon agreed. The demon then stood before him with one wing touching heaven, and the other reaching to the earth. Snatching up Solomon, who had parted with his protecting ring, he flung him four hundred parasangs away from Jerusalem, and then palmed himself off as the king .... After long wanderings Solomon returned to reclaim his throne' Giṭ. 68; parallel passages, Midr. Teh. on Ps. lxxviii. 45; Yalḳ. ii. 182; compare Num. R. xi. 3; Targ. on Eccl. i. 12, and the extract from a manuscript Midrash in "Z. D. M. G." xxi. 220, 221).
65. Other forms of this name are Abyzou, Obizou, Bizou, Obizouth, among others. This demon is Lilith and is linked to the primordial sea or 'abyss' of Sumerian myth (i.e., Abzu).
66. Conybeare, 'The Testament of Solomon'.
67. Nicholas Clapp, *Sheba: Through the Desert in Search of the Legendary Queen*. Boston: Houghton Mifflin, 2001. The composite tale is based mostly on Muhammad al-Kisa'i, *The Tales of the Prophets of al-Kisa'i*.
68. According to Wahb ibn Munabbih.
69. Lady Anne Blunt, *A Pilgrimage to Nejd: The Cradle of the Arab Race*, 2 vols., London: Frank Cass and Co., 1881, reprinted 1968. Lady Anne Blunt was the granddaughter of Lord Byron and was married to Sir Wilfred Scawen Blunt.
70. King Solomon lived a thousand years before the Christian era.
71. Lady Anne Blunt, *A Pilgrimage to Nejd*, footnote.
72. Al-Hamdani, who lived in the tenth century AD, wrote an acclaimed history of ancient South Arabia called *Al-Iklil* (The Crown). Only two

books of this 10-volume opus have survived. One of these deals with, in al-Hamdani's words, 'the public buildings of al-Yaman [Yemen], its inscriptions, buried treasures, and castles' as well as Himyaritic inscriptions and other writings. This book also contains references to jinn. Nabih Amin Faris, *The Antiquities of South Arabia [Al-Hamdani].* Princeton, NJ: Princeton University Press, 1938.

73. Oswald Spengler, *The Decline of the West*. Vol. II: Perspectives of World History. New York: Alfred A. Knopf, 1980.
74. Al-Hamdani does not address the possibility that both accounts could be true, and that jinn builders worked under local human supervision.
75. Rev. Samuel Rapaport, *Tales and Maxims from the Midrash*, London: George Routledge & Sons, 1907.
76. Faris, *The Antiquities of South Arabia*.
77. Heinrich F. von Minutoli, *Reise zum Tempel des Jupiter Ammon*, etc., Berlin: 1825, quoted in Walter Cline, *Notes on the People of Siwah and El Garah in the Libyan Desert*. No. 4, General Series in Anthropology. Menasha, WI: George Banta Publishing Co., 1936.

Chapter Two

1. H.T. Norris, *The Berbers in Arabic Literature*. London: Longman, 1982.
2. This story is retold in Washington Irving, *Legends of the Conquest of Spain*, London: John Murray, 1835.
3. The Umayyads claimed descent from the Prophet's tribe, the Quraysh of Mecca.
4. See R.W.J. Austin, trans., *Sufis of Andalusia: The Ruh al-quds and al-Durrat al-fakhirah of Ibn 'Arabi*. London: George Allen & Unwin Ltd., 1971.
5. Al-Bukhari records the following hadith: 'Narrated Abu Huraira: "The Prophet said, 'Last night a big demon (afreet) from the jinns came to me and wanted to interrupt my prayers ... but Allah enabled me to overpower him. I wanted to fasten him to one of the pillars of the mosque so that all of you could see him in the morning but I remembered the statement of my brother Solomon'" [as stated in the Qur'an]: "My Lord! Forgive me and bestow on me a kingdom such as shall not belong to anybody after me (38:35)".' The sub narrator Rauh said, 'He (the demon) was dismissed humiliated' (Book #8, Hadith #450m).
6. Claudius Galen (130–201 AD), anatomist and physician, and the most celebrated of ancient medical writers. He was born in Pergamum in Asia Minor. A prolific author, he is said to havewritten over 600medicalworks,

of which only 20 survive, and those because they were rescued and preserved by Arab physicians.

7. Yahya Grammaticus, a Jacobite/Monophysite bishop in Egypt who translated from the Greek and wrote philosophical and polemical books, lived in the first half of the seventh century of our era.
8. C. Edward Sachau, trans. and ed., *The Chronology of Ancient Nations: An English Version of the Arabic Text of the Athar-ul-Bakiya of Albiruni*. London: William H. Allen and Co., 1879.
9. Spanish Arabist Miguel Asín Palacios and others have argued that *The Epistle of Forgiveness* influenced and indeed may have inspired Dante Alighieri's classic work.
10. R. A. Nicholson (trans.), *Journal of the Royal Asiatic Society* (1900), pp. 692–696. This translation was reprinted most recently in Irwin, *Night, Horses and the Desert*. Irwin provides a helpful commentary at the end.
11. Miguel Asín Palacios, *Islam and the Divine Comedy.* Translated and abridged by Harold Sunderland. London: John Murray, 1926.
12. Ibid.
13. Ibid.
14. Jamshid's reign was known for its gigantic buildings, which presumably were constructed with the help of the jinn. However, Jamshid's father Tahmurath may actually have been the one to achieve control over the demons, since he is known as *Div-Band* or 'the Binder of Demons'. See Edward G. Browne, *A Literary History of Persia,* London: T. Fisher Unwin, 1902. Vol. 1, Section 27.
15. Samuel P. Scott, *History of the Moorish Empire in Europe*, Philadelphia: J.B. Lippincott, 1904.
16. Ibid.
17. This Sufi tradition is related in Ernest Scott, *The People of the Secret*. London: Octagon Press, 1983.
18. Ernest Scott, *The People of the Secret*.
19. This view was expressed in an exhibit of the Robert E. Schlueter-Paracelsus Collection, Bernard Becker Medical Library, Washington University School of Medicine, St. Louis.
20. Paracelsus introduced these intermediate beings to European alchemy. See E.J. Holmyard, *Alchemy*, Harmondsworth, UK: Penguin, 1968.
21. The remaining three non-jinn categories of spirits in the Paracelsian world included good angels, human souls and infernal spirits. The last could qualify as evil jinn. Paracelsus' spirits are cited in Lynn Thorndyke's definitive work, *A History of Magic and Experimental Science*, Vol. VII, New York: Columbia University Press, 1958, p. 344.

Chapter Three

1. For example, 'Then they brought him a demon-possessed man who was blind and mute, and Jesus healed him, so that he could both talk and see' (Matthew 12:22).
2. Charles Doughty, *Travels in Arabia Deserta*. London: Jonathan Cape, 1924.
3. Richard Francis Burton, *The Gold-Mines of Midian and the Ruined Midianite Cities (1878)*. Cambridge: Oleander Press, 1979.
4. Graeco-Syrian geographer Yaqut al-Hamawi (1179–1229), in his *Kitab Mu'jam al-Buldan* (Geographical Dictionary), said that most sources placed Ubar in the sands of the southwest Rub' al-Khali between the Yemeni cities of Shihir and Sana'. See Bertram Thomas, *Arabia Felix: Across the Empty Quarter of Arabia*. London: Jonathan Cape, 1932.
5. Nicholas Clapp, *The Road to Ubar: Finding the Atlantis of the Sands*. Boston: Houghton Mifflin, 1998.
6. The team of discoverers also included adventurer Ranulph Fiennes, archaeologist Juris Zarins and lawyer George Hedges. The site they identified with Ubar was located near a water well at Shisur in Dhofar. The discovery was notable for its use of NASA remote-sensing satellites and ground-penetrating radar. Australian geologist Prof. Henry Stewart Edgell writes in the *Seminar for Arabian Studies* 2003: 'Fiennes (1992) and Clapp (1998) claim discovery of the lost city of Ubar, at the once walled sinkhole at Shisur in interior Dhofar. NASA has satellite images and online articles about 'Ubar' since 1994, showing the sinkhole at Shisur, but this is 175 km southeast of Ramlat Shu'ait and is the stony desert (najd) not in the sands. This sinkhole exposes the Middle Eocene Dammam limestone aquifer and is an isolated waterhole. There is no evidence that Shisur was once a city called Ubar, although it was probably a caravanserai on overland frankincense trade routes. Arab historians state that Ubar, or Wabar, refers to a wide land in southern Arabia.'
7. Interestingly, the jinn-name *nisnas* is now used by zoologists to refer to a white-nosed subspecies of the ground-dwelling Patas monkey *(Erythrocebus patas pyrrhonotus). This monkey often avoids woodlands and* thrives in the treeless savannas and semi-deserts of eastern West Africa.
8. Thomas, *Arabia Felix*.
9. See Appendix A: Edward Lane's Notes on the Jinn.
10. H. St. J. B. Philby, 'Two Notes from Central Arabia', *The Geographical Journal*, Vol. 113, Jan.–Jun. 1949.

11. H. St. J. B. Philby, *Heart of Arabia*. London: Constable and Company, 1922.
12. Thomas, *Arabia Felix*.
13. Clapp, *The Road to Ubar*, and Ranulph Fiennes, *Atlantis of the Sands: The Search for the Lost City of Ubar*, London: Bloomsbury, 1992.
14. Zayn Bilkadi, 'The Wabar Meteorite', *Aramco World*, Nov./Dec. 1986.
15. Apparently the guardian jinn have not left this area. Iraqi-born architect Dr. Salma Samar al-Damluji writes about a visit to al-Hamra' and the Yafa' highlands: 'I enquired the name of the highest peak across the wadi and was told that it was Jebel al-Darfan, "kingdom of jinns", where no one could build. The story goes that some people did once build a house there and slept the night inside, only to wake next morning to find themselves out in the open!' Salma Samar Al-Damluji, 'Letter from Yafa' ', *Journal of the British-Yemeni Society*, July 2000.
16. Alois Musil, 'Arabia Deserta: A Topographical Itinerary'. *Oriental Explorations and Studies* No. 2. New York: American Geographical Society of New York, 1927. Reprint: New York: AMS Press, 1978.
17. Abu Ameenah Bilal Philips, *The Exorcist Tradition in Islaam*. Sharjah, United Arab Emirates: Dar Al Fatah Printing, 1997.
18. Ibid.
19. Ibid.
20. Abu Ameenah Bilal Philips, ed. and trans. *Ibn Taymeeyah's Essay on the Jinn*. Riyadh: Tawheed Publications, 1989.
21. Ibid., op cit.
22. 'Death Investigation, Culture Conflicted', St. Paul Pioneer Press, St. Paul, Minnesota, 17 March 2002.
23. Ahmed Fakhry, *The Oases of Egypt, Vol. I: Siwa Oasis*. Cairo: American University of Cairo Press, 1973.
24. This account from 'Abdallah's *Siwan Customs* (1917) is reported in Walter Cline, *Notes on the People of Siwah and El Garah*.
25. According to Sudanese doctor Ahmad Al-Safi, Zar is 'an ambivalent word that indicates both the name of the possessing spirits and the propitiatory ceremonial dances performed to appease them'. See Ahmad Al-Safi et al., eds., *Women's Medicine: The Zar-Bori Cult in Africa and Beyond*. International African Seminars. Edinburgh: Edinburgh University Press; 1991.
26. Heba Fatteen Bizzari, 'The Zar Ceremony'. *Tour Egypt* : http://www.touregypt.net/featurestories/zar.htm.
27. Ahmad Al-Safi, 'The Zar and the Tambura Cults'. Paper posted on author's web site: http://aalsafi.tripod.com/tm/management/possession.htm.

28. 'Mass Hysteria behind Scared Teachers at "Haunted" School', *Arab News*, 5 Nov. 2000, and 'Two More Teachers Have Fits at "Haunted" School', *Arab News*, 7 Nov. 2000.
29. Indo-Asian News Service (IANS), 'Spooky Mosques Haunt the Devout in Bhopal', published in the *India News* and other newspapers on 22 Oct. 2006.
30. Cyril A. Mango, 'Antique Statuary and the Byzantine Beholder', *Dumbarton Oaks Papers 17* (1963): 55–75.
31. Comments in Translator's Foreword of Ameen's *The Jinn and Human Sickness: Remedies in the Light of the Qur'aan and* Sunnah. Trans. by Nasiruddin Al-Khattab. Riyadh: Maktaba Dar-us-Salam, 2005.
32. Dodge, *The Fihrist of al-Nadim.*
33. Ibn Ja'far and Ibn Zurayq were tenth-century magicians.
34. *Al-tast* (basin) here probably refers to a large copper vessel. The worker of magic spoke from under it to give an air of mystery to the proceedings.
35. Venetia Porter, 'Islamic Seals: Magical or Practical?' *University Lectures in Islamic Studies,* Vol. 2 (1998).
36. David Pingree, ed., *Picatrix: The Latin Version of the Ghayat al-Hakim.* London: The Warburg Institute, University of London, 1986.
37. A solid mass from the stomach or intestine of an animal, used in medieval times as an antidote for poison.
38. Sylvain Matton, 'Picatrix', *La Magie Arabe Traditionelle*, Paris: 1977, and Pingree, *Picatrix*, both cited in Porter, 'Islamic Seals'.
39. Dodge, *The Fihrist of al-Nadim.*
40. Tewfik Canaan, 'The Decipherment of Arabic Talismans', *Berytus 4* (Beirut, 1937); *Berytus 5* (Beirut, 1938). For a current reprint, see References.
41. Ibid.
42. Elizabeth Marie Sharpe, *Into the Realm of Smokeless Fire: (Qur'an 55:14): A Critical Translation of Al-Damiri's Article on the Jinn from 'Hayat al-Hayawan al-Kubra' (Egypt, Mamluk).* M.A. Thesis, University of Arizona, 1992.
43. From al-Damiri, as translated in Sharpe, *Into the Realm of Smokeless Fire.*
44. Sharpe, *Into the Realm of Smokeless Fire.*
45. Hasan M. El-Shamy, ed. and trans. *Folktales of Egypt.* Chicago: University of Chicago Press, 1980.
46. Walker, John, trans., *Folk Medicine in Modern Egypt: Being the Relevant Parts of the* Tibb al-Rukka *or* Old Wives' Medicine *of 'Abd al-Rahman Isma'il.* London: Luzac & Co., 1934.
47. Michael Rice, *Search for the Paradise Land: An Introduction to the Archaeology of Bahrain and the Arabian Gulf, from the Earliest Times to the Death of Alexander the Great.* London: Longman, 1985.

48. *The Siyar A'lam al-Nubala* (The Lives of Noble Figures) is a 23-volume encyclopaedia of biographical history. This story appears at 2/135–201.
49. Muhammad ibn Ahmad al-Dhahabi, *Siyar A'lam al-Nubala* (The Lives of Noble Figures). 4 Vols. Beirut: Al-Maktabah al-Asriyah, n.d.
50. 'Aisha bint Talha was a niece of the Prophet's wife 'Aisha. She was a celebrity in her day, not only because she was an aristocrat of great beauty but also because she refused to wear a veil.
51. 'Aisha bint Abi Bakr was celebrated for her stories about the Prophet. The Battle of Badr, fought near Medina in 624, was the Muslims' first decisive victory over their pagan opponents from Mecca. It established Muhammad's authority as a leader and encouraged local tribes to join his cause.
52. 'Yemeni Superstitions', *Yemen Times*, Sanaa, Yemen, 15–21 Jan. 2001.
53. Sharpe, *Into the Realm of Smokeless Fire.*
54. He ruled from 717 to 720 and should not be confused with the second caliph, 'Umar ibn al-Khattab, or 'Umar the Great, who ruled from 634 to 644.
55. Paul Lucas, *Voyage du Sieur Paul Lucas dans la Turquie, l'Asie, Haute et Basse Egypte, etc.*, Amsterdam: 1720, Vol. 2.
56. Giovanni Canova, 'Uno sheykh-serpente dell'Alto Egitto: al-Haridi', *Quaderni di Studi Arabi,* 10 (1992).
57. E.S. Stevens, *Folk-Tales of Iraq: Set Down and Translated from the Vernacular.* London: Oxford University Press, 1931. Stevens was so successful in recording these tales that they were 'back-translated' into Arabic half a century later: Abdullah Al-Muhanna and Dawud Salloum, *Qisas Sha'abiyyah 'Iraqiyyah.* Kuwait: Dar Kazima lil-Nashr wal-Tawzi' wal-Tarjima, 1983.
58. Another Arabic form of this jinn's name is *si'la* (pl. *si'layat*).
59. The poet 'Amirah, son of Ju'al, of Taghlib, in Charles J. Lyall, ed. and trans., *The Mufaddaliyat: An Anthology of Ancient Arabian Odes Compiled by al-Mufaddal, Son of Muhammad, etc.* Oxford: At the Clarendon Press, 1918.
60. Sharpe, *Into the Realm of Smokeless Fire.*
61. R.B. Serjeant, 'Two Yemenite Djinn', *Bulletin of the School of Oriental and African Studies*, University of London, Vol. 13, No. 1 (1949).
62. Lena Jayyusi, trans., *The Adventures of Sayf Ben Dhi Yazan: An Arab Folk Epic.* Bloomington: Indiana University Press, 1996.
63. 'The Hadeeth of the Ghoul', adapted by Abu Khaliyl from Mashhur Hassan Salman, *Al-Ghoul*, 7 Aug. 2004.
64. Sabine Baring-Gould, *The Book of Werewolves*, Reprint: London: Senate, 1995.

65. Baring-Gould attributes the story to Fornari in his *History of Sorcerers*. This is presumably Mathias de Giraldo, pseud., *Histoire curieuse et pittoresque des sorciers, devins, magiciens, astrologues, ... etc. ... depuis l'antiquité jusqu' à nos jours ...* Revue et augmentée par M. Fornari, etc., Paris: 1849.
66. Baring-Gould is referring to French historian Pierre de Marcassus (1584–1664) and his history of the Greeks: *Histoire grecque, où se void fidèlement déduit par la suite des temps et l'ordre des matières tout ce qui est arrivé de plus mémorable parmy les Grecs*, Paris: P. Rocolet, 1647.
67. Abu Ameenah Bilal Philips, ed. and trans., *Ibn Taymeeyah's Essay on the Jinn.* Riyadh: Tawheed Publications, 1989.
68. *Sahih Muslim*, Book 4, No. 903 and others.
69. Abdul Rahman ibn Sakhr al-Azdi, or Abu Hurayrah (Father of the Kitten), born in Baha in the Tihama region in western Arabia, was a member of the Bani Daws tribe. He is the most quoted source of hadiths accepted by Sunnis. Shi'ites reject almost all of his hadiths and consider him an enemy of Ali.
70. Philips, *Ibn Taymeeyah's Essay on the Jinn.*
71. Marco Polo, *The Travels of Marco Polo: The Complete Yule-Cordier Edition (Vol. 1).* Reprint edition. New York: Dover Publications, 1993.
72. Curzon, Marquess of Kedleston, *Tales of Travel.* New York: George H. Doran Company, 1923.
73. Called *'azf, 'azîf.* See Lane. The opinion above quoted from al-Asma'i will be found in the commentary to Labid, *Diwan*, p. 109 (al-Khalidi's edition). – Lyall
74. Charles Lyall, *Translations of Ancient Arabian Poetry.* New York: Columbia University Press, 1930.
75. Michael Schirber, 'Singing Sand Dunes: The Mystery of Desert Music'. www.livescience.com. 11 Jan. 2005.
76. Norris, *The Berbers in Arabic Literature.*
77. Westermarck, *Ritual and Belief in Morocco.*
78. Walker, *Folk Medicine in Modern Egypt.*
79. For more on the prophylactic value of the cross among Muslims, Walker recommends: Frederick W. Hasluck, *Christianity and Islam under the Sultans*, I, Oxford: Clarendon Press, 1929.
80. Ameen, *The Jinn and Human Sickness*, p. 128.
81. Sharpe, *Into the Realm of Smokeless Fire.*
82. Westermarck, *Ritual and Belief in Morocco.*
83. Sir James George Frazer, *The Golden Bough: A Study in Magic and Religion.* 1 Volume, Abridged Edition. New York: Collier Books, 1963.

84. Maria Leach, ed. *Funk and Wagnalls Standard Dictionary of Folklore, Mythology, and Legend.* New York: Harper & Row, 1984.
85. Jalaluddin al-Suyuti, *Laqat al-Marjan fi-Ahkam al-Jann* (The Gleanings of Coral: Rulings Concerning the Jinn). 1989.
86. Abu 'Uthman 'Amr ibn Bahr al-Kinani al-Fuqaimi al-Basri (781–869), known to most as al-Jahiz (the Goggle-eyed), was a prolific Arabic prose writer and scientist who authored many works on biology, zoology, philosophy, psychology and other fields. *The Telegraph* of London recently called him one of 'Islam's forgotten geniuses' of science (*The Telegraph*, 29 Jan. 2008).
87. Al-Jahiz 1:88, cited in Sharpe, *Into the Realm of Smokeless Fire.*
88. Sharpe, *Into the Realm of Smokeless Fire.*
89. Robert Irwin, The Arabian Nights*: A Companion.* London: Allen Lane / Penguin Press, 1994.
90. One of the major collections of Hanafi legal opinions, this compendium, also called *Fatawae-e-Alamgiri*, was current in India in the seventeenth century. It was compiled for the Moghul emperor Muhyiddin Alamgir.
91. Stevens, *Folk-Tales of Iraq.*
92. Khaled Ahmed, 'Nuggets from the Urdu Press', *The Friday Times*, Lahore, Pakistan, 10–16 Nov. 2000.

Chapter Four

1. Much of the material in this section is drawn from Zbinden, *Die Jinn des Islam und der Altorientalische Geisterglaube,* one of the most comprehensive studies of the jinn in any language. Translated by Robert W. Lebling.
2. W. Robertson Smith, *Kinship and Marriage in Early Arabia*. London: 1903.
3. Theodor Noeldeke, 'Ancient Arabs', in Hastings, James, ed., *Encyclopaedia of Religion and Ethics*, Edinburgh: T.&T. Clark, 1908–1926.
4. The Hutaim (or Htem) are said to be descended from a people who refused to accompany the Prophet on his expeditions. Said Dutch diplomat Marcel Kurpershoek, 'The prophet is supposed to have said of them, "*Hattimu*, boycott them, avoid all contact with them!" From that day on, the true Arabs have looked down on the tribe of Htem.' The Sulaib are described as untouchables, not true Arabs, who work with metal and are skilled desert trackers. Both tribes are said to ride donkeys instead of camels. See Marcel Kurpershoek, *Arabia of the Bedouins*. London: Saqi Books, 1995.
5. Frazer, *The Golden Bough*.
6. William Robertson Smith, *Lectures on the Religion of the Semites*, 1894.
7. Ibid.

8. Smith says the stories in which apparitions take such shapes are clearly late. The riding beasts of *jinn* include jackals, gazelles and hedgehogs. Interestingly, the desert hare is not ridden by jinn, and for this reason amulets are sometimes made from parts of its body.
9. Smith, *Lectures on the Religion of the Semites.*
10. Ibid.
11. Doughty, *Travels in Arabia Deserta.*
12. Ibid.
13. Ibid.
14. Erik A. Mandaville, 'Crossing the Rub', *Aramco World*, May/June 1989.
15. The Jinn Group, Yahoo Groups, 20 Feb. 2001.
16. Stevens, *Folk-Tales of Iraq.*
17. Also known as the *sa'lawiya* to the Hanajre tribe, the *si'reh* and *sa'aliya* to the Utaibi tribe, and the *sa'alu* to the Shararat (among others).
18. Reginald Campbell Thompson. *The Devils and Evil Spirits of Babylonia: Being Babylonian and Assyrian Incantations against the Demons, etc.* London: Luzac, 1903.
19. Wilfred Thesiger, *The Marsh Arabs*, London: Penguin, 1964.
20. From the editors' introduction of 'In the Marshes of Iraq', written and photographed by Wilfred Thesiger, in *Aramco World*, Nov./Dec. 1966.
21. Thesiger, *The Marsh Arabs.*
22. Bayard Dodge, 'The Sabians of Harran', *American University of Beirut Festival Book (Festschrift).* Beirut: American University of Beirut, 1967.
23. Dodge, *The Fihrist of al-Nadim.*
24. J.E. Hanauer, *Folk-Lore of the Holy Land: Moslem, Christian and Jewish.* London: Sheldon Press, 1907 and 1935 [revised]. Hanauer was the elder son of a converted Bavarian Jew and a British Christian mother. He was well known as a scholar, teacher and clergyman. He was a student of history, archaeology and geology and studied the flora and fauna of the Holy Land. He published numerous articles as well as five books.
25. Orthodox Jews also believed in the existence and general character of jinn as described here but called them *shedim.*
26. None but the poorest Palestinians would sleep without a night light, for fear of the jinn.
27. A village about nine miles southwest of Jerusalem, and on the Jerusalem-Jaffa railway line.
28. Kohl is an ancient cosmetic, made from soot (such as charcoal) and other ingredients. It is applied to the eyelids to darken them and is also used as a mascara for the eyelashes.

29. Frances W. Pritchett, trans. and ed., *The Romance Tradition in Urdu: Adventures from the Dastan of Amir Hamzah*. New York: Columbia University Press, 1991.
30. Robert S. Robins and Jerrold M. Post, *Political Paranoia: The Psychopolitics of Hatred*. New Haven, CT: Yale University Press, 1997.
31. Celia E. Rothenberg, *Spirits of Palestine: Gender, Society, and Stories of the Jinn*. Lanham, MD: Lexington Press, 2004.
32. Zbinden, *Die Jinn des Islam und der Altorientalische Geisterglaube*.
33. The article was translated into English for The Jinn Group by member Mohamed El-Hag and was rewritten and edited by the author. It appeared online at an Arabic web site called 'Good News 4ME', www.gn4me.com.
34. Zbinden, *Die Jinn des Islam und der Altorientalische Geisterglaube*. This work features a comprehensive discussion of the jinn phenomenon among the people of Egypt.
35. Winifred S. Blackman, 'Some Beliefs among the Egyptian Peasants with Regard to "Afarit", *Folklore,* Vol. 35, No. 2 (30 June 1924).
36. For more of Lane's observations on jinn, see Appendix A.
37. See p. 95 of this book.
38. Walker, *Folk Medicine in Modern Egypt*.
39. Translator Walker's footnote: 'These are the Jinn, who, according to Moslem legends, were forced to assist King Solomon in his works of magic.'
40. Walker: 'Gaga is the goddess of guidance.'
41. Walker, 'The name of a king of the Unbelieving Jinn'.
42. This account is loosely derived from an article on an unofficial Web site hosted by members of the Multinational Force and Observers (MFO), the Sinai peacekeepers: Larry W. Roeder, Jr., 'Tales from the Sinai: In Search of Ghouls and High Adventure', www.iaw.on.ca/~awoolley/mfotale1.html.
43. 'Cryptid canines', The Cryptodominion web site (crassigyrinus@yahoo.ca), http://www.angelfire.com/bc2/cryptodominion/canids.html
44. In ancient Egyptian art, Set was usually portrayed as a mysterious creature that Egyptologists call the Set animal or Typhonic beast. It has a curved snout, square ears, forked tail and canine body. Sometimes Set is shown with a human body and an animal head. This creature does not totally resemble any known creature, but it does look like a composite of an aardvark, a donkey and a jackal, all three of which are desert creatures.
45. AUC Fox Information Site: http://auc-fox-site.blogspot.com/2008/11/salawa-fact-or-fiction.html

46. ANE Digest Archive, The Oriental Institute of the University of Chicago, 1997: http://oi.uchicago.edu/research/library/ane/digest/1997/v1997.n024.
47. Laouste's vivid portrayal of Moroccan jinn appears in Eugene Guernier, ed., *L'Encyclopedie Coloniale et Maritime*. Paris: 1940.
48. American Semiticist and Islamic scholar Duncan Black Macdonald was of the opinion that jinn exorcisms of this kind, popular throughout the Islamic world, were a late nineteenth-century development and were actually 'parodies' of the Sufi rituals, with the addition of animal sacrifices (thus indicating that the rites were actually African, even Voodoo, in origin). See Duncan Black Macdonald, *Aspects of Islam*. New York: Macmillan, 1911. See also Samuel M. Zwemer, *The Influence of Animism on Islam: An Account of Popular Superstitions*. New York: Macmillan, 1920.
49. Zwemer, *The Influence of Animism on Islam*.
50. Horst Nachtigall, 'Akkulturationsprobleme bei den Beni Mguild', *Ethnos*, Vol. 31, No. 1, 1966.
51. Douglas A. Davis and Susan Schaefer Davis, 'Possessed by Love: Gender and Romance in Morocco', www.haverford.edu/psych/ddavis/romance.html. A version of this paper appeared in William R. Jankowiak, ed., *Romantic Passion: A Universal Experience?* New York: Columbia University Press, 1995.
52. Vincent Crapanzano, *The Hamadsha: A Study in Moroccan Ethnopsychiatry*, Berkeley: University of California Press, 1973; V. Crapanzano, 'Saints, Jnun, and Dreams', *Psychiatry* (1975), 38, 145–159; and V. Crapanzano, 'Mohammed and Dawia: Possession in Morocco', in V. Crapanzano and V. Garrison, eds., *Case Studies in Spirit Possession*. New York: John Wiley, 1997.
53. Davis and Davis, 'Possessed by Love'.
54. Ibid.
55. Ibid.
56. Liner notes by lead musician Patrick Jabbar El-Shaheed, 'El Buya' (The Chameleon) by 'Aisha Qandisha's Jarring Effects. Recorded at Larbi Studio, Agadir, 1989, and at Shaidic Studio, Marrakesh, 1988. See Deborah Anne Kapchan, *Traveling Spirit Masters: Moroccan Gnawa Trance and Music in the Global Marketplace*. Middletown, CT: Wesleyan University Press, 2007.
57. Rosita Forbes, *Adventure*. London: Cassell & Co. Ltd., 1930.
58. Marie-Louise Dubouloz-Laffin, *Le Bou-Mergoud: Folklore Tunisien – Croyances et Coutumes Populaires de Sfax et de sa Region*. Paris: G.P. Maisonneuve, 1946.

59. Ibid.
60. Ibid.
61. The pilgrimage to the Ghriba synagogue, which draws Jewish worshippers from throughout North Africa, continues to this day.
62. Dobouloz-Laffin, *Le Bou-Mergoud*.
63. Ibid.
64. Nancy Elizabeth Gallagher, *Medicine and Power in Tunisia, 1780–1900.* Cambridge: Cambridge University Press, 2002.
65. Ibid.
66. Tuygun Sevki, 'Jinni: Man's Oldest Ancestor or Worst Nightmare?' *Turcoman*, 2000.
67. Barbara K. Walker, *The Art of the Turkish Tale*. Lubbock, TX: Texas Tech University Press, 1990.
68. Foreword by Talat Sait Halman in Walker, ibid.
69. Sevki, 'Jinni'.
70. The 1923 population exchange, agreed upon in a Greek-Turkish convention signed at Lausanne, Switzerland, involved some two million people displaced by the Balkan Wars, World War I and the Turkish War of Independence. Those who swapped countries were Greeks of the Muslim faith and Turks of the Greek Orthodox faith.
71. Fazile Zahir, 'Exorcising Turkey's Islamic Imps', *Asia Times*, Hong Kong, 13 March 2009.
72. Much information in this chapter is derived from Bess Allen Donaldson's thoughtful study of Iranian magic and folklore, *The Wild Rue: A Study of Muhammadan Magic and Folklore in Iran*. London: Luzac and Co., 1938.
73. Muhammad Rida al-Imami b. Muhammad Mu'min, *Jannat al-Khulud* (Garden of Eternity). Manuscript dated 2 Dhu al-Qa'ada 160 AH/13 Nov. 1844 AD. This work is a short encyclopaedia on the lives of the prophets and imams, world religions, Muslim rulers and other information.
74. Reynold A. Nicholson, ed. and trans., *The Mathnawi of Jalalu'ddin Rumi.* Vols. V & VI. London: Luzac and Co., 1924–1940.
75. The water of life (in Arabic *ma' al-hayat*), or fountain of life, is a secret spring whose waters, according to pre-Islamic legend, confer eternal life. Some believe it is located at Kataragama in Sri Lanka. The only human to have tasted its waters and thus attained immortality was said to be al-Khidr (The Green Man, also called al-Khadir or Kizr), a mysterious holy man or prophet associated with Alexander the Great. See Patrick Franke, *Begegnung mit Khidr: Quellenstudien zum Imaginären in Traditionellen Islam* (Encountering Khidr). Stuttgart: Franz Steiner Verlag, 2000.

76. Keightley, *The Fairy Mythology*.
77. The philosopher Abu Hamid Muhammad ibn Muhammad al-Ghazali (1058–1111). Of Persian origin, he wrote in Arabic and was one of the most celebrated scholars of Sunni Islamic thought. Al-Ghazali repudiated Greek philosophy, which had heretofore dominated Islamic thinking. He was known to European scholars as Algazel.
78. Donaldson, *The Wild Rue*.
79. These are four short chapters of the Qur'an: Suras 109, 112, 113 and 114.
80. Yazdanism groups three separate but related ancestral religions: Alevism, Ahl-e Haqq and Yezidism.
81. Michael M. Gunter, 'The Kurdish Minority Identity in Iraq', in Maya Shatzmiller, ed., *Nationalism and Minority Identities in Islamic Societies*. Montreal and Kingston: McGill-Queen's University Press, 2005. See also Margaret Kahn, *Children of the Jinn: In Search of the Kurds and Their Country*. New York: Seaview Books, 1980.
82. Andrew Collins, *From the Ashes of Angels: The Forbidden Legacy of a Fallen Race*. London: Michael Joseph Ltd., 1996.
83. Mehrdad R. Izady, *The Kurds: A Concise Handbook*. Washington, DC: Crane Russak, 1992.
84. See Victoria Arakelova's informative article on spirit possession entitled 'The Caucasus, Central Asia, Iran and Afghanistan' in Suad Joseph and Afsaneh Najmabadi, *Encyclopedia of Women and Islamic Cultures: Family, Body, Sexuality and Health*. Leiden: Brill, 2003.
85. Ghalib Lakhnavi and Abdullah Bilgrami, *The Adventures of Amir Hamza*. Trans. Musharraf Ali Farooqi. New York: Modern Library, 2007.
86. William Dalrymple, *City of Djinns: A Year in Delhi*. London: HarperCollins, 1993.
87. Ibid.
88. Ibid.
89. The Jumna is a major tributary of the Ganges River.
90. A. Hameed, 'LAHORE LAHORE AYE: When the Fairy Queen Came to Lahore', *The Daily Times* (Pakistan), 5 Nov. 2006.
91. Ibid.
92. The young woman's identity is unknown. Her account appeared on a web page hosted by AOL's Hometown community and won a competition called the 'Amazing but Incredibly True Story Contest'. Hometown closed down permanently on Halloween, 31 Oct. 2008, and the web page can no longer be traced.
93. An experience shared in the Yahoo Jinn Group.

94. The tale is related by bush pilot Tom Claytor in his journal about his 1996 visit to the Comoros, www.claytor.com/archive/16net.html
95. Aiman Rasheed, 'Possessed: The Story of the Makunodhoo Jinni', *Minivan News*, Maldives, 18 May 2008.
96. H.C.P. Bell, *The Maldive Islands: Monograph on the History, Archaeology, and Epigraphy,* Colombo: Ceylon Government Press, 1940.
97. Ibid. Cited in Thor Heyerdahl, *The Maldive Mystery*, London: George Allen & Unwin, 1986.
98. Heyerdahl, *The Maldive Mystery.*
99. Lisa Mackenrodt, 'The Jinn Fly on Friday. On Spiritual Healing Practices of the Swahili Coastal People in Contemporary Tanzania', Beiträge zur 1. Kölner Afrikawissenschaftlichen Nachwuchstagung (KANT I), 12–14 May 2006.
100. Ibid.
101. Caroline Mango, 'Evil Exploits of the Invisible People', *The Standard*, Nairobi, Kenya, 30 June 2008.
102. Persian traders visited Africa over many centuries. Indian Parsi merchants were particularly active in such trade in the eighteenth century.
103. Joseph Greenberg, 'The Influence of Islam on a Sudanese Religion', *Monographs of the American Ethnological Society, X.* New York: J.J. Augustin, 1946.
104. *Weekly Trust*, Kaduna, Nigeria, 6 Sept. 2002.
105. R.O. Winstedt, *Shaman, Saiva and Sufi: A Study of the Evolution of Malay Magic.* London: Constable and Co., 1925.
106. Ibid.
107. Many Muslim scholars, dating back to such classical authorities as Ibn Hisham, al-Farabi and Ibn Sina, identify Alexander the Great with the mysterious figure in the Qur'an referred to as Dhu al-Qarnain (He of the Two Horns) (Qur'an 18:83). Various Muslim accounts of Alexander have drawn on medieval romances of the Greek conqueror, for the most part written in Europe but now part of the global corpus of Alexander legends.
108. Winstedt, *Shaman, Saiva and Sufi.*
109. Ibid.
110. Ibid.

Chapter Five

1. The actual name of this work is *Qit'a Nunniya* [Short Poem Rhyming in the Letter Nun] and the translation appeared in Suzanne Pinckey

Stetkevych's *The Mute Immortals Speak: Pre-Islamic Poetry and the Poetics of Ritual.* Ithaca, NY: Cornell University Press, 1993.

2. Robert Irwin discusses some of this lore in his informative work, The Arabian Nights*: A Companion* (1994). Parts of this chapter draw upon that work.
3. Richard F. Burton, *Supplemental Nights to the Book of* The Thousand and One Nights *with Notes Anthropological and Explanatory.* Vol. 3. Printed by the Burton Club for Private Subscribers Only. n.d.
4. Irwin, The Arabian Nights*: A Companion*.
5. Burton, *Supplemental Nights*.
6. The following is a retelling of Lane's translated tale, 'The Story of the City of Brass', for modern readers. See Edward William Lane, trans. *Stories from the* Thousand and One Nights. Revised by Stanley Lane-Poole. Harvard Classics, Vol. 16, New York: P.F. Collier & Son Co., 1909–1914.
7. Mas'oudi, *Prairies d'or.*
8. Mai I. Gerhardt, *The Art of Storytelling: A Literary Study of the Thousand and One Nights.* Leiden: E.J. Brill, 1963.
9. Güneli Gün, *On the Road to Baghdad: A Picaresque Novel of Magical Adventures, Begged, Borrowed, and Stolen from The Thousand and One Nights.* London: Virago Press, 1991.
10. Stephen Greenblatt (general editor) et al., *The Norton Anthology of English Literature*, 8th edition. New York: W.W. Norton & Co., 2006.
11. Maurice H., Fitzgerald, ed., *The Poems of Robert Southey*, London: Oxford University Press, 1909. The poet's notes are from Robert Southey, *Thalaba the Destroyer*, Vols. 1 and 2. London: Longman, Hurst, Rees, and Orme, Paternoster-Row, 1809.
12. Alex Watson, 'Annotating Empire: Robert Southey's Footnotes for *Thalaba the Destroyer* (1801)', *Material Cultures and the Creation of Knowledge 2005*, Center for the History of the Book, University of Edinburgh, 21 July 2005, and Herbert F. Tucker, 'Southey the Epic-Headed', *Romanticism on the Net*, Université de Montréal, Nos. 32–33, Nov. 2003. Southey's many pages of notes for *Thalaba the Destroyer* include quotations from numerous works of Orientalist scholarship, travel narratives and literary curiosities which as Watson puts it 'blur the boundaries between Southey's poem and the text from which it was created'. The sources included: George Sale's translation of The Koran (1736); John Hoole's translations of Torquato Tasso's *Jerusalem Delivered* (1763) and Ludovico Ariosto's *Orlando Furioso* (1783); Sir William Jones' *The Enchanted Fruit* (1784); W.H. Roberts' *Judah Restored* (1774); and Samuel Henley's notes for William Beckford's *Vathek* (1786).

13. In his notes, Southey quotes Godwyn's *Moses and Aaron*: 'The manner how the Teraphim were made is fondly conceived thus among the Rabbies. They killed a man that was a first-born son, and wrung off his head, and seasoned it with salt and spices, and wrote, upon a plate of gold, the name of an unclean spirit, and put it under the head upon a wall, and lighted candles before it, and worshipped it.' He then cites Rabbi Eleazar: 'It is said to be the head of a child.'
14. Fitzgerald, *The Poems of Robert Southey*, p. 34.
15. Actually, the *ghul*, not the *afreet,* is the type of jinn commonly portrayed as a man-eater, but Southey claims poetic license. The afreet (*afrit*, *ifrit*) is a very powerful jinn explicitly mentioned in the Qur'an as faithfully serving King Solomon (Sura An-Naml, 27:39–40). But as Southey demonstrates, there are also evil or 'rebel' afreets. In his notes, the poet paints a vivid picture of an evil afreet by quoting from the *Bahar-Danush*, or *Garden of Knowledge*, a Persian romance written by Einaiut Oolah and translated by Jonathan Scott in 1799:

    > On his entrance, he beheld a black demon heaped on the ground like a mountain, with two large horns upon his head, and a long proboscis, fast asleep. In his head the Divine Creator had joined the likeness of an elephant and the wild bull. His teeth grew out as the tusks of a boar, and all over his monstrous carcase hung shaggy hairs, like those of the bear. The eye of mortal-born was dimmed at his appearance, and the mind, at his horrible form, and frightful figure, was confounded.

16. Carol Bolton, '*Thalaba the Destroyer*: Southey's Nationalist "Romance"', *Romanticism on the Net*, Université de Montréal, Nos. 32–33, Nov. 2003.
17. Jorge Luis Borges, *Book of Imaginary Beings*, Mexico City: 1957.
18. Graham Robb, *Victor Hugo,* New York: W.W. Norton & Co., 1998.
19. Blavatsky, an influential figure in the Western 'esoteric tradition', is rarely turned to by serious researchers. Her 'mystical' approach to antiquity is off-putting for many academics, and there is considerable scepticism about her alleged psychic abilities. However, her writings show a talent for indefatigable research, and the sources she cites are often worth a closer look. If nothing else, her writings are a contribution to Orientalist literature.
20. H.P. Blavatsky, *Isis Unveiled*. 2 Vols. Pasadena, CA: Theosophical University Press, 1976. Vol. II, p. 29.
21. Charles Perry (1698–1780) travelled extensively between 1739 and 1742 in France, Italy and the East. He travelled up the Nile to Aswan,

providing the earliest known description of the Temple of Isis at Behbit el-Hagar, and the frescoes in the tombs of the Beni Hasan necropolis. Perry was known for his unusual observations. For example, in *A View of the Levant*, he has been quoted as observing that 'the ancient Pelusiens, a people of lower Egypt, did venerate a Fart, which they worshipped under the symbol of a swelled paunch'.

22. Kurt H. Sethe, *Amun und die acht Urgotter von Hermopolis. eine Untersuchung iiber Ursprung und Wesen des Egyptischen Gotterkonigs*. Berlin: Akademie der Wissenschaften, 1929.
23. R.O. Faulkner, trans., *The Ancient Egyptian Pyramid Texts.* Oxford: Clarendon Press, 1969, § 446.
24. Inea Bushnaq, ed. and trans. *Arab Folktales.* New York: Pantheon Books, 1986.
25. For the scope of such lore, see Gary R. Varner, *Creatures of the Mist: Little People, Wild Men and Spirit Beings around the World*. New York: Algora Publishing, 2007.

Appendix B

1. Reprinted with permission, The Book Foundation.

Appendix C

1. Chris Line, 'Jinn from a Scientific (?) Viewpoint', *Flying Saucer Review*, Dec. 1989.
2. This material is summarised in Gordon Creighton's 'A Brief Account of the True Nature of the UFO Entities', published originally in *Flying Saucer Review (FSR)* 29/1 (Oct. 1983) and reprinted in *FSR 33/3* (Sept. 1988).
3. Gerald Feinberg and Robert Shapiro, *Life beyond Earth: The Intelligent Earthling's Guide to Life in the Universe*, New York: William Morrow & Co., 1980.
4. Dr. Ibrahim B. Syed, 'The Jinn – A Scientific Analysis', Islamic Research Foundation International, Inc., www.irfi.org.
5. Jay Alfred, *Our Invisible Bodies: Scientific Evidence for Subtle Bodies*, Victoria, BC, Canada: Trafford Publishing, 2006.
6. Jay Alfred, 'Jinns – Plasma Aliens from a Parallel Earth', www ezinearticles.com.
7. For more on the holographic memory systems of plasma life forms, see Jay Alfred, *Our Invisible Bodies*, 2006.
8. 'Jinn: Born of Fire', a special report in *The Economist*, 19 Dec. 2006.

References

Ahmad, Salim. *Revealing the Mystery behind the Hidden World of Jinn*. Booksurge, 2009.

Ali, Abdullah Yusuf (trans.). *The Meaning of the Holy Quran*. Beltsville, MD: Amana Publications, 2004.

Ameen, Dr. Abu'l-Mundhir Khaleel ibn Ibraaheem. *The Jinn and Human Sickness: Remedies in the Light of the Qur'aan and* Sunnah. Trans. by Nasiruddin Al-Khattab. Riyadh: Maktaba Dar-us-Salam, 2005.

Asad, Muhammad, trans. and ed. *The Message of the Qur'an*. Gibraltar: Dar al-Andalus, 1984.

Al-Ashqar, Umar S., and Jamaal A. Zarabozo (trans.). *The World of Jinn and Devils*. Denver: Al-Basheer Publications and Translations, 1998.

Asín Palacios, Miguel. *Islam and the Divine Comedy*. Translated and abridged by Harold Sunderland. London: John Murray, 1926.

Austin, R.W.J., trans. *Sufis of Andalusia: The Ruh al-quds and al-Durrat al-fakhirah of Ibn 'Arabi*. London: George Allen & Unwin Ltd., 1971.

Bearman, P.J., et al. (eds.) *Encyclopaedia of Islam. New Edition*. 13 Vols. Leiden: E.J. Brill, 2005.

Bell, H.C.P. *The Maldive Islands: Monograph on the History, Archaeology, and Epigraphy*. Colombo: Ceylon Government Press, 1940.

Blavatsky, H.P. *Isis Unveiled: A Master-Key to the Mysteries of Ancient and Modern Science and Theology*. Pasadena, CA: Theosophical University Press, 1976.

Blunt, Lady Anne. *A Pilgrimage to Nejd: The Cradle of the Arab Race*, 2 Vols., London: Frank Cass and Co., 1881, reprinted 1968.

Bohm, David. *Wholeness and the Implicate Order*. New York: Routledge, 1996.

Browne, Edward G. *A Literary History of Persia*. London: T. Fisher Unwin, 1902–24.

Al-Bukhari, Muhammed ibn Ismaiel, and Muhammad Muhsin Khan. *Sahih al-Bukhari: The Translation of the Meanings*. 9 Vols. Riyadh: Dar-us-Salam Publications, 1997.

Burton, Richard F. *The Book of the Thousand Nights and a Night: A Plain and Literal Translation of the Arabian Nights Entertainment.* 10 Vols. Benares: Kamashastra Society, 1885–1886.

Bushnaq, Inea, ed. and trans. *Arab Folktales.* New York: Pantheon Books, 1986.

Canaan, Tewfik. 'The Decipherment of Arabic Talismans', *Berytus* 4 (Beirut, 1937) and *Berytus* 5 (Beirut, 1938), reprinted in Savage-Smith, Emilie, ed. *Magic and Divination in Early Islam.* Aldershot, UK: Ashgate Publishing, 2004.

Clapp, Nicholas. *The Road to Ubar: Finding the Atlantis of the Sands.* Boston: Houghton Mifflin, 1998.

Clapp, Nicholas. *Sheba: Through the Desert in Search of the Legendary Queen.* Boston: Houghton Mifflin, 2001.

Claus, Peter J., Sarah Diamond and Margaret Ann Mills. *South Asian Folklore: An Encyclopedia: Afghanistan, Bangladesh, India, Nepal, Pakistan, Sri Lanka.* London: Taylor & Francis, 2003.

Cline, Walter. *Notes on the People of Siwah and El Garah in the Libyan Desert.* No. 4, General Series in Anthropology. Menasha, WI: George Banta Publishing Co., 1936. Reprinted AMS, 1979.

Collins, Andrew. *From the Ashes of Angels: The Forbidden Legacy of a Fallen Race.* London: Michael Joseph Ltd., 1996.

Conybeare, F.C., trans. 'The Testament of Solomon', *The Jewish Quarterly Review*, Vol. 11, No. 1 (Oct. 1898).

Crapanzano, Vincent. *The Hamadsha: A Study in Moroccan Ethnopsychiatry.* Berkeley: University of California Press, 1973.

Crapanzano, Vincent, and V. Garrison, eds. *Case Studies in Spirit Possession.* New York: John Wiley and Sons, 1997.

Curzon, Marquess of Kedleston. *Tales of Travel.* New York: George H. Doran Company, 1923.

Dalrymple, William. *City of Djinns: A Year in Delhi.* London: HarperCollins, 1993.

Dodge, Bayard, ed. and trans. *The Fihrist of Al-Nadim: A Tenth-Century Survey of Muslim Culture.* New York: Columbia University Press, 1970.

Donaldson, Bess Allen. *The Wild Rue – A Study of Muhammadan Magic and Folklore in Iran.* London: Luzac & Co., 1938.

Doughty, Charles. *Travels in Arabia Deserta.* London: Jonathan Cape, 1924.

Dubouloz-Laffin, Marie-Louise. *Le Bou-Mergoud: Folklore Tunisien – Croyances et Coutumes Populaires de Sfax et de sa Région.* (Vol. X of *Les Littératures Populaires de toutes les Nations.*) Paris: G.P. Maisonneuve, 1946.

Fahd, Toufic. *La Divination Arabe. Études religieuses, sociologiques et folkloriques sur le milieu natif de l'Islam.* Paris: Sindbad, 1987.

Fakhry, Ahmed. *The Oases of Egypt, Vol. I: Siwa Oasis*. Cairo: American University of Cairo Press, 1973.

Faris, Nabih Amin. *The Antiquities of South Arabia [Al-Hamdani]*. Princeton, NJ: Princeton University Press, 1938.

Faris, Nabih Amin. *The Book of Idols: Being a Translation From the Arabic of the Kitab Al-Asnam By Hisham Ibn-Al-Kalbi*. Princeton, NJ: Princeton University Press, 1952.

Fiske, John. *Myths and Myth-Makers: Old Tales and Superstitions Interpreted by Comparative Mythology*. Boston: Houghton Mifflin, 1899.

Forbes, Duncan, trans. *The Adventures of Hatim Tai*. 3rd Edition. Bombay: Cherag Office, 1911.

Forbes, Rosita. *Adventure*. London: Cassell & Co. Ltd., 1930.

Frazer, Sir James George. *The Golden Bough: A Study in Magic and Religion*. 1 Volume, Abridged Edition. New York: Collier Books, 1963.

Greenberg, Joseph. 'The Influence of Islam on a Sudanese Religion', *Monographs of the American Ethnological Society, X*. New York: J.J. Augustin, 1946.

Guernier, Eugene, ed. *L'Encyclopedie Coloniale et Maritime*. Paris: 1940.

Gün, Güneli. *On the Road to Baghdad: A Picaresque Novel of Magical Adventures, Begged, Borrowed, and Stolen from the Thousand and One Nights*. London: Virago Press, 1991.

Hanauer, J.E. *Folk-Lore of the Holy Land: Moslem, Christian and Jewish*. London: Sheldon Press, 1907 and 1935 [revised].

Hasluck, Frederick W. *Christianity and Islam under the Sultans*. Oxford: Clarendon Press, 1929.

Hastings, James, ed. *Encyclopedia of Religion and Ethics*. Edinburgh: T. & T. Clark, 1908–1926.

Henninger, Joseph, and Gwendolyn Goldbloom (trans.). 'Belief in Spirits Among the Pre-Islamic Arabs', in Savage-Smith, Emilie, ed. *Magic and Divination in Early Islam*. Aldershot, UK: Ashgate Publishing, 2004.

Heyerdahl, Thor. *The Maldive Mystery*. London: George Allen & Unwin, 1986.

Houtsma, M.Th. et al. (eds.) *E.J. Brill's First Encyclopedia of Islam: 1913–1936*. Reprint Edition. Leiden: E.J. Brill, 1993.

Hughes, Thomas Patrick. *A Dictionary of Islam: Being a Cyclopaedia of the Doctrines, Rites, Ceremonies, and Customs, Together With the Technical and Theological Terms, of the Muhammadan Religion*. London: W.H. Allen, 1885.

Irwin, Robert. *The Arabian Nights: A Companion*. London: Allen Lane / Penguin Press, 1994.

Irwin, Robert. *Night, Horses and the Desert: An Anthology of Classical Arabic Literature.* New York: Overlook Press, 2000.

Jankowiak, William R., ed. *Romantic Passion: A Universal Experience?* New York: Columbia University Press, 1997.

Jayyusi, Lena, trans. *The Adventures of Sayf Ben Dhi Yazan: An Arab Folk Epic.* Bloomington: Indiana University Press, 1996.

Jones, Alan, ed. *University Lectures in Islamic Studies Volume 2.* London: Altajir World of Islam Trust, 1998.

Joseph, Suad, and Afsaneh Najmabadi. *Encyclopedia of Women and Islamic Cultures: Family, Body, Sexuality and Health.* Leiden: Brill, 2003.

Kahn, Margaret. *Children of the Jinn: In Search of the Kurds and Their Country.* New York: Seaview Books, 1980.

Katibah, H.I. *Other Arabian Nights.* New York: Charles Scribner's Sons, 1928.

Keightley, Thomas. *The Fairy Mythology: Illustrative of the Romance and Superstition of Various Countries.* New and Revised Edition. London: Henry G. Bohn, 1850.

Knappert, Jan. *Islamic Legends: Histories of the Heroes, Saints and Prophets of Islam.* Leiden: Brill, 1985.

Lakhnavi, Ghalib, and Abdullah Bilgrami. *The Adventures of Amir Hamza.* Trans. by Musharraf Ali Farooqi. New York: Modern Library, 2007.

Lane, Edward W., trans. *The Thousand and One Nights.* Cambridge: The Harvard Classics, 1909–1914.

Leach, Maria, ed. *Funk and Wagnalls Standard Dictionary of Folklore, Mythology, and Legend.* New York: Harper & Row, 1984.

Levy-Bruhl, Lucien. *The 'Soul' of the Primitive.* London: George Allen & Unwin 1965.

Lyall, Charles James. *Translations of Ancient Arabian Poetry.* New York: Columbia University Press, 1930.

Macdonald, Duncan Black. 'The Attitude of the Semites Toward the Unseen World; Prophecy as a Semitic Phenomenon and Especially Among the Arabs', Lecture I, *Haskell Lectures in Comparative Religion*, University of Chicago, 1906, pp. 1–39.

Macdonald, Duncan Black. 'Djinn', in Houtsma, M.Th. et al. (eds.) *E.J. Brill's First Encyclopedia of Islam: 1913–1936.* Reprint Edition. Leiden: E.J. Brill, 1993.

Macdonald, Duncan Black. 'Intercourse through the Jinn; Spirits, Demons, Ghosts in Islam', Lecture V, *Haskell Lectures in Comparative Religion*, University of Chicago, 1906, pp. 130–156.

Mackenrodt, Lisa. 'The Jinn Fly on Friday: On Spiritual Healing Practices of the Swahili Coastal People in Contemporary Tanzania'. Kölner Afrikawissenschaftliche Nachwuchstagung (KANT I), May 12–14, 2006.

Mango, Cyril A. 'Antique Statuary and the Byzantine Beholder', *Dumbarton Oaks Papers* 17 (1963): 55–75.

Miller, Anthony G., and Miranda Morris. *Plants of Dhofar, The Southern Region of Oman: Traditional, Economic and Medicinal Uses.* Muscat: Office of the Adviser for Conservation of the Environment, Diwan of Royal Court, Sultanate of Oman, 1988.

Newby, Gordon Darnell. *The Making of the Last Prophet: A Reconstruction of the Earliest Biography of Muhammad.* Columbia, SC: University of South Carolina Press, 1989.

Norris, H.T. *The Berbers in Arabic Literature.* London: Longman, 1982.

Owadally, Mohamad Yasin. *Qaf: The Mysterious, Emerald Mountain Decoded.* Kuala Lumpur: A.S. Noordeen, 2002.

Patai, Raphael. *The Hebrew Goddess.* New York: Avon Books, 1978.

Perry, Charles. *A View of the Levant: Particularly of Constantinople, Syria, Egypt, and Greece, in which their Antiquities, Government, Politics, Maxims, Manners, and Customs (with many other Circumstances and Contingencies) are attempted to be Described and Treated on.* London: T. Woodward, C. Davis and J. Shuckburgh, 1743.

Philby, H. St. J. B. *Heart of Arabia.* 2 Vols. London: Constable and Company, 1922.

Philips, Abu Ameenah Bilal, ed. and trans. *Ibn Taymeeyah's Essay on the Jinn.* Riyadh: Tawheed Publications, 1989.

Philips, Abu Ameenah Bilal. *The Exorcist Tradition in Islaam.* Sharjah, United Arab Emirates: Dar Al Fatah Printing, 1997.

Pinckey Stetkevych, Suzanne. *The Mute Immortals Speak: Pre-Islamic Poetry and the Poetics of Ritual.* Ithaca, NY: Cornell University Press, 1993.

Pingree, David, ed., *Picatrix: The Latin Version of the Ghayat al-Hakim.* London: Warburg Institute, University of London, 1986.

Robins, Robert S., and Jerrold M. Post. *Political Paranoia: The Psychopolitics of Hatred.* New Haven, CT: Yale University Press, 1997.

Rothenberg, Celia E. *Spirits of Palestine: Gender, Society, and Stories of the Jinn.* Lanham, MD: Lexington Press, 2004.

Sachau, C. Edward, trans. and ed. *The Chronology of Ancient Nations: An English Version of the Arabic Text of the Athar-ul-Bakiya of Albiruni.* London: William H. Allen and Co., 1879.

Sagan, Carl. *The Demon-Haunted World: Science as a Candle in the Dark.* London: Headline, 1997.

Sakr, Ahmad. *Al-Jinn.* Chicago: Foundation of Islamic Studies, 1994.

Al-Saleh, Khairat. *Fabled Cities, Princes and Jinn from Arab Myths and Legends.* New York: Schocken Books, 1985.

Saletore, R.N. *Indian Witchcraft: A Study in Indian Occultism.* India: Abhinav Publications, 1990.

Sarruf, Fuad, and Suha Tamim, eds. *American University of Beirut Festival Book (Festschrift).* Beirut: American University of Beirut, 1967.

Savage-Smith, Emilie, ed. *Magic and Divination in Early Islam.* (Vol. 42, The Formation of the Classical Islamic World.) Aldershot, UK: Ashgate Publishing, 2004.

Scott, Ernest. *The People of the Secret.* London: Octagon Press, 1983.

Scott, Samuel P. *History of the Moorish Empire in Europe.* 3 Vols. Philadelphia: J.B. Lippincott, 1904.

Sengers, Gerda. *Women and Demons: Cult Healing in Islamic Egypt.* International Studies in Sociology and Social Anthropology, Vol. 86. Leiden: Brill, 2003.

Serjeant, R.B. 'Two Yemenite Djinn', *Bulletin of the School of Oriental and African Studies.* University of London, Vol. 13, No. 1 (1949).

Shah, Idries. *The Secret Lore of Magic.* London: Frederick Muller, 1957.

Shah, Tahir. *The Caliph's House: A Year in Casablanca.* London: Doubleday, 2006.

Shah, Tahir. *In Arabian Nights: A Caravan of Moroccan Dreams.* New York: Bantam Books, 2008.

El-Shamy, Hasan M., ed. and trans. *Folktales of Egypt.* Chicago: University of Chicago Press, 1980.

Sharpe, Elizabeth Marie. *Into the Realm of Smokeless Fire: (Qur'an 55:14): A Critical Translation of Al-Damiri's Article on the Jinn from 'Hayat al-Hayawan al-Kubra' (Egypt, Mamluk).* M.A. Thesis, University of Arizona, 1992.

Silberman, Neil Asher. *Digging for God and Country: Exploration, Archeology, and the Secret Struggle for the Holy Land, 1799–1917.* New York: Knopf, 1982.

Smith, William Robertson. *Kinship and Marriage in Early Arabia.* London: 1903.

Smith, William Robertson, *Lectures on the Religion of the Semites. First Series, The Fundamental Institutions.* London, A. & C. Black, 1894..

Soucek, Priscilla P. 'Solomon's Throne/Solomon's Bath: Model or Metaphor?' *Ars Orientalis*, Vol. 23, 1993.

Spence, Lewis. *Myths and Legends of Babylonia and Assyria.* London: George G. Harrap & Co., 1916. Republished: Detroit: Gale Research Co., 1975.

Spengler, Oswald. *The Decline of the West.* 2 Vols. New York: Alfred A. Knopf, 1980.

Stern, David, and Mark Jay Mirsky. *Rabbinic Fantasies: Imaginative Narratives from Classical Hebrew Literature.* Philadelphia: Jewish Publication Society, 1990.

Stevens, E.S. *Folk-Tales of Iraq: Set Down and Translated from the Vernacular.* London: Oxford University Press, 1931.

Swartz, Merlin L., trans. and ed. *Studies on Islam.* New York: Oxford University Press, 1981.

Al-Tabari, Mohammed ibn Jarir. (Hermann Zotemberg, trans.) *Chronique de Tabari: Histoire des Prophètes et des rois: De la création à la dernière Révélation.* Paris: Editions La Ruche, 2006.

Talbot, Michael. *The Holographic Universe.* New York: HarperCollins, 1991.

Teixidor, Javier. *The Pantheon of Palmyra.* Leiden: E.J. Brill, 1979.

Thompson, R. Campbell. *Semitic Magic: Its Origins and Development.* London, Luzac & Co., 1908.

Thorndyke, Lynn. *A History of Magic and Experimental Science*, 8 Vols., New York: Columbia University Press, 1958.

Walker, Barbara K. *The Art of the Turkish Tale.* Lubbock, TX: Texas Tech University Press, 1990.

Walker, John. *Folk Medicine in Modern Egypt: Being the Relevant Parts of the* Tibb al-Rukka *or* Old Wives' Medicine *of 'Abd al-Rahman Isma'il.* London: Luzac & Co., 1934.

Westermarck, Edward. *Ritual and Belief in Morocco.* London: Macmillan and Co., 1926.

Winkler, H.A. *Siegel und Charaktere in der Muhammedanischen Zauberei.* (*Seals and Characters in Islamic Magic.*) Berlin: Walter de Gruyter & Co., 1930.

Winstedt, R.O. *Shaman, Saiva and Sufi: A Study of the Evolution of Malay Magic.* Glasgow: University Press, 1925.

Zbinden, Ernst. *Die Jinn des Islam und der Altorientalische Geisterglaube.* (*The Jinn of Islam and Ancient Eastern Spirit Belief.*) Bern and Stuttgart: Verlag Paul Haupt, 1953.

Zwemer, Samuel M. *The Influence of Animism on Islam: An Account of Popular Superstitions.* New York: Macmillan Company, 1920.

Index